Framework 8

MATHS E

David Capewell   Formerly Westfield School, Sheffield

Marguerite Comyns   Queen Mary's High School, Walsall

Gillian Flinton   All Saints Catholic High School, Sheffield

Paul Flinton   Chaucer School, Sheffield

Geoff Fowler   Maths Strategy Manager, Birmingham

Derek Huby   Mathematics Consultant, West Sussex

Peter Johnson   Wellfield High School, Leyland, Lancashire

Penny Jones   Waverley School, Birmingham

Jayne Kranat   Langley Park School for Girls, Bromley

Ian Molyneux   St. Bedes RC High School, Ormskirk

Peter Mullarkey   Netherhall School, Maryport, Cumbria

Nina Patel   Ifield Community College, West Sussex

OXFORD
UNIVERSITY PRESS

OXFORD
UNIVERSITY PRESS

Great Clarendon Street, Oxford OX2 6DP

Oxford University Press is a department of the University of Oxford.
It furthers the University's objective of excellence in research,
scholarship, and education by publishing worldwide in

Oxford New York

Auckland Bangkok Buenos Aires Cape Town
Dar es Salaam Delhi Hong Kong Istanbul Karachi Kolkata
Kuala Lumpur Madrid Melbourne Mexico City Mumbai Nairobi
São Paulo Shanghai Taipei Tokyo Toronto

Oxford is a registered trade mark of Oxford University Press
in the UK and in certain other countries

British Library Cataloguing in Publication Data

Data available

ISBN 0 19 914853 8

10 9 8 7 6 5 4 3 2 1

Typeset by Mathematical Composition Setters Ltd.

Printed and bound by G. Canale & C. S.p.A.-Turin.

Acknowledgements

The photograph on the cover is reproduced courtesy of Graeme Peacock.

The publisher and authors would like to thank the following for permission
to use photographs and other copyright material:
Stone, page 1, Corbis, page 15 and 72, Empics, page 29, Science Photo Library,
page 57, Alamy Images, page 72 and 126, Rex Features, page 119, Ordnance
Survey, page 214.

Figurative artwork by Paul Daviz.

The authors would like to thank
Sarah Caton, Kam Grewal-Joy, Karl Warsi and Phil Sage for their help in
compiling this book.

About this book

This book has been written specifically for Year 8 of the Framework for Teaching Mathematics. It is aimed at higher ability students who are following the Year 9 teaching programme from the Framework.

The authors are experienced teachers and maths consultants who have been incorporating the Framework approaches into their teaching for many years and so are well qualified to help you successfully meet the Framework objectives.

The book is made up of units based on the sample medium term plans which complement the Framework document, thus maintaining the required pitch, pace and progression.

The units are:

Each unit comprises double page spreads that should take a lesson to teach. These are shown on the full contents list.

Problem solving is integrated throughout the material as suggested in the Framework.

How to use this book

This book is made up of units of work which are colour coded into: Number/Algebra (Purple), Algebra (Blue), Data (Pink), Number (Orange), Shape, space and measures (Green) and Problem solving (Light Green).

Each unit of work starts with an overview of the content of the unit, as specified in the Framework document, so that you know exactly what you are expected to learn.

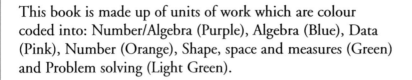

This unit will show you how to:

▶▶ Solve problems using properties of angles, of parallel and intersecting lines, and of triangles and other polygons.

▶▶ Explain how to find, calculate and use the interior and exterior angles of polygons.

▶▶ Know the definition of a circle and its parts.

▶▶ Explain why inscribed regular polygons can be constructed by equal divisions of a circle.

▶▶ Use straight edge and compasses to construct a triangle, given right angle, hypotenuse and side (RHS).

▶▶ Solve increasingly demanding problems and evaluate solutions.

▶▶ Present a concise, reasoned argument.

The first page of a unit also highlights the skills and facts you should already know and provides Check in questions to help you revise before you start so that you are ready to apply the knowledge later in the unit:

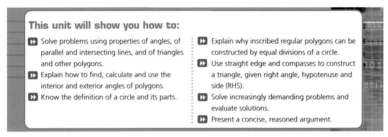

Before you start

You should know how to ...

1 Calculate angles on:
   a a straight line
   b in a triangle
   c at a point.

Check in

1 Calculate the unknown angles.

Inside each unit, the content develops in double page spreads which all follow the same structure.

The spreads start with a list of the learning outcomes and a summary of the keywords:

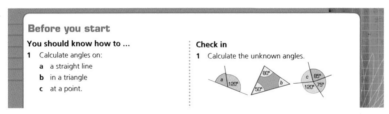

This spread will show you how to:

▶▶ Know the parts of a circle.

▶▶ Construct inscribed regular polygons in a circle.

KEYWORDS

Circumference   Arc

Chord   Diameter

Sector   Segment

Inscribe   Radius

The keywords are summarised and defined in a Glossary at the end of the book so you can always check what they mean.

Key information is highlighted in the text so you can see the facts you need to learn.

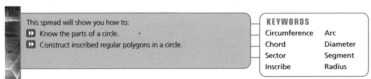

▶ If you raise any number to a zero index, the answer will be 1.

$x^0 = 1$ $(3^0 = 1, 4^0 = 1, 100^0 = 1 ...)$

Examples showing the key skills and techniques you need to develop are shown in boxes. Also hint boxes show tips and reminders you may find useful:

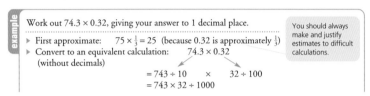

Work out 74.3×0.32, giving your answer to 1 decimal place.

▸ First approximate: $75 \times \frac{1}{3} = 25$ (because 0.32 is approximately $\frac{1}{3}$)
▸ Convert to an equivalent calculation: 74.3×0.32
  (without decimals)

$$= 743 \div 10 \quad \times \quad 32 \div 100$$
$$= 743 \times 32 \div 1000$$

You should always make and justify estimates to difficult calculations.

Each exercise is carefully graded, set at three levels of difficulty:

▸ The first few questions provide lead-in questions, revising previous learning.
▸ The questions in the middle of the exercise provide the main focus of the material.
▸ The last few questions are challenging questions that provide a link to Year 10 material.

At the end of each unit is a summary page so that you can revise the learning of the unit before moving on.

Check out questions are provided to help you check your understanding of the key concepts covered and your ability to apply the key techniques.

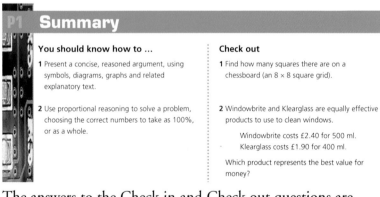

P1 Summary

You should know how to ...

1 Present a concise, reasoned argument, using symbols, diagrams, graphs and related explanatory text.

2 Use proportional reasoning to solve a problem, choosing the correct numbers to take as 100%, or as a whole.

Check out

1 Find how many squares there are on a chessboard (an 8 × 8 square grid).

2 Windowbrite and Klearglass are equally effective products to use to clean windows.

Windowbrite costs £2.40 for 500 ml.
Klearglass costs £1.90 for 400 ml.

Which product represents the best value for money?

The answers to the Check in and Check out questions are produced at the end of the book so that you can check your own progress and identify any areas that need work.

Contents

This unit will show you how to:

▶▶ Extend mental methods of calculation, working with decimals, factors, powers and roots.

▶▶ Use standard column procedures to add and subtract integers and decimals of any size.

▶▶ Use the sign change key on a calculator, and function keys for powers and roots.

▶▶ Use the prime factor decomposition of a number.

▶▶ Use index notation for integer powers.

▶▶ Make and justify estimates and approximations of calculations.

▶▶ Generate terms of a sequence using term-to-term and position-to-term definitions.

▶▶ Write an expression to describe the nth term of an arithmetic sequence.

▶▶ Solve increasingly demanding problems and evaluate solutions.

▶▶ Solve substantial problems by breaking them into simpler tasks.

▶▶ Use trial and improvement where a more efficient method is not obvious.

Six is a triangular number.

Before you start

You should know how to ...

1 Add and subtract integers.

2 Substitute integers into simple expressions.

Check in

1 Work out mentally:

  a $^-3 - ^-120 + ^-6$

  b $^-21 + 58 - ^-12$

  c $^-60 + 72 - 93 + 101$

2 If $a = 3$, $b = 4$ and $c = ^-2$ evaluate:

  a $4a - b$ **b** bc **b** $4a^2$

  d $c^2 - 1$ **e** $b^3 - a$ **f** $3a - 2c$

Adding and subtracting negative numbers

This spread will show you how to:
- ▶▶ Order positive and negative integers and decimals.
- ▶▶ Add and subtract integers and decimals.

KEYWORDS

Integer   Positive

Negative   Inequality

You can use negative decimals to describe money that is owed.

> **example**
>
> Matt, Phoebe and Justine are students.
> They are all overdrawn at the bank.
> Their bank statements read ⁻£34.28, ⁻£7.43
> and ⁻£12.89 respectively.
>
>
>
> **a** Who owes **i** the most amount of money
>   **ii** the least amount of money?
> **b** How much do the three students owe the
>   bank in total?
>
> ....
>
> **a** **i**   Matt owes the most amount of money (£34.28).
>   **ii**   Phoebe owes the least amount of money (£7.43).
> **b**   34.28 + 7.43 + 12.89 = 54.6 (using a written method).
>   The students owe £54.60 in total.
>
> Line up the decimal points:
> 34.28
> 7.43
> 12.89
> 54.60

To compare decimal numbers, first check the sign and then compare the place values of each digit.

> **example**
>
> Complete these inequalities, using either of the symbols > or <.
>
> **a**   0.0234   0.3
>
> **b**   ⁻32.4   4.3
>
> **c**   ⁻3.1246   ⁻3.1252
>
> **a** Compare the first decimal place:
>   0.0234 < 0.3
>
> **b** Compare the sign:
>   ⁻32.4 < ⁺4.3
>
> **c** Compare the third decimal place:
>   ⁻3.1246 < ⁻3.1252

You can add and subtract negative numbers either mentally or using a written method.
You need to remember these rules:

> ▶ Adding a negative number is the same as subtracting a positive number.
> 3.4 + ⁻2.3 = 3.4 − 2.3 = 1.1
>
> ▶ Subtracting a negative number is the same as adding a positive number.
> 3.4 − ⁻2.3 = 3.4 + 2.3 = 5.7

Exercise NA1.1

1 Look at these integers.

$$5 \quad {}^-3 \quad 2 \quad {}^-6 \quad {}^-10$$

a Which pair of integers gives:

  i the largest answer when added?

  ii the largest answer when subtracted?

  iii the smallest answer when added?

  iv the smallest answer when subtracted?

b What is the sum of all the integers?

2 Calculate, using a mental or written method:

a $4.3 + 3.69$ **b** $4.3 + {}^-2.7$

c $1.037 + 3.063$ **d** $12.65 - {}^-3.48$

e $4.005 + 5.095$ **f** ${}^-6.13 + {}^-2.8$

3 Write all the decimal numbers with exactly two decimal places that lie between ${}^-1.4$ and ${}^-1.3$.

4 Puzzle

1.551 is a palindromic number.

It reads the same backwards and forwards.

a How many other palindromic numbers can you find between ${}^-2$ and 2 that contain:

  i no zeros?

  ii exactly four digits

b What is the total of all of these palindromic numbers?

5 a Add together each pair of numbers in the brackets. What do you notice?

$$(3.43, {}^-3.2) \quad ({}^-6.7, 6.93) \quad ({}^-7.56, 7.79)$$

b Subtract the larger number in each bracket from the smaller.

6 Calculate the following using a mental or written method, or, where appropriate, using a calculator.

a ${}^-4.3 + 2.7$ **b** $37 - {}^-19 + 99$

c $42.1 + 36.7 + 12.4$

d ${}^-37.5 + {}^-12.5$ **e** $143 + 16.8 - {}^-4.9$

f $16.03 - 8.4 + 11.25 - {}^-3.75$

g ${}^-\frac{3}{4} + {}^-\frac{2}{3}$ **h** $\frac{2}{5} - {}^-1\frac{3}{4}$

7 Puzzle

Here are six numbers.

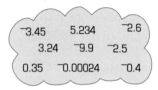

12.23	${}^-6.7$
${}^-2.3$	5.02
${}^-11.8$	0.28

You can add or subtract the numbers to make a target number, for example:

$12.23 - {}^-6.7 = 18.93$.

a Find two numbers to make ${}^-18.5$.

b Find three numbers that you can use to make 12.

c Find four numbers that you can use to make 16.48.

8 Look at the numbers in the cloud:

${}^-3.45$ 5.234 ${}^-2.6$

3.24 ${}^-9.9$ ${}^-2.5$

0.35 ${}^-0.00024$ ${}^-0.4$

a What is the total of the numbers in the cloud?

b What is the mean of these numbers?

c Which number is closest to zero?

d What number lies exactly halfway between the largest and the smallest number?

9 Investigation

In an arithmagon you add the numbers in the circles to produce the numbers in the squares.

a Solve this arithmagon.

b Describe and explain your method for solving this problem.

c Invent an arithmagon problem of your own which involves **subtracting** the numbers in the circles to give the numbers in the squares.

d Explain your method for solving subtraction arithmagons.

Comment upon any problems in designing a subtraction arithmagon.

This spread will show you how to:

▶▶ Multiply and divide integers and decimals.

KEYWORDS

Multiplication   Factor

Division   Product

When you multiply or divide negative numbers you need to look at the sign.

Multiplication

▶ Negative number × positive number = negative product
For example, $^-0.6 \times 8 = ^-4.8$

▶ Negative number × negative number = positive product
For example, $^-0.6 \times ^-8 = 4.8$

This also means that:
positive number × negative
number = negative product.

Division

▶ Negative number ÷ positive number = negative quotient
For example, $^-4.8 \div 8 = ^-0.6$

▶ Positive number ÷ negative number = negative quotient
For example, $4.8 \div -8 \div ^-0.6$

▶ Negative number ÷ negative number = positive quotient
For example, $^-4.8 \div ^-8 = 0.6$

This table may help you remember:

× or ÷	+	−
+	+	−
−	−	+

You can use mental strategies to help multiply and divide with negative integers and decimals.

You could use factors...

example

Calculate, using a mental method:

a $^-1.4 \times 20$ **b** $^-360 \div 30$

a $^-1.4 \times 20 = ^-1.4 \times 10 \times 2$
$\qquad = ^-14 \times 2$
$\qquad = ^-28$

b $^-360 \div 30 = ^-360 \div 10 \div 3$
$\qquad = ^-36 \div 3$
$\qquad = ^-12$

Or you could use an equivalent calculation...

example

Calculate, using a mental method:

a $^-50 \times ^-1.3$ **b** $^-1.9 \div 25$

÷ 25 is the same
as ÷ 100 and × 4.

a $^-50 \times ^-1.3 = ^-50 \times ^-13 \div 10$
$\qquad = ^-50 \div 10 \times ^-13$
$\qquad = ^-5 \times ^-13$
$\qquad = 65$

b $^-1.9 \div 25 = ^-1.9 \div 100 \times 4$
$\qquad = ^- \ ^-9 \times 4 \div 100$
$\qquad \div 100$

Exercise NA1.2

1 Copy and complete this multiplication grid.

×	⁻4	⁻2	0	2	4
3					
2					
1					
0					
⁻1					
⁻2					
⁻3					

2 Here are four integers:

$$⁻3 \qquad ⁻4 \qquad ⁻5 \qquad 10$$

Answer the following questions.

a Which pairs of numbers, when multiplied, will give a negative answer?

b Which pairs of numbers, when divided, will give a positive answer?

c Find a product of three numbers that will give an answer of 120.

3 Calculate these, using a mental or written method.

a $⁻0.6 \times ⁻7$ **b** $240 \div ⁻48$

c $1.7 \times ⁻9$ **d** $⁻2.6 \times ⁻40$

e $⁻18 \times 19$ **f** $43 \times ⁻24$

g $⁻60 \times ⁻1.4$ **h** $⁻644 \div ⁻28$

4 Puzzle

Use two or more of the numbers in Box A, together with the operators × or ÷ , to make the target number.

For example, for target number ⁻2.4:

$⁻6 \times 2 \div 5 = ⁻2.4$

Target numbers

a ⁻4.2

b 4.43 (to 2 d.p.)

c 8.3̇

d 323 to the nearest whole number

Box A

⁻6	2
⁻10	⁻0.31
5	0.7

5 Investigation

Here is the ⁻1.45 times table!

$1 \times ⁻1.45 = ⁻1.45$	$6 \times ⁻1.45 =$
$2 \times ⁻1.45 =$	$7 \times ⁻1.45 =$
$3 \times ⁻1.45 = ⁻4.35$	$8 \times ⁻1.45 =$
$4 \times ⁻1.45 =$	$9 \times ⁻1.45 =$
$5 \times ⁻1.45 =$	$10 \times ⁻1.45 = ⁻14.5$

Write down strategies for calculating each of the missing products.

For example,

$$5 \times ⁻1.45 = \frac{10 \times ⁻1.45}{2} = \frac{⁻14.5}{2} = ⁻7.25$$

6 Use the sign change key on your calculator to work these out.

In each case estimate your answer first.

a $⁻1.34 \times 4.5$

b $4.87 + ⁻0.2$

c $⁻3.1 + ⁻6.7$

d $0.004 \times ⁻3\,000\,000$

7 Find the value of each of the expressions given, using these values:

$$a = ⁻3 \qquad b = ⁻4 \qquad c = ⁻5$$
$$d = 10 \qquad e = ⁻0.5$$

a $3a^2$ **b** $e - 2(\frac{a}{d})$

c $c^2 + 0.5b$ **d** $abc \div de$

In each case, show your working.

8 In these arithmagons the numbers in the squares are the products of the numbers in the circles on either side.

Solve these arithmagons.

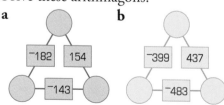

This spread will show you how to:

▶▶ Use the prime factor decomposition of a number.

KEYWORDS

Multiple	Divisible
Common factor	HCF
Prime factor	LCM

The factors of 12 are 1, 2, 3, 4, 6 and 12.
The **prime factors** of 12 are 2 and 3.

▶ You can write any number as the product of its prime
factors.

There are two common methods:

<table>
<tr><td>Factor trees</td><td>Division by primes</td></tr>
</table>

Factor trees

250
10 × 25
2 × 5 × 5 × 5

$250 = 2 \times 5 \times 5 \times 5$
$= 2 \times 5^3$

Each number is split into two factors until you reach
prime numbers.

Division by primes

$$2)\underline{250}$$
$$5)\underline{125}$$
$$5)\underline{\ 25}$$
$$5)\underline{\ \ 5}$$
$$1$$

$250 = 2 \times 5 \times 5 \times 5$
$= 2 \times 5^3$

Divide by prime numbers starting with 2, ignoring
any that give a remainder.

You can use prime factors to find the **HCF** and
LCM of two or more numbers.

Remember:
HCF and LCM are short for highest common factor
and lowest common multiple respectively.

example

Find:

a the HCF of 240 and 460

b the LCM of 24 and 174

. . . .

a List the prime factors:
$240 = 2 \times 2 \times 5 \times 2 \times 3 \times 2$
$460 = 2 \times 2 \times 5 \times 23$
$HCF = 2 \times 2 \times 5 = 20$

Use the common factors.

b List the prime factors as powers:
$24 = 2 \times 2 \times 2 \times 3 = 2^3 \times 3$
$174 = 2 \times 3 \times 29$
$LCM = 2^3 \times 3 \times 29 = 696$

Use the highest power of each common factor.

Exercise NA1.3

1 Find the HCF of each pair of numbers:
  a 25 and 46
  b 40 and 48
  c 24, 46 and 60
  d 15, 30 and 40

2 Find the LCMs of these sets of numbers:
  a 16 and 5
  b 12 and 20
  c the first three square numbers
  d the first three triangular numbers

3 Express each of these numbers as a product of its prime factors:
  a 34
  b 54
  c 485
  d 350
  e 83
  f 62
  g 815
  h 648

4 Find the HCF of each of these pairs of numbers.
  a 215 and 326
  b 532 and 359
  c 468 and 324
  d 238 and 430
  e 4950 and 4840
  f $6d$ and $24d$

5 Find the LCM of each of these sets of numbers:
  a 31 and 26
  b 34 and 39
  c 278 and 694
  d 648 and 132
  e 12, 18 and 30
  f 16, 9 and 12

6 Work out these problems involving fractions.
(Hint: first find the LCM of the denominators.)
  a $\frac{23}{72} + \frac{12}{90}$
  b $\frac{13}{24} - \frac{60}{122}$
  c $\frac{24}{125} - \frac{24}{200}$
  d $\frac{43}{56} + \frac{67}{80}$

7 Puzzle
  a Which of these numbers is 2004 divisible by? Explain your method.
    i 15
    ii 12
    iii 22
    iv 25
    v 30
  b What is the smallest number that can be divided by 12, 15, 22, 25 and 30 without leaving a remainder?

8 Puzzle
Find all the pairs of numbers that have an HCF of 30 and an LCM of 3150.

9 Puzzle
Use the digits 0, 1, 5, 6, 7, and 8 to make two 3-digit numbers with an HCF of 45. Explain your method.

10 Puzzle
  a Write down a 2-digit number (for example, 47).
  b Reverse the digits (74).
  c Subtract the smaller number from the larger number ($74 - 47 = 27$).
  d Prove that the answer is always a multiple of 9.

Powers and roots

This spread will show you how to:
▶▶ Estimate square roots and cube roots.
▶▶ Use index notation for small integer powers.
▶▶ Use simple instances of the index laws.

KEYWORDS
Power   Square root
Cube root   Index notation
Trial and improvement
Index laws

Powers

You can represent powers of 10, including fractions, using index notation:

Remember: You can represent powers of **any** number using index notation.
$6^5 = 6 \times 6 \times 6 \times 6 \times 6 = 7776$.

Numbers being divided by 10

100 ($= 10 \times 10$)	10	1	.	$\frac{1}{10} = 0.1$	$\frac{1}{100} = 0.01$
10^2	10^1	10^0	.	10^{-1}	10^{-2}

You say 10^{-2} as '10 raised to the power of $^-2$'.

Powers decreasing by 1

Roots

▶ A positive integer has two square roots, one positive and one negative.
$\sqrt{25} = 5$ or $^-5$ because $5 \times 5 = 25$ and $^-5 \times ^-5 = 25$

▶ A positive number has a positive cube root ... $^3\sqrt{27} = 3$

... and a negative number has a negative cube root $^3\sqrt{^-27} = ^-3$

You can write:
$\sqrt{25} = \pm 5$

You can use **trial and improvement** to estimate square roots and cube roots.

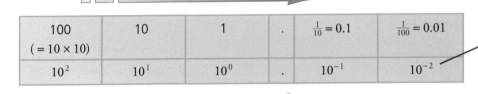

example

Find $^3\sqrt{30}$ to one decimal place.

$3^3 = 27$ and $4^3 = 64$ so $^3\sqrt{30}$ lies in between 3 and 4.
$3.5^3 = 42.875$ (> 30)   so $^3\sqrt{30}$ lies in between 3 and 3.5
Try $3.1^3 = 29.791$ (< 30)   so $^3\sqrt{30}$ lies in between 3.1 and 3.5
Try $3.2^3 = 32.768$ (> 30)   so $^3\sqrt{30}$ lies in between 3.1 and 3.2
Now find 3.15^3 to see if the root is between 3.1 and 3.15 or 3.15 and 3.2.
$3.15^3 = 31.256 (>30)$ so $^3\sqrt{30} =$ lies between 3.1 and 3.15.
                             so $^3\sqrt{30} = 3.1$ to 1 decimal place.

Exercise NA1.4

1 Write each of these numbers using index notation:
  a 10
  b 1000
  c one hundred thousand
  d one million

2 Use an appropriate method to work out:
  a $^-6^3$ **b** 5^4 **c** $^-10^3$
  d 0.1^2 **e** $(\frac{1}{4})^3$ **f** 0.5^3
  g $\sqrt{361}$ **h** $\sqrt[3]{343}$ **i** 17^3

3 Investigation
  a Use your calculator to work out the value of:
    i 3^0 **ii** $^-10^0$ **iii** $(\frac{1}{4})^0$
  b Try other numbers raised to the power of zero. What do you notice?

4 Calculate these using an appropriate method:
  a $3^2 + 4^2$ **b** $4^3 \times 4^2$
  c $5^2 - 5^3$ **d** $7^2 \times 4^2$
  e $3^5 \div 3^2$ **f** $12^3 \times 2^3$

5 Game – Root targets
  Working with a partner, take it in turns to try to 'hit' the target number without using the $\sqrt{}$ key on your calculator. Here is an example:

  Target $\sqrt{5.76}$

  Player 1 guesses 2.1
  Check: $2.1 \times 2.1 = \mathbf{4.41}$ too small

  Player 2 guesses 2.7
  Check: $2.7 \times 2.7 = \mathbf{7.29}$ too big

  Player 1 guesses 2.4
  Check: $2.4 \times 2.4 = \mathbf{5.76}$ just right!

  a Target $\sqrt{31.4721}$
  b Target $\sqrt{237.16}$
  c Target $\sqrt{123.4321}$

6 Investigation
  $1^2 = 1$
  $11^2 = 121$
  a Use a calculator to work out the answers to **i** 111^2 **ii** 1111^2.
  b Extend the pattern and comment on what you notice.

7 Estimate the cube root of 40 to 1 decimal place.

8 Investigation
  a Which of these statements are true?
    i $\sqrt{16} + \sqrt{9} = \sqrt{(16 + 9)}$
    ii $\sqrt{16} \div \sqrt{9} = \sqrt{(16 \div 9)}$
    iii $\sqrt{16} - \sqrt{9} = \sqrt{(16 - 9)}$
  b Try to find out which of the statements are always true for **any** pair of numbers.

9 Mary says that $7^2 \times 4^3 = 28^5$.
  Tom disagrees.
  Explain why Tom disagrees with Mary.

10 Use a calculator to work out these, writing your answer:
  i as a decimal   **ii** as a fraction
  a 2^{-1} **b** 2^{-2} **c** 2^{-3}
  d Look carefully at your fraction answers. Write down anything you notice.

11 Investigation
  a Work out, writing your answer in index notation:
    i $5^2 \times 5^3$ **ii** $6^2 \times 6^2$ **iii** $10^4 \times 10^3$
  b Use your answers to part **a** to help you write a rule for multiplying numbers in index form.
  c Work out, writing your answers in index form:
    i $7^4 \div 7^1$ **ii** $8^3 \div 8^2$ **iii** $10^6 \div 10^4$
  d Use your answers to part **c** to help you write a rule for dividing numbers in index form.

Generating sequences

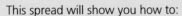

This spread will show you how to:

▶▶ Generate and describe sequences.

▶▶ Review general properties of linear sequences of the form $an + b$.

▶▶ Find the nth term of a linear sequence, justifying its form.

KEYWORDS

Term	Difference
Sequence	Justify
Linear sequence	
Position-to-term rule	

▶ A **sequence** is a set of numbers that follow a rule.

▶ A **linear sequence** is a set of numbers that:

go up by the same amount ... 1, 8, 15, 22, 29, ...

... or down by the same amount ... 30, 23, 16, 9, 2, ...

▶ You can use algebra to find any term of a sequence if you know its position.

APRIL						
M	**T**	**W**	**Th**	**F**	**S**	**S**
	1	2	3	4	5	6
7	8	9	10	11	12	13
14	15	16	17	18	19	20
21	22	23	24	25	26	27
28	29	30				

Here is an example of a **position-to-term rule**: $T(n) = 5n + 1$

$T(n)$ is the nth term n is the position

Use the formula to find the first term ($n = 1$) like this: $T(1) = 5 \times 1 + 1 = 6$
You can construct a table of values:

Position	1st	2nd	3rd	4th	...	100th	...
Term	$5 \times 1 + 1$ $= 6$	$5 \times 2 + 1$ $= 11$	$5 \times 3 + 1$ $= 16$	$5 \times 4 + 1$ $= 21$	...	$5 \times 100 + 1$ $= 501$	...

Linear sequences behave like times tables.
You can use this fact to find the formula.

Here is a linear sequence:

8,   11,   14,   17,   20,   ...

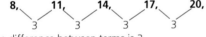

The difference between terms is 3.

Here is the 3 times table:

3,   6,   9,   12,   15, ...

The difference between terms is 3.

The algebra formula for the sequence 8, 11, 14, 17, 20, ... is connected to the 3 times table.

To get each term you × 3 then + 5.
The formula is $T(n) = 3n + 5$

Position n	1	2	3	4	5	×3
$3 \times$ table	3	6	9	12	15	
Term $T(n)$	8	11	14	17	20	+5

Diagrams often contain linear sequences.

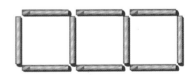

1 Construct a table:

Squares, n	1	2	3	4	...
$3 \times$ table	3	6	9	12	...
Straws, s	4	7	10	13	...

2 Find a rule:
Number of straws = 3 × number of squares +1
$n = 3s + 1$

3 Justify the formula:
Each new square needs 3 straws to make it plus the 1 at the start.

Exercise NA1.5

1 Here is a page from a calendar.

JULY						
M	T	W	Th	F	S	S
		1	2	3	4	5
6	7	8	9	10	11	12
13	14	15	16	17	18	19
20	21	22	23	24	25	26
27	28	29	30	31		

Write down as many **linear** sequences as you can find.

2 Copy and complete these linear sequences:
  a 5, 16, 27, 38, __, __, ...
  b 36, 33, 30, 27, __, __, ...
  c 4, __, 8, __, 12, ...
  d 3, __, __, 33, __, ...
  e 6, __, __, __, 26, ...
  f 98, __, __, __, 78, ...

3 a Write down the first five terms of the sequences described by these position-to-term rules:

  i $T(n) = 4n + 1$ **ii** $T(n) = 6n - 3$

  iii $T(n) = 7n$ **iv** $T(n) = 18 - 3n$

  b Name the sequence you have generated in **a** part **iii**.

4 a Generate the linear sequence that this flow chart describes.

  b Design your own flow chart for the sequence 4, 7, 10, 13, 17, 20, 23.

5 Find a formula for $T(n)$, the general term of each sequence, in terms of n, the term number:
  a 4, 9, 14, 19, 24, ...
  b 3, 5, 7, 9, 11, ...
  c 17, 30, 43, 56, 69, ...
  d 20, 18, 16, 14, 12, ...
  e multiples of 12
  f counting down from 100 in 5s.

6 a Write down three different linear sequences with a third term of 10.
  b Find a formula for $T(n)$ in each case and give the 500th term.

7 The general formula for a linear sequence is $T(n) = an + b$, where a and b are constants (numbers).
What can you say about:
  a a if the linear sequence is increasing in threes?
  b b if the sequence is multiples of 10
  c sequences where the value of a is 2
  d a if the linear sequence is going down by a constant amount?

8 The 100th, 101st and 102nd terms of a linear sequence are 307, 310 and 313.
  a Find a formula for $T(n)$.
  b Use it to generate the first five terms of the sequence.

9 Use this pattern to find a formula connecting the length of the middle square (L) and the number of white tiles (T). Justify why the formula works.

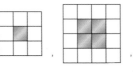

1 × 1   2 × 2   3 × 3

Quadratic sequences

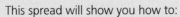

This spread will show you how to:

▶▶ Begin to generate a quadratic sequence.

▶▶ Substitute positive numbers into expressions involving powers.

▶▶ Find the next term and the *n*th term of a quadratic sequence.

KEYWORDS

Power	Sequence
Formula	*n*th term
Second difference	
Quadratic sequence	

Before calculators, the Chinese worked out square roots by repeatedly subtracting odd numbers.

The method works because you can write each square number as the sum of consecutive odd numbers.

The sequence of square numbers is an example of a **quadratic sequence**. It includes an n^2 term.

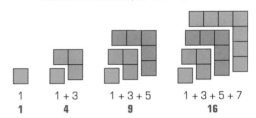

▶ A quadratic sequence contains a squared term as its highest power.

The general term of a particular quadratic sequence is given by the formula $T(n) = 3n^2$.
Find the first five terms of the sequence.

Position, *n*	1	2	3	4	5
Term, T(*n*)	$3 \times 1^2 = 3$	$3 \times 2^2 = 12$	$3 \times 3^2 = 27$	$3 \times 4^2 = 48$	$3 \times 5^2 = 75$

The quadratic sequence is 3, 12, 27, 48, 75, ...

Remember:
BIDMAS
Indices before
Multiplying.

In a quadratic sequence, the **second difference** is constant.

Find an expression for T(*n*), the general term of the sequence 6, 9, 14, 21, 30, ...

First look at the differences:

6   9   14   21   30

First difference   3   5   7   9

Second difference   2   2   2

Draw a table:

Position *n*	1	2	3	4	5
Square numbers, n^2	1	4	9	16	25
Term T(*n*)	6	9	14	21	30

square

+5

Write a formula: You square and add 5 to get each term.   ⟹ $T(n) = n^2 + 5$

Exercise NA1.6

1

prime numbers   10, 40, 90, 160, 250, ... *square numbers*

3, 6, 9, 12, 15, ...   2, 4, 8, 16, 32, 64, ...

triangular numbers   *multiples of 11*

0, 3, 8, 15, 24, ...

Find all of the quadratic sequences in the box.

2 Generate the next five terms of each of these quadratic sequences.

   a 2, 5, 10, 17, 26, ...
   b ⁻1, 2, 7, 14, 23, ...
   c 4, 16, 36, 64, 100, ...
   d 2, 6, 12, 20, 30, ...
   e 10, 13, 18, 25, 34, ...

3 **a** For a particular sequence
     $T(n) = (n + 2)(n + 3)$.
     Generate the first five terms of this sequence.
   b Using differences, decide if the sequence is quadratic. Explain how you might have known this from the formula.

4 Copy and complete this crossword by finding the specified term for each clue.

Across
   1 $T(n) = n^2 + 3$ ... 3rd term
   3 $T(n) = n(n + 1)$ ... 6th term
   4 $T(n) = n^2$ ... 24th term
   6 $T(n) = \frac{n^2}{2}$ ... 2nd term

Down
   1 $T(n) = n^2 - 1$ ... 14th term
   2 $T(n) = 2n^2$ ... 4th term
   3 $T(n) = 3n^2 - 2$ ... 4th term
   5 $T(n) = (n + 3)(n + 4)$ ... 5th term

5 **a** Copy and complete the table.

	Sequence	Value of second difference	Position-to-term formula
i	1, 4, 9, 16, 25, ...		
ii	2, 8, 18, 32, 50		
iii	3, 12, 27, 48, 75		
iv	4, 16, 36, 64, 100		
v	5, 20, 45, 80, 125		

   b Explain what you notice and use this to help you to find a general formula for
     i 10, 16, 26, 40, 58, ...
     ii 9, 39, 89, 159, 249, ...

6 For each sequence of diagrams, find a formula connecting the given quantities. Try to explain why this formula works.

   a

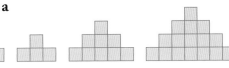

     Height of staircase, number of blocks

   b

     Height of rectangle, number of blocks

   c

     Height of staircase, number of blocks
     (Hint: Connect to **b**).
     What is this sequence called?

7 **Challenge**
   Find the *n*th term formula for:
   a 4, 9, 16, 25, 36, ...
   b 6, 12, 20, 30, 42, ...
   c $\frac{1}{9}, \frac{4}{16}, \frac{9}{25}, \frac{16}{36}, \frac{25}{49}, ...$

You should know how to ...

1 Make and justify estimates and approximations of calculations.

2 Solve substantial problems by breaking them into simpler tasks.

3 Generate terms of a sequence using term-to-term and position-to-term definitions of the sequence.

4 Write an expression to describe the *n*th term of an arithmetic sequence.

Check out

1 a Estimate the number of drawing pins in 267 tubs that are labelled 'approximate contents 1500'.

   b Estimate the distance covered by a person who walks 23 times around the perimeter of a regular pentagon of side 8.6 m.
Justify your answer.

2 Find the dimensions of the rectangle with the largest area whose perimeter is 10 m.

3 a Generate the first five terms of the sequences described by these position-to-term formulae.

     i $T(n) = 3n + 7$ **ii** $T(n) = n^2 + 2$

     iii $T(n) = 7 - 2n$ **iv** $T(n) = 2n^2 + 1$

   b Decide if each sequence in part (**a**) is linear, quadratic or neither.

   c Match, without a calculator, the formula of a sequence with its 10th term:

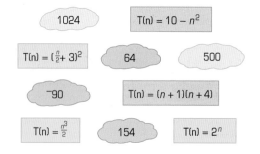

1024 $T(n) = 10 - n^2$

$T(n) = (\frac{n}{2} + 3)^2$ 64   500

⁻90 $T(n) = (n + 1)(n + 4)$

$T(n) = \frac{n^3}{2}$ 154 $T(n) = 2^n$

4 a Derive a formula for $T(n)$, the *n*th term of each sequence:

     i 3, 8, 13, 18, 23, ... **ii** 0, 3, 8, 15, 24, ...

     iii 30, 27, 24, 21, 18, ...

     iv 3, 12, 27, 48, 75, ...

     v $\frac{8}{3}, \frac{14}{6}, \frac{20}{11}, \frac{26}{18}, \frac{32}{27} \ldots$

   b i Generate the first five terms of $T(n) = (n + 2)^2$.

     ii Use what you notice to write a formula for the sequence 36, 49, 64, 81, 100 ...

This unit will show you how to:

▶▶ Solve problems using properties of angles, of parallel and intersecting lines, and of triangles and other polygons.

▶▶ Explain how to find, calculate and use the interior and exterior angles of polygons.

▶▶ Know the definition of a circle and its parts.

▶▶ Explain why inscribed regular polygons can be constructed by equal divisions of a circle.

▶▶ Use straight edge and compasses to construct a triangle, given right angle, hypotenuse and side (RHS).

▶▶ Solve increasingly demanding problems and evaluate solutions.

▶▶ Present a concise, reasoned argument.

Circles are all around us.

Before you start

You should know how to ...

1 Calculate angles on:
   a   a straight line
   b   in a triangle
   c   at a point.

2 Know the names of polygons.

Check in

1 Calculate the unknown angles.

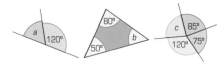

2 Name these shapes.

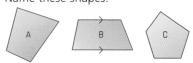

KEYWORDS

Parallel   Intersection

Corresponding

Alternate

Supplementary

Vertically opposite

This spread will show you how to:

▶▶ Know and use angle properties of parallel and intersecting lines to solve problems and explain reasoning.

▶▶ Understand a proof that the sum of the angles in a triangle is 180° and of a quadrilateral is 360°.

When you draw a straight line across two parallel lines, you create:

corresponding angles   **alternate** angles   **supplementary** angles

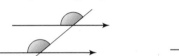      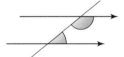

▶ Corresponding angles are equal. Alternate angles are equal. Supplementary angles add up to 180°.

You also create **vertically opposite** angles at the intersections.

▶ Vertically opposite angles are equal.

Remember: Angles in a straight line add to 180°.

You can use these facts with angles in polygons.

example

a Prove that the angles in a triangle add up to 180°.

b Use this fact to prove that the angles in a quadrilateral add up to 360°.

....

a Draw a triangle ABC between two parallel lines.

$x + c + y = 180°$ (angles on a straight line) $x = a$ (alternate angles)
                                                        $y = b$ (alternate angles)

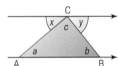

So $a + b + c = 180°$.

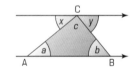

b Draw a quadrilateral ABCD and split it into two triangles.

Angles in $\triangle ABD = 180°$.
Angles in $\triangle BCD = 180°$.

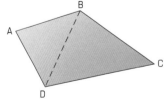

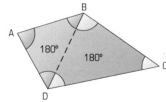

So the sum of angles in ABCD $= 180° + 180° = 360°$.

Exercise S1.1

Calculate the unknown angles, giving reasons for your answers.

1

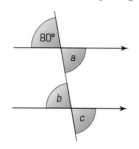

2

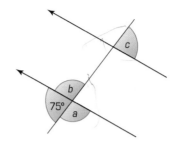

3

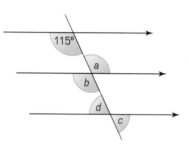

4

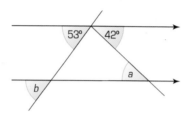

5

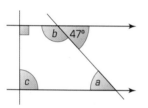

6

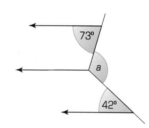

7

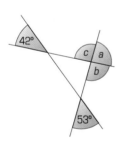

8

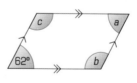

9

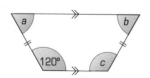

10

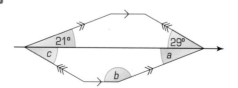

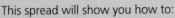

S1.2 Triangle properties

This spread will show you how to:
- ▶▶ Find, calculate and use properties of the interior and exterior angles of triangles.
- ▶▶ Understand a proof that the exterior angle of a triangle equals the sum of the two interior opposite angles.

A triangle has three **interior** angles.

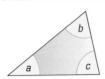

If you extend one of the lines, you create an **exterior** angle d.

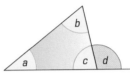

$a + b + c = 180°$ (angles in a triangle)

$c + d = 180°$ (angles on a straight line)

So $a + b + c = c + d$

Therefore $a + b = d$

▶ **The exterior angle of a triangle is equal to the sum of the two interior opposite angles.**

You can use this fact to find angles both inside and outside triangles.

example

Find the unknown angles.

Do not measure the angles. You are meant to **calculate** them.

a

b

a $a = 120° - 42°$
  $= 78°$

b $b = 140° - 90°$
  $= 50°$

example

a Find angle x.

b Find angle a.

Always **sketch** a diagram and fill in any angles that you know.

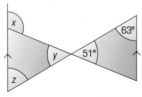

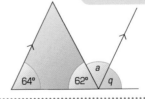

$y = 51°$ (vertically opposite angles)
$z = 63°$ (alternate angles)
So $x = 63° + 51°$ (exterior angle)
  $= 114°$

$q = 64°$ (corresponding angles)
$a = 180° - 64° - 62°$ (angles on a straight line)
  $= 54°$

Exercise S1.2

Find the unknown angles, giving reasons for your answers.

1

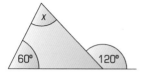

2

3

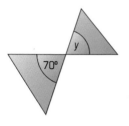

4

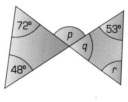

5

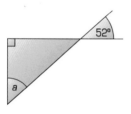

6

7

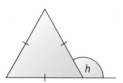

8

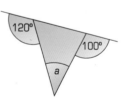

9

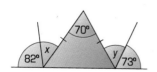

10

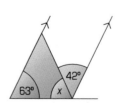

S1.3 Calculating angles in polygons

This spread will show you how to:

▶▶ Find, calculate and use the interior and exterior angles of regular polygons.

▶▶ Find, calculate and use the sums of the interior and exterior angles of quadrilaterals, pentagons and hexagons.

KEYWORDS

Pentagon   Hexagon
Polygon
Interior angle
Exterior angle
Regular polygon

You can split a ...

... quadrilateral into two triangles

The sum of the interior angles is $2 \times 180° = 360°$.

... pentagon into three triangles

The sum of the interior angles is $3 \times 180° = 540°$.

... hexagon into four triangles.

The sum of the interior angles is $4 \times 180° = 720°$.

▶ A polygon with n sides can be split into $(n - 2)$ triangles, each with an angle sum of 180°.

▶ The interior angle sum S of any polygon with n sides is given by the formula: $S = (n - 2) \times 180°$.

Check the formula for a hexagon where $n = 6$:
$S = (6 - 2) \times 180° = 720°$.

▶ At each vertex of any polygon, the sum of the interior and exterior angles is 180°.

For a hexagon, the sum of six interior and six exterior angles is $6 \times 180°$.
But the sum of the interior angles is $4 \times 180°$, so the sum of the exterior angles is $2 \times 180° = 360°$.

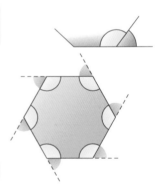

▶ The sum of the exterior angles of any polygon is 360°.

In a regular polygon all the angles are equal.

▶ The interior angle of a regular polygon is $S \div n$ where S = the interior angle sum and n is the number of sides.

Remember:
Each of the interior angles in an equilateral triangle is
$180° \div 3 = 60°$.

Exercise S1.3

Calculate the unknown angles, giving reasons for your answers.

1

2

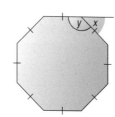

3

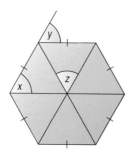

4

5

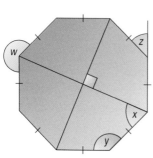

6

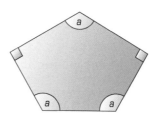

7

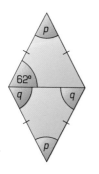

8

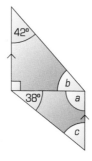

9 How many sides has a regular polygon with interior angles of 140°?
Explain your answer.

10 How many sides has a regular polygon with interior angles of 135°?
Explain your answer.

11 Can a regular polygon have an interior angle of 100°? Explain your answer.

12 a If the exterior angle of a regular polygon is 30°, how many sides does it have?
b What are the sizes of the interior angles?

Circle properties

This spread will show you how to:
▶▶ Know the parts of a circle.
▶▶ Construct inscribed regular polygons in a circle.

KEYWORDS
Circumference   Arc
Chord   Diameter
Sector   Segment
Inscribe   Radius

You need to know the names of parts of a circle.

The **circumference** is the distance around a circle.

An **arc** is part of the circumference.

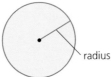

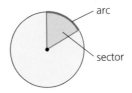

The **radius** is the distance from the centre to the circumference.

A **sector** is a region bounded by an arc and two radii.

Radii is the plural of radius.

A **chord** is a straight line joining any two points on the circumference.

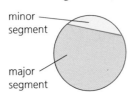

A chord divides the circle into two **segments**.

A chord that passes through the centre is called a **diameter**.

A diameter is twice the length of a radius, and it splits the circle into two semicircles.

You can draw, or **inscribe**, regular polygons within a circle.

example

By dividing a circle into equal parts, construct a regular octagon.

1 Draw a circle using compasses.

2 $360° \div 8 = 45°$, so draw radii at 45° angles.

3 Join the chords. The resulting shape is a regular octagon.

Note:
The octagon is regular because it is made from congruent isosceles triangles.

▶ Inscribed regular polygons can be constructed by equal divisions of a circle.

Exercise S1.4

1 Copy the diagrams and label the parts of the circle.

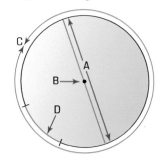
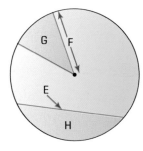

2 **a** Draw a circle with radius 8 cm.
   b Draw in one diameter AB.
   c From AB draw two lines AC and BC where C is on the
      circumference.
   d Measure accurately the angles A, B and C.
   e Repeat for four more positions of C and record your
      results in a table.

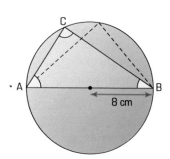

	Angle A	Angle B	Angle C
1			
2			
3			
4			
5			

   f What do you notice about your results?

3 **a** If chords of length equal to the radius are constructed around
      a circle, explain why the inscribed polygon is a regular hexagon.
   b Construct a regular hexagon with side 4 cm.

4 Find the unknown angles.
   Use your results from question 2 to help you.

   a 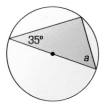   **b** 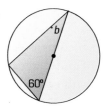   **c**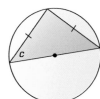

This spread will show you how to:

▶▶ Use straight edge and compasses to construct a triangle.

KEYWORDS

Construction

Compasses

How you construct a triangle will depend on the information that you are given.

Angle, side, angle (ASA)

example

It is useful to do a sketch first.

Construct △XYZ where XY = 9 cm, ∠X = 50° and ∠Y = 40°.

1 Draw the baseline XY with a ruler.

2 Draw ∠X using a protractor.

3 Draw ∠Y using a protractor.

4 Extend the lines from X and Y, and label the intersection Z.

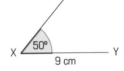 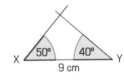 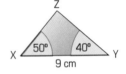

Side, angle, side (SAS)

example

Construct △PQR where PQ = 6 cm, QR = 5 cm and ∠Q = 40°.

1 Draw the baseline PQ.

2 Draw ∠Q.

3 Mark 5 cm along the line from Q.

4 Join PR.

 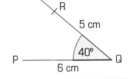 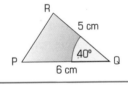

Side, side, side (SSS)

Leave on the construction lines. They show evidence of your working.

example

Construct △ABC where AB = 7 cm, BC = 5 cm and AC = 4 cm.

1 Draw the baseline AB.

2 Open compasses to 5 cm and draw an arc with centre B.

3 Open compasses to 4 cm and draw an arc with centre A.

4 Join A and B to the intersection C.

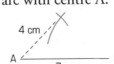 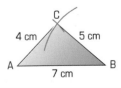

Exercise S1.5

1 Construct △PQR with PQ = 6 cm, QR = 8 cm and RP = 7 cm.

2
a Construct △XYZ with XY = 5 cm, ∠X = 40°, ∠Y = 50°.
b Measure angle Z.
c What type of triangle is △XYZ?

3 Construct △ABC with AB = 6.2 cm, BC = 7.4 cm, ∠B = 43°.

4 Using only a pair of compasses construct:
a △XYZ where XY = YZ = XZ = 5.4 cm
b △PQR where PQ = QR = 4.2 cm and ∠Q = 60°.

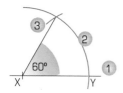

To construct an angle of 60°, draw a base line ①, draw an arc ② from X, draw a second arc ③ from Y.

c What type of triangle is PQR?

5
a Construct △DEF where DE = 8 cm, EF = 9 cm, DF = 7 cm.
b Bisect each side using compasses.

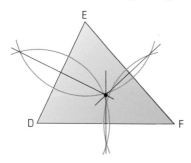

c Label the point P where the bisectors meet and draw a circle, centre P, through DEF.

Note:
This is known as a **circumcircle**.

6 Is it possible to construct these triangles?
Give reasons for your answer.
a △ABC: AB = 5 cm, BC = 3 cm, CA = 1 cm
b △PQR: PQ = QR = RP = 4 cm
c △XYZ: XZ = 5 cm, ∠X = 95°, ∠Y = 90°
d △EFG: EF = 9 cm, ∠E = 90°, EG = 4 cm
e △WXY: ∠X = 40°, ∠Y = 50°, ∠Z = 90°
f △MNO where ∠M = 50°, ∠N = 50° and ∠O = 90°.

7 Draw △PQR, where PQ = QR = RP = 7 cm.
Bisect each angle and use the point of intersection of the bisectors as the centre of an inscribed circle.

Constructing right-angled triangles

This spread will show you how to:
▶▶ Construct the perpendicular from a point on a line.
▶▶ Construct a triangle given right angle, hypotenuse and side.

You can use a pair of compasses to construct an angle of 90°.

Construct a perpendicular at the point P on the line PQ.
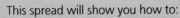

1 Extend the line QP.
2 With centre P, draw two arcs to cut the line at A and B
3 With centre A, draw an arc above PQ.

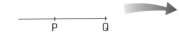

5 Join XP.
Angle XPQ is 90°.

4 With centre B and the same radius, draw an arc to cut the first at X.

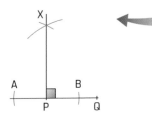

You can use this technique to construct a right-angled triangle.

Construct △PQR where ∠P = 90°, QR = 7 cm and PR = 5 cm.

1 First sketch the triangle.
2 Draw the base PR 5 cm long.
3 Construct a perpendicular PX at P.

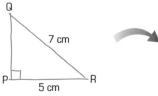
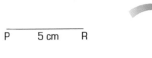
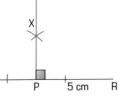

5 Label the intersection Q. This is the completed triangle.
4 Open compasses to 7 cm and draw an arc from R.

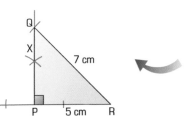
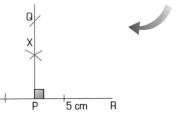

Exercise S1.6

1 **a** Draw a base line AB 10 cm long.
  b Construct a 90° angle at A.
  c From B find C_1 where $BC_1 = 11$ cm.
  d From B find C_2 where $BC_2 = 12$ cm.
  e From B find C_3 where $BC_3 = 13$ cm.
  f Measure **i** C_1C_2 **ii** C_2C_3, giving
      your answers to the nearest millimetre.

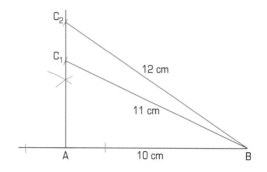

2 **a** Construct $\triangle ABC$ where $\angle A = 90°$, AB = 5 cm and
      AC = 5 cm.
  b Measure CB and construct $\triangle CBD$ where $\angle C = 90°$
      and CB = CD.
  c Construct $\triangle BDE$ where $\angle D = 90°$ and DE = BD.
  d Construct $\triangle BEF$ where $\angle E = 90°$ and BE = EF.
      Continue your pattern.
      Describe what happens.

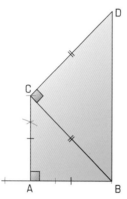

3 A ladder 5 m long rests up against a wall.
   The wall is perpendicular to the ground.
   How far up the wall does the ladder reach if it is 1.5 m
   away from the base of the wall?
   Use a scale drawing to solve this problem.

4 A boat is 50 m away from the bottom of a vertical cliff.
   The distance from the boat directly to the top of the
   cliff is 90 m.
   How high is the cliff? (Use a scale 1 cm : 10 m.)

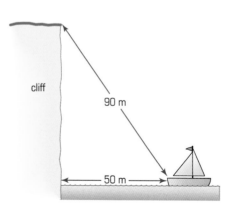

You should know how to ...

1 Solve problems using properties of angles, of parallel and intersecting lines, and of triangles and other polygons.

2 Present a concise, reasoned argument, using symbols, diagrams, graphs and related explanatory text.

3 Solve substantial problems by breaking them into simpler tasks.

4 Use straight edge and compasses to construct a triangle.

Check out

1 Find a, b and c.

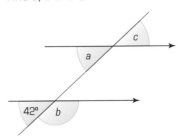

2 Give reasons for each of your answers to question 1.

3 Construct a regular octagon by drawing a circle.

4 Construct these triangles.
   a △ABC: AB = 4.7 cm, BC = 5.3, ∠B = 62°
   b △PQR: PQ = 4 cm = QR, PR = 7 cm
   c △XYZ: XY = 4.3 cm, ∠Y = 90°, YZ = 5.2 cm.

1 Probability

This unit will show you how to:

▶▶ Use the vocabulary of probability in interpreting results involving uncertainty and prediction.

▶▶ Identify all the mutually exclusive outcomes of an experiment.

▶▶ Estimate probabilities from experimental data.

▶▶ Compare experimental and theoretical probabilities in a range of contexts.

▶▶ Find and record all possible outcomes.

▶▶ Appreciate the difference between mathematical explanation and experimental evidence.

▶▶ Solve increasingly demanding problems and evaluate solutions.

▶▶ Solve substantial problems by breaking them into simpler tasks.

▶▶ Present a concise reasoned argument.

Most games contain an element of chance.

Before you start

You should know how to ...

1 Find and justify simple probabilities based on equally likely outcomes.

2 Calculate with fractions and decimals.

3 Collate data into a tally chart.

Check in

1 A ten-sided dice numbered 1–10 is thrown. What is the probability of getting:

a 2 **b** 7 or 8?

2 Calculate:

a $1 - \frac{1}{3}$ **b** $1 - 0.24$ **c** $\frac{2}{5} \times \frac{3}{8}$

3 Draw a tally chart to show these frequencies of pets owned by a group of students.

Dog (D), Cat (C), Rabbit (R)

D C D R C D D D C D R C C D

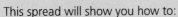

This spread will show you how to:
- ▶▶ Use the vocabulary of probability in interpreting results involving uncertainty and prediction.
- ▶▶ Know that if the probability of an event occurring is p, then the probability of it not occurring is $1 - p$.
- ▶▶ Appreciate that random processes are unpredictable.

KEYWORDS

Equally likely   Event
Outcome   Trial
Theoretical probability
Sample space
Random process

In probability an **event** is a collection of possible outcomes.
When you roll an ordinary dice the event 'factors of 5' has outcomes 1 and 5.

The set of all possible outcomes is called the sample space.
When you roll an ordinary dice the sample space is {1, 2, 3, 4, 5, 6}.

If each outcome in the sample space is equally likely to occur then:

> ▶ Theoretical probability of an event = $\dfrac{\text{number of favourable outcomes}}{\text{total number of outcomes in sample space}}$

example

Martine rolls an ordinary dice.
Find the probability of the top face showing:

a a multiple of 3   **b** a number that is not a multiple of 3

a The multiples of 3 are 3 and 6 $\Rightarrow$ there are two favourable outcomes.

Probability (multiple of 3) $= \dfrac{2}{6}$ $\dfrac{\text{two favourable outcomes}}{\text{six possible outcomes}}$

b There are two favourable outcomes $\Rightarrow$ there are four unfavourable outcomes.

Probability (not a multiple of 3) $= \dfrac{4}{6}$ $\left(1 - \dfrac{2}{6} = \dfrac{4}{6}\right)$

> ▶ If Probability (event occurs) $= p$
> then Probability (event does not occur) $= 1 - p$

In real situations involving **random** events, the outcome of a trial is uncertain.

> ▶ An experiment such as rolling a dice is a random process, and so the outcome is unpredictable.

Exercise D1.1

1 For each of these trials, list all the outcomes in the sample space.

  a The school year of a student chosen at random from an 11–16 secondary school.

  b The way a drawing pin points when dropped.

  c The score from a single dart thrown at a dartboard. (Ignore doubles, trebles and bulls'-eyes)

  d The colour of traffic lights at a busy junction.

  e The result of a football match.

  f The suit chosen when picking a card from a pack of ordinary playing cards.

2 For each of the trials outlined in question 1:

  ▸ State whether or not all the outcomes are equally likely.

  ▸ If they are equally likely, write down the probability of each outcome occurring.

  If they are not equally likely give a reason why not.

3 For each of these trials explain why you cannot easily list all the outcomes in the sample space.

  a The colour of the next car to arrive in the school car park.

  b The first name of a person chosen at random in the high street.

4 For each of these events:

  i List the favourable outcomes.

  ii Use your answer to **a** to write down the theoretical probability that the event occurs.

    a Obtaining an even number when rolling an ordinary dice.

  b Obtaining a prime number when rolling an ordinary dice.

  c Choosing an ace from a pack of ordinary playing cards.

  d Choosing a picture card from an ordinary pack of playing cards.

  e Choosing a diamond from an ordinary pack of playing cards.

  f Choosing the correct answer in a multiple-choice test question that has five possible answers.

5 Copy and complete the table, working out the probabilities that the events do not occur.

Event	A	B	C	D	E
Probability (event occurs)	$\frac{1}{4}$	0.82	$\frac{2}{3}$	$\frac{5}{12}$	0.36
Probability (event does not occur)					

6 Marsha has a bag of coloured sweets. They are red, blue, green or yellow.
She has partly completed a table showing the probabilities of choosing a particular colour.

  a Copy and complete the table.

Outcome	Red	Blue	Green	Yellow
Probability (event occurs)	0.45			0.1
Probability (event does not occur)		0.8		

  b There are 20 sweets in total. How many of each colour are there?

This spread will show you how to:
- ▶▶ Identify all the mutually exclusive outcomes of an experiment.
- ▶▶ Find and record all possible outcomes in a systematic way.
- ▶▶ Know that the sum of probabilities of all mutually exclusive outcomes is 1.

KEYWORDS
Mutually exclusive
Outcome   Systematic
Sample space diagram
Tree diagram   Event

▶ Two events are **mutually exclusive** if they cannot occur at the same time.

In a bag of marbles some are yellow and the rest are blue.

The events 'choose a yellow marble' and 'choose a blue marble' are mutually exclusive.
If p(yellow) = 0.7, then p(blue) = 0.3

▶ The sum of probabilities of all the mutually exclusive outcomes is 1.

A second bag contains marbles that are either green or white or red. One marble is chosen from each of the two bags. Here are two ways to record all possible outcomes.

1. A **sample space diagram** is a table that shows all the possible outcomes.

	Green	White	Red
Yellow	Y and G	Y and W	Y and R
Blue	B and G	B and W	B and R

2. A **tree diagram** shows each event on a set of branches.

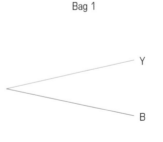

The six possible outcomes are found by travelling along the branches.

Bag 1   Bag 2

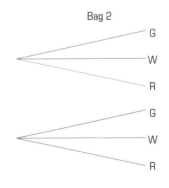

Y
⟨ G
  W
  R
B
⟨ G
  W
  R

One possible outcome is (Y, R), shown by the orange line.

Exercise D1.2

1 Hari buys an ice-cream. He can choose to have one flake, two flakes or none.
He can choose nut topping, chocolate sauce, strawberry sauce or no topping.
Draw a sample space diagram to show all the combinations of ice-cream that Hari can choose.

2 Two tetrahedral (four-sided) dice are rolled.
One is numbered 1, 2, 3, 4. The other is numbered 2, 4, 6, 8.

Draw a sample space diagram to show all possible outcomes when:
a the base numbers are added together
b the base numbers are multiplied together.

3 On a restaurant set menu you can choose a starter and a main course.

menu

starters	main
melon	lemon chicken
prawn cocktail	baked trout
soup	lasagne
	vegetarian flan

The starters are melon, prawn cocktail or soup.
The main courses are lemon chicken, baked trout, lasagne or vegetarian flan.
a Draw a sample space diagram to show the different combinations that someone could choose.
b How many different combinations are there?
c Write down how you could work out the total number of combinations without drawing the sample space diagram.

d How many combinations would there be if there were:
  i 4 starters and 5 main courses
  ii 7 starters and 6 main courses
  iii 4 starters, 6 main courses and 3 puddings?

4 Jerome has three coins: a 1p, 2p and 10p.
He throws all the coins in the air and notes whether they show heads or tails.
a Copy and complete the tree diagram to show all the different ways the coins could land.

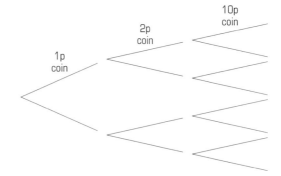

b How many combinations are there?
c How many of these combinations will give you two heads and a tail?

5 Jenny has three bags of coins.
In one bag she has 1p and 2p coins.
In a second bag she has 5p and 10p coins.
In a third bag she has 5p and 20p coins.

Jenny chooses one coin from each of the three bags.
Draw a tree diagram to show all the possible combinations of coins that Jenny can choose.

KEYWORDS

Equally likely outcome

Theoretical probability

Tree diagram

This spread will show you how to:

▶▶ Identify all the mutually exclusive outcomes of an experiment.

▶▶ Record all possible outcomes for two successive events using diagrams and tables.

Listing outcomes helps you to work out probabilities.

example

Two ordinary dice are rolled. Their scores are added.

a Draw a sample space diagram to show all possible outcomes.

b What is the probability of getting a total score of 6?

a

+	1	2	3	4	5	6
1	2	3	4	5	6	7
2	3	4	5	6	7	8
3	4	5	6	7	8	9
4	5	6	7	8	9	10
5	6	7	8	9	10	11
6	7	8	9	10	11	12

b There are 36 possible outcomes.

Each outcome is equally likely to occur.

There are five ways to score a total of 6.

$p(6) = \frac{5}{36}$

In the example, there are 36 possible outcomes, but only 11 **different** possible outcomes: 2, 3, 4, 5, 6, 7, 8, 9, 10, 11 and 12.

▶ You can use a **sample space diagram** to calculate theoretical probabilities for two successive events containing equally likely outcomes.

If the probabilities in each event are **not** equally likely then you need to draw a tree diagram.

example

Jenna has two bags of marbles.

In the first bag six are yellow and four are blue.

In the second bag five are green, three are white and two are red.

Jenna chooses a marble from each bag at random.

a Draw a tree diagram to show all possible outcomes.

b Find the probability that Jenna chooses a yellow and a white marble.

a

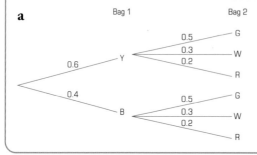

b To find the probability of choosing a yellow and a white marble you follow along the branch multiplying their probabilities.

$p(Y, W) = 0.6 \times 0.3$

$\qquad = 0.18$

Exercise D1.3

1 Tom is having pizza for his tea. He is allowed two extra toppings on his pizza. He chooses from ham, mushroom, pineapple, sweetcorn and extra cheese.
  a Draw a sample space diagram to show all the possible combinations of toppings Tom could choose. (He could choose two lots of the same topping.)
  b How many outcomes are there?

2 Use the sample space diagram on the opposite page to find the following probabilities of these events when two ordinary dice are rolled and their scores are added.
  a The score is odd.
  b The score is less than 5.
  c The score is a factor of 12.

3 Ursula rolls a dice and tosses a coin.

  a Draw a sample space diagram to show all possible outcomes.
     If she gets a factor of 6 she will wash her hair. If she gets a tail she will also use conditioner.
  b What is the probability that Ursula will wash her hair and use conditioner?

4 Use the tree diagram on the opposite page to find the probabilities of these events when one marble is chosen from each of Jenna's two bags of marbles.
  a A yellow and a green marble.
  b A blue and a red marble.

5 Thierry collects coins in two jars.

In one jar there are ten 1p coins and forty 2p coins.
In the second jar there are seventy 1p coins and thirty 2p coins.
Thierry chooses, at random, one coin from each of the two jars.
  a Draw a tree diagram showing the different combinations of coins that Thierry could choose. Write on your tree diagram the probability of choosing each coin.
  b Work out the probability that Thierry chooses coins with a total value of:
     i 2p   **ii** 3p   **iii** 4p

6 Maria empties a box containing three drawing pins on the floor.
  a Draw a tree diagram to show if they land point up (U) or point down (D).
  b One possible outcome is UUU. How many ways are there that the drawing pins could land?
  c How many ways would there be if Maria had
     i four drawing pins
     ii five drawing pins
     iii six drawing pins?
  d Write down a quick method that Maria could use to calculate the number of ways the drawing pins could land for any number of pins.

Experimental probability

This spread will show you how to:
▶▶ Estimate probabilities based on experimental data.

KEYWORDS
Tally chart
Experimental probability

Outcomes are not often equally likely.
You can estimate the probability of an outcome using an **experiment**.

Laura and Lucy are doing a project on the length of words in limericks.
They want to estimate the probability of choosing a five-letter word in a limerick.
Laura wrote a limerick.

Laura's limerick

> There was a young lady from Dover
> Who once found a fifteen-leaf clover
> Her friend said 'Oh dear –
> But your eyes have gone queer!
> You counted each leaf five times over.'

Lucy compiled a frequency table for the number of letters in each word.

Number of letters	1	2	3	4	5	6	7
Tally	II	I	IIII	IIII IIII IIII	IIII I	II	II
Frequency	2	1	5	14	6	2	2

There are 32 words in the limerick.
Six words have five letters.

$$p(5 \text{ letter word}) = \frac{6}{32}$$
$$= 0.1875$$
$$\simeq 0.2$$

This is only an estimate because it is based on the data that the girls collected from Laura's limerick.

Laura and Lucy **estimate** that the probability of choosing a five-letter word at random from any limerick is 0.2.

In an experiment:

▶ **Experimental probability** $= \dfrac{\text{number of successes}}{\text{total number of trials}}$

Exercise D1.4

1 Peter wrote a limerick.

> There once was a woman from Ealing
> Who walked upside down on a ceiling.
> She fell on her neck
> And said 'Oh my heck,
> What a peculiar feeling'.

a Draw a tally chart to show the length of each word.

b What is the probability that a word chosen at random will have
  i 3 letters
  ii 4 letters
  iii 6 or more letters?

2 Suzy counted the number of drawing pins in each of 40 boxes.

Here are her results:

35 37 42 36 36 35 40 41 41 39
41 42 34 37 38 39 39 93 42 36
41 42 40 38 37 38 37 34 36 35
42 35 35 39 36 42 42 35 41 39

a Suzy studied the results and decided that the result 93 had been incorrectly recorded. Give a reason for Suzy to reach this decision.

b Rewrite 93 as 39 and collate all the results in a tally chart.

c Use your chart to determine the probability of choosing a box of drawing pins containing:
  i 38 pins
  ii 42 pins
  iii 37 or fewer pins.

3 The table shows the number of goals scored by Warren Juniors Football Club in their last 20 games.

Goals scored	Number of games
0	3
1	6
2	4
3	2
4	3
5	1
6	0
7	0
8	1

a Estimate the probability that in their next game Warren JFC will score:
  i 1 goal
  ii 3 goals or fewer
  iii 5 or more goals.

b Explain why you think your answer to **iii** may be unrealistic.

4 A class of 32 students noted how many brothers and sisters they had.
Their results are summarised in the table.

Brothers

		0	1	2	3
S i s t e r s	0	4	5	1	0
	1	7	6	3	0
	2	0	4	0	0
	3	1	0	0	1

One student from the class is chosen at random.
What is the probability that this student will:

a be an only child

b have one brother and no sisters

c have one sister and two brothers

d have no brothers

e be in a family of seven children?

Probability and estimation

This spread will show you how to:
- ▶▶ Use the vocabulary of probability in interpreting results involving uncertainty and prediction.
- ▶▶ Estimate probabilities based on experimental data.

When you repeat an experiment you often get different results.

Ten students were asked to estimate the probability that a randomly chosen word in a book would contain the letter *s*.

Each student chose a different page and counted the number of words with the letter *s* in the first 40 words of the page.

Their results are summarised in the table.

Student	Amy	Beth	Cath	Dolores	Elena	Freya	Gina	Holly	Ivy	Jasmine
Words with an *s*	13	29	30	24	18	22	32	15	11	26

The probability of choosing a word with the letter *s* varies a lot.

If you use Amy's result the estimated probability is $\frac{13}{40} = 0.325$

If you use Gina's result the estimated probability is $\frac{32}{40} = 0.8$

A better estimate of the probability would come from combining all the results.

Number of words with an $s = 13 + 29 + 30 + 24 + 18 + 22 + 32 + 15 + 11 + 26 = 220$
Total number of words $= 10 \times 40 = 400$
p(word contains s) $= \frac{220}{400} = 0.55$

▶ If you use a small sample the experimental probability can vary a lot.

▶ Increasing the number of trials generally leads to better estimates of probability.

Remember: a trial is a repetition of an experiment.

Exercise D1.5

1 **a** Toss a coin ten times and write down how many times you get a tail.
Use this to estimate the probability of getting a tail.

 b Toss the coin a further ten times and use all 20 throws to estimate the probability of throwing a tail.

 c Toss the coin a further ten times and use all 30 throws to estimate the probability of throwing a tail.

 d Repeat the experiment until you have thrown the coin 100 times.
Write all ten estimated probabilities in a table.
Comment on how the estimated probabilities change as the number of trials increases.

2 Choose a book, preferably a novel, and select a page at random.

 a **i** Select a passage of 100 words from the page and count the number of words that contain the letter *t*.

 ii Use your data to estimate the probability that a word in the book will contain the letter *t*.

 b Repeat this experiment a further four times, each time selecting a different page at random.
Comment on the different estimates of probability you found each time.

 c Use your data to write down a better estimate of the probability that a word chosen at random will contain the letter *t*.

 d How could you improve your estimate further?

3 This is a dice game for two players.

Rules

Player 1 rolls a dice.

▶ If the dice shows a six, player 1 scores nothing and it is player 2's turn.

▶ If the dice shows a number other than a six, player 1 scores 1 point.

Player 1 can roll the dice as many times as they like, and will score 1 point each time, as long as they don't get a 6 on the dice.
At any time, player 1 can say 'bank' instead of rolling the dice. When this happens:

▶ The score for this go is added to player 1's banked total.

▶ It is then player 2's go to roll the dice.

The first player to bank 10 points is the winner.
Remember – only banked scores count towards the winning total!

When you think you have worked out some good strategies, you could try altering the rules.

Comparing theoretical and experimental probability

This spread will show you how to:
▶▶ Compare experimental and theoretical probabilities in a range of contexts.
▶▶ Appreciate the difference between mathematical explanation and experimental evidence.

KEYWORDS
Experimental probability
Theoretical probability

Saira wants to estimate the probability of choosing a blue marble from a large bag of different coloured marbles.
She decides to choose ten marbles and count how many are blue.

Saira records her results for 12 trials:

Trial	1	2	3	4	5	6	7	8	9	10	11	12
Number of blue marbles	6	5	4	2	2	3	5	3	7	4	3	5

Experimental probability (1st trial) = $\frac{6}{10}$ = 0.6
Experimental probability (all trials) = $\frac{49}{120}$ = 0.41
Saira emptied the bag and found 200 marbles, of which 80 were blue.
Theoretical probability (blue marble) = $\frac{80}{200}$ = 0.4

Saira would expect four out of every ten marbles to be blue.

Saira draws a line graph.

As more results are included the experimental probability gets closer to the theoretical probability.

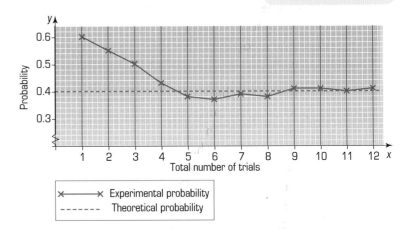

▶ Experimental probability from a large number of trials is a good approximation to theoretical probability.

Sometimes results of an experiment do not support a mathematical explanation.

Ben threw a coin four times and each time it came up tails.
He said that on the next throw he was bound to get heads – but the probability is **still** only $\frac{1}{2}$!

Tails again!

▶ Mathematical explanation and experimental evidence will not always agree.

Exercise D1.6

In questions 1 and 2 it may be easier to give probabilities in decimals correct to 3 decimal places.

1 Govinder made an electronic dice.
He wanted to test it to see if it was fair or biased.
The first 100 scores he got using the dice were:

Score	1	2	3	4	5	6
Frequency	18	19	17	12	16	18

a Compare the results Govinder got with the theoretical probabilities he should get if the dice is fair. Comment on your results.

b Gemma used the same dice 1000 times. Her results were:

Score	1	2	3	4	5	6
Frequency	166	160	172	177	165	160

Compare the results Gemma got with the theoretical probabilities.

c Use both sets of results to comment on whether you think the dice is biased.

2 Two dice were rolled 100 times. Each time their scores were added together.

Score	2	3	4	5	6	7	8	9	10	11	12
Frequency	3	6	8	11	15	18	13	9	12	4	1

a Using a sample space diagram, or otherwise, calculate the theoretical probabilities of achieving each total score.

b Compare the theoretical and experimental probabilities to comment on whether or not the dice are fair.

3 A pack of ordinary playing cards is shuffled and a card chosen at random.
Its suit is noted and the card replaced.
The first three cards chosen were a Heart, a Club, and a Diamond in that order.

a What is the probability that the fourth card chosen will be a Spade?
Give a reason for your answer.

The fourth card chosen was a Diamond.

b What is the probability that the fifth card chosen will be a Diamond?
Give a reason for your answer.

4 Patrick, Adam and John play the national lottery every Saturday.
Patrick always picks the six winning numbers from the previous week.
Adam always picks the numbers 2, 3, 4, 5, 6 and 7.
John always picks the multiples of 8 namely 8, 16, 24, 32, 40 and 48.
Explain, giving reasons for your answer, who has the best chance of winning the lottery.

You should know how to ...

1 Use the fact that the sum of all mutually exclusive outcomes is 1 when solving problems.

2 Present a concise, reasoned argument, using symbols, diagrams, graphs and related explanatory text.

Check out

1 Simon divides a circle into eight equal sectors. Each sector is coloured either red, green or yellow.
Only one sector is coloured yellow.
Simon asks a friend to choose one sector.
  a What is the probability of choosing a sector that is not yellow?
  The probability of choosing a red sector is 0.25.
  b How many red sectors are there?
  c Find the probability of choosing a green sector.

2 Two four-sided dice have faces labelled 1, 2, 3 and 4. Pran rolls both dice together 100 times, and adds the scores on the uppermost faces. Here are Pran's results.

Score	2	3	4	5	6	7	8
Frequency	6	14	16	24	18	15	8

  a Using a sample space diagram, or otherwise, calculate the theoretical probabilities of each score.
  b Use the table to calculate the experimental probability of each score.
  c Compare the theoretical and experimental probabilities and comment on whether the dice are fair.

Fractions, decimals and percentages

This unit will show you how to:

▶▶ Know that a recurring decimal is an exact fraction.

▶▶ Use efficient methods to add, subtract, multiply and divide fractions.

▶▶ Cancel common factors before multiplying or dividing.

▶▶ Recognise when fractions or percentages are needed to compare proportions.

▶▶ Solve problems involving percentage changes.

▶▶ Use proportional reasoning to solve a problem.

▶▶ Extend mental methods of calculation, working with decimals, fractions and percentages.

▶▶ Make and justify estimates and approximations.

▶▶ Multiply and divide by decimals.

▶▶ Enter numbers on a calculator and interpret the display in context.

▶▶ Solve increasingly demanding problems and evaluate solutions.

▶▶ Solve substantial problems by breaking them into simpler tasks.

▶▶ Give solutions to problems to an appropriate degree of accuracy.

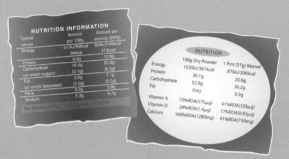

Nutritional information is often expressed using decimals and percentages.

Before you start

You should know how to ...

1 Find the HCF and LCM by prime factor decomposition.

2 Convert between fractions, decimals and percentages.

3 Find simple fractions and percentages of amounts.

Check in

1 a Write 36 and 48 as the product of their prime factors.

   b Use your answers to **a** to find:

     i the HCF of 36 and 48

     ii the LCM of 36 and 48

2 Express each of these numbers in the other two forms (percentage or decimal or fraction)

   a $\frac{9}{20}$ **b** 0.145   **c** 26%

3 Work out:

   a i $\frac{3}{8}$ of 248 mg   **ii** $\frac{8}{15}$ of £300

   b i 23% of 40   **ii** $17\frac{1}{2}$% of £240

Fractions and decimals

This spread will show you how to:

▶▶ Use fraction notation to describe a proportion of a shape.
▶▶ Express one number as a fraction of another.
▶▶ Order fractions.
▶▶ Know that a recurring decimal is an exact fraction.

KEYWORDS

Proportion   Decimal
Recurring

You use fractions to describe a proportion of a whole.

To work out the fraction shaded purple ...

... divide the shape into equal parts

$\frac{6}{16}$ of the shape is shaded, or $\frac{3}{8}$

You can express a number as a fraction of another number.

example

Class 8Y were asked to name their favourite subject.
This pie chart shows the results.
What fraction of students prefers Art?

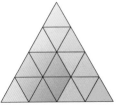

Add up the angles: $60° + 90° + 40° + 110° = 300°$
Find the missing angle: $360° - 300° = 60°$
Express as a fraction: $\frac{60}{360} = \frac{1}{6}$ ⟹ $\frac{1}{6}$ of students in class 8Y prefer Art.

Converting to decimals is a good way to order fractions.

example

Which is the larger, $\frac{4}{7}$ or $\frac{2}{3}$?

Convert to decimals: You could use equivalent fractions instead:
$\frac{4}{7} = 4 ÷ 7 = 0.5714 ...$ $\frac{4}{7} = \frac{12}{21}$ $\frac{2}{3} = \frac{14}{21}$
$\frac{2}{3} = 2 ÷ 3 = 0.6666 ...$ Compare numerators: $\frac{2}{3}$ is larger than $\frac{4}{7}$.
Compare the first digit:
$\frac{2}{3}$ is larger than $\frac{4}{7}$.

The last example contained two **recurring** decimals.
$\frac{2}{3} = 0.66666 ... = 0.\dot{6}$ $\frac{4}{7} = 0.5714285714 ... = 0.\dot{5}7142\dot{8}$

▶ **You can write a recurring decimal as an exact fraction.**

In a recurring decimal the
sequence of digits will repeat
forever.

Exercise N2.1

1 Identify the larger fraction in each pair.

a $\frac{3}{8}$ $\frac{5}{14}$

c $\frac{4}{9}$ $\frac{3}{7}$

e $\frac{3}{11}$ $\frac{5}{16}$

b $\frac{3}{5}$ $\frac{7}{12}$

d $\frac{2}{3}$ $\frac{7}{11}$

f $\frac{1}{9}$ $\frac{2}{13}$

2 A square has side 5 cm.
A, B, C and D are the midpoints of each side of the square.

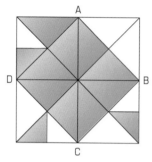

a i Calculate the area of the whole square.

ii Calculate the area of the shaded part.

iii What fraction of the whole square is unshaded?

b The diagram shows the same square shaded differently.

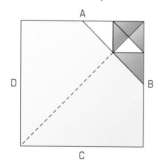

By dividing the square up into equal parts express the shaded part as a fraction of the whole in its simplest terms.

3 The gradient of the line segment AB is $\frac{2}{3}$.

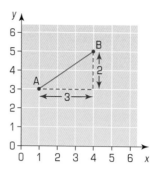

On graph paper draw axes from 0 to 10.

a On the same axes, draw line segments with these gradients:

i $\frac{1}{2}$ **ii** $\frac{3}{5}$ **iii** $\frac{1}{6}$

b Put the fractions $\frac{1}{2}$, $\frac{3}{5}$ and $\frac{1}{6}$ in order of size from smallest to largest.

c What can you say about the gradients that you drew in part **a** as the fractions get bigger?

4 The pie chart represents the votes cast for six candidates in a school council election.

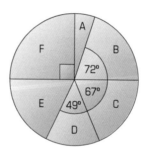

What fraction of the votes was cast for each candidate? Express these answers as:

a a fraction

b a decimal

5 **Puzzle**
Find a fraction that is equivalent to each of these recurring decimals.

a $0.4\dot{2}857\dot{1}$

b $0.3\dot{8}461\dot{5}$

Adding and subtracting fractions

This spread will show you how to:

▶▶ Add and subtract fractions.

You can add or subtract fractions easily when they have the same denominator.

When the denominators are different, you need to change them to equivalent fractions.

$\frac{3}{16}$ + $\frac{5}{16}$ = $\frac{8}{16}$ or $\frac{1}{2}$

---

example

Calculate $\frac{7}{12} + \frac{9}{20} - \frac{2}{3}$.

▶ First find the LCM of the denominators, 12, 20 and 3:

$$12 = 2 \times 2 \times 3$$
$$20 = 2 \times 2 \times 5$$
$$3 = 3$$
$$LCM = 2^2 \times 3 \times 5 = 60$$

▶ Rewrite as equivalent fractions: $\frac{7}{12} = \frac{35}{60}$ $\frac{9}{20} = \frac{27}{60}$ $\frac{2}{3} = \frac{40}{60}$

▶ Combine the fractions: $\frac{35}{60} + \frac{27}{60} - \frac{40}{60} = \frac{22}{60}$

▶ Simplify: $\frac{22}{60} = \frac{11}{30}$

Remember:
You find the LCM by multiplying the highest power of each prime factor.

When the denominators are larger you may need to use a written method to find the LCM.

---

example

Calculate $\frac{17}{28} + \frac{29}{70}$, leaving your answer as a mixed number.

▶ Find the LCM of 28 and 70 by prime factor decomposition:

2) 28
2) 14
7) 7
1

2) 70
5) 35
7) 7
1

$$28 = 2^2 \times 7$$
$$70 = 2 \times 5 \times 7$$
$$LCM = 2^2 \times 5 \times 7$$
$$= 140$$

▶ Convert to equivalent fractions: $\frac{17}{28} = \frac{85}{140}$ $\frac{29}{70} = \frac{58}{140}$

▶ Add the fractions: $\frac{85}{140} + \frac{58}{140} = \frac{143}{140}$

▶ Convert to a mixed number: $\frac{143}{140} = 1\frac{3}{140}$

Alternatively, you could convert to decimals:
$\frac{17}{28} = 0.6071$ (to 4 d.p.)
$\frac{29}{70} = 0.4143$ (to 4 d.p.)
$\frac{17}{28} + \frac{29}{70} = 0.6071 + 0.4143$
$= 1.0214$
This method is not as accurate in this case.

Exercise N2.2

1 Convert each of these fractions into decimals, giving your answer to 3 decimal places where appropriate.

a $\frac{3}{8}$ **b** $\frac{6}{25}$ **c** $\frac{9}{20}$ **d** $\frac{5}{9}$ **e** $\frac{2}{11}$

2 Calculate:

a $\frac{3}{4} + \frac{2}{5}$ **b** $\frac{4}{5} + \frac{1}{3}$ **c** $\frac{3}{4} + \frac{2}{7}$

d $\frac{5}{9} - \frac{2}{5}$ **e** $2\frac{7}{10} + 1\frac{1}{4}$ **f** $1\frac{5}{6} - \frac{7}{9}$

3 a List the prime factors of these numbers:

    i 36 **ii** 54 **iii** 120 **iv** 435

b Use your answers to part **a** to answer these questions.

    i What is the LCM of 36 and 54?

    ii What is the LCM of 54, 120 and 435?

    iii What is the lowest common multiple of all four numbers?

4 Calculate these, expressing each answer in its simplest form.

a $\frac{4}{9} + \frac{5}{6}$ **b** $\frac{5}{18} + \frac{17}{20}$

c $\frac{24}{45} - \frac{13}{24}$ **d** $\frac{31}{41} + \frac{17}{34} - \frac{2}{15}$

e $5\frac{2}{13} - 3\frac{4}{9}$ **f** $6\frac{23}{25} + \frac{5}{4} - 10\frac{5}{11}$

5 A plank of wood is $3\frac{2}{15}$ m long. A piece of length $1\frac{5}{8}$ m is sawn off. What length of wood is left?

6 Use the fractions in the box to complete these number sentences:

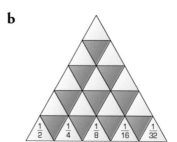

7 Emilio says that if you repeatedly subtract $\frac{2}{31}$ from $\frac{5}{8}$ you will eventually reach $^-1$. Is he correct? Show working to justify your answer.

8 Joe worked out that he spent $\frac{3}{8}$ of his spare time watching TV, $\frac{1}{3}$ with friends and $\frac{2}{5}$ in other activities. Show that this is impossible and explain your answer.

9

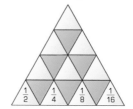

a For each question **i**, **ii** and **iii** choose two fractions from the cloud that have the difference indicated.

    i $\frac{49}{162}$ **ii** $\frac{43}{155}$ **iii** $\frac{14}{891}$

b What is the sum of:

    i the two largest fractions

    ii the two smallest fractions?

10 In a Fraction Pyramid, the number in each triangle is the sum of the two triangles directly below. Copy and complete these diagrams.

a

b

This spread will show you how to:
» Calculate fractions of numbers, quantities or measurements.
» Multiply a fraction by a fraction.
» Divide a fraction by a fraction.

KEYWORDS
Integer
Unit fraction

You can use various methods to find a fraction of an amount.
To find $\frac{5}{8}$ of 85 kg you could ...

Divide first:
$\frac{5}{8} \times 85$ kg
$= 5 \times \frac{1}{8}$ of 85 kg
$= 5 \times (85 \div 8)$ kg
$= 53.125$ kg

Multiply first:
$\frac{5}{8} \times 85$ kg
$= \frac{1}{8} \times 5 \times 85$ kg
$= \dfrac{5 \times 85}{8}$ kg
$= \frac{425}{8}$ kg $= 53\frac{1}{8}$ kg

Use an equivalent decimal:
$\frac{5}{8} \times 85$ kg
$= (5 \div 8) \times 85$ kg
$= 0.625 \times 85$ kg
$= 53.125$ kg

You can multiply a fraction by another fraction.
$$\frac{3}{5} \times \frac{2}{3} = \left(\frac{1}{5} \times 3\right) \times \left(\frac{1}{3} \times 2\right)$$
$$= \frac{3 \times 2}{5 \times 3} = \frac{6}{15} = \frac{2}{5}$$

» When you multiply two fractions:
  » multiply the numerators
  » multiply the denominators

$\dfrac{a}{b} \times \dfrac{c}{d} = \dfrac{ac}{bd}$

You can divide an integer by a fraction.

$1 \div \frac{1}{6} = 6$ $2 \div \frac{1}{6} = 12$ $1 \div \frac{2}{6} = 3$

Ask: How many sixths are there in one whole?

Ask: How many sixths are there in two wholes?

Ask: How many two-sixths are there in one whole?

You can divide a fraction by a fraction.

» Dividing by $\frac{a}{b}$ is the same as multiplying by $\frac{b}{a}$.

$$\frac{5}{7} \div \frac{3}{4} = \frac{5}{7} \times \frac{4}{3}$$
$$= \frac{5 \times 4}{7 \times 3}$$
$$= \frac{20}{21}$$

$$3\frac{1}{4} \div \frac{2}{5} = \frac{13}{4} \div \frac{2}{5}$$
$$= \frac{13}{4} \times \frac{5}{2}$$
$$= \frac{13 \times 5}{4 \times 2}$$
$$= \frac{65}{8} = 8\frac{1}{8}$$

Exercise N2.3

1 Calculate:

  a $\frac{4}{5}$ of £220   **b** $\frac{3}{8} \times 4$

  c $1\frac{1}{4} \times 22$ m   **d** $\frac{11}{24}$ of 3 days

  e $\frac{3}{7} \times 63$ **f** $27 \times \frac{2}{9}$

2 Puzzle

There are 550 sweets in a jar.
$\frac{2}{5}$ of these are for Hani, and $\frac{1}{2}$ are for Jane.
The rest remain in the jar.

  a Who gets most: Hani or Jane? Explain your answer.

  b What fraction of the sweets remains in the jar?

  c How many sweets remain in the jar?

Samantha gets $\frac{3}{11}$ of those that remain in the jar.

  d How many sweets does Samantha get?

3 Work out each of these amounts:

  a $\frac{3}{5}$ of £33   **b** $\frac{5}{13}$ of 450 m

  c 0.4×25 cm   **d** $\frac{1}{17}$ of £42

  e 23% of 540 g   **f** 0.8×145 kg

  g 52% of £563   **h** 0.875×560 mm

  i $\frac{4}{11} \times £45$

4 Calculate these products, leaving your answer as a mixed number where appropriate.

  a $\frac{5}{9} \times 27$ **b** $\frac{3}{8} \times 44$

  c $\frac{7}{24} \times 15$ **d** $28 \times \frac{17}{21}$

  e $2\frac{5}{8} \times 6$ **f** $2\frac{7}{10} \times 5$

5 In a competition, Julie won $\frac{2}{13}$ of £304 and Jasmine won $\frac{3}{17}$ of £230.
Who won the most money? Show all your working.

6 Boris says: 'If you multiply a number by another number, you will always increase the amount you started with.'
Mikhail disagrees. Suggest a reason why Mikhail might disagree.

7 Work out:

  a $\frac{2}{5}$ of $\frac{3}{4}$ **b** $\frac{4}{3}$ of $\frac{6}{7}$ **c** $0.4 \times \frac{8}{9}$

  d $\frac{3}{7} \div \frac{1}{4}$ **e** $30\% \div \frac{5}{8}$ **f** $0.3 \div 52$

  g $\frac{6}{11}$ of $\frac{6}{5}$ **h** $0.75 \div \frac{6}{7}$ **i** $\frac{3}{10} \times \frac{5}{7}$

8 Puzzle

Here is a fraction sequence:
$$\frac{3}{4}, \frac{3}{8}, \frac{3}{16}, \frac{3}{32}, \underline{\quad}, \underline{\quad}$$
You can find each term by multiplying the previous term by $\frac{1}{2}$:
$$\frac{3}{4} \times \frac{1}{2} = \frac{3}{8}, \quad \frac{3}{8} \times \frac{1}{2} = \frac{3}{16}, \ldots$$
The next two terms will be:
$$\frac{3}{32} \times \frac{1}{2} = \frac{3}{64}$$
$$\frac{3}{64} \times \frac{1}{2} = \frac{3}{128}$$
Find the next two terms of these fraction sequences:

  a $\frac{1}{2}, \frac{3}{5}, \frac{3}{10}, \frac{9}{50}, \underline{\ }, \underline{\ }, \underline{\ }$

  b $3, \frac{2}{3}, 2, \frac{4}{3}, \frac{8}{3}, \underline{\ }, \underline{\ }, \underline{\ }$

  c $\frac{3}{4}, \frac{4}{5}, \frac{3}{5}, \frac{12}{25}, \underline{\ }, \underline{\ }, \underline{\ }$

9 A rectangular window is $2\frac{1}{4}$ m high and $1\frac{1}{5}$ m wide.
Calculate its area.

10 The area of a rectangle is 340 cm^2 and its length is $15\frac{2}{5}$ cm.
What is the width of the rectangle?
Give your answer as a mixed number.

11 Investigation
$$\frac{2}{5} \times 11 = \frac{22}{5} = 4\frac{2}{5}$$
$$\frac{3}{7} \times 15 = \frac{45}{7} = 6\frac{3}{7}$$

  a What is the smallest integer that can be multiplied by $\frac{2}{9}$ so that the result is a mixed number whose fractional part is also $\frac{2}{9}$?

  b Investigate for any starting fraction. Explain your answer.

Percentages of amounts

This spread will show you how to:

▶▶ Calculate percentages of numbers, quantities and measurements.

▶▶ Use percentage changes to solve problems.

KEYWORDS

Percentage decrease

Percentage increase

To work out 23% of 60 kg, you could ...

Multiply first:
23% of 60
$= \frac{23}{100} \times 60$
$= \frac{1}{100} \times (23 \times 60)$
$= \frac{1380}{100}$
$= 13.8$ kg

Divide first:
23% of 60
$= \frac{23}{100} \times 60$
$= (23 \div 100) \times 60$
$= 0.23 \times 60$
$= 13.8$ kg

Convert to a decimal:
23% of 60
$= 23 \times 1\%$ of 60
$= 23 \times \frac{1}{100} \times 60$
$= 23 \times 0.6$
$= 13.8$ kg

There is more than one way to work out a percentage increase or decrease.

example

Robbie's spending money is £3 per week.
Next month it will increase by 15%.
How much will Robbie's spending money be from next month?

You could add the increase on at the end ...
Increase = 15% of £3
$= \frac{15}{100} \times £3$
$= 0.15 \times £3$
$= £0.45$

New spending money
= original amount + increase
$= £3 + £0.45$
$= £3.45$

... or you could calculate the new
amount in one go.
New spending money = 115% of £3
$= \frac{115}{100} \times £3$
$= 1.15 \times £3$
$= £3.45$

The single calculation method is
quicker.

You can show the single calculation method on a number line.
You represent the original amount as 100%.

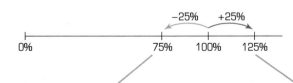

If you **decrease** an amount by
25% then it is 75% of the original
amount.

If you **increase** an amount by 25%
then it is 125% of the original
amount.

Exercise N2.4

1 Find these percentages of amounts.
In each case, choose a mental, written or calculator method.

  a 13% of £650   **b** 43% of 80 cl
  c 17.5% of 25 m   **d** 16.4% of €400
  e 7.5% of £2.40   **f** 0.03% of 1600 kg
  g 0.8% of 3 million   **h** 1.3% of 8 g

2 For each pair of items, work out which is cheaper. Show your working.

  a A television costing £546, or the same television originally priced at £674 with 18% discount.
  b A DVD costing £124 including VAT (value added tax) or the same DVD for £99 plus VAT at 17.5%.

3 Show your workings in each of these problems. You may use a calculator.

  a Henry's father offered him two choices: a £1.20 per week increase in his spending money or a 12% increase. Henry currently receives £9 per week.
  i Which should Henry choose to receive the greatest increase?
  ii What amount would he need to receive now for the 12% increase to equal the £1.20 increase?
  b A railway engineer calculates that the points on a railway track will increase in width by 0.03% on a very hot summer day. If the width of the points is normally 90 mm calculate:
  i the increase in width that would occur
  ii the new width.
  c At a local youth club, the secretary states that the membership subscriptions in the previous 12 months decreased from £3610 by 14%. Calculate the amount the youth club needs to raise to bring the income to the level of the previous year.

4 Three years ago, Adam and Jayne received a gift of £500 from their aunt. They put it into a bank account and saved it.
After one year, the value of their savings grew by 5%.

  a How much did Adam and Jayne have in their account after one year?

After the second year, the new value of their savings increased again by 5%.

  b How much did they have in their account after two years?
  c How much money do Adam and Jayne have in their bank account now?

5 Investigation
Bus fares rose by 8% in January.
They rose by a further 12% in February.
Azad says 'The new bus fare is 20% more than the old fare'.
Sabina disagrees.
Explain why Sabina disagrees.

6 Investigation
Morrissey wants to hire a tractor to plough his land.
Here are the rates from three different hire companies.

The maximum hire period for a tractor is 20 days.

  a If Morrissey takes 10 days to plough his land, from which company should he hire a tractor?
  b Investigate which company Morrissey should use for different lengths of time.

Problems involving percentage change

This spread will show you how to:

▶▶ Use percentage changes to solve problems.

▶▶ Enter numbers into a calculator and interpret the display in context.

KEYWORDS

Original price

Unitary method

In a shop sale, items are often reduced by a percentage.

Here are three different ways you could work out the **original** price of the dress shown on the right.

Reduced 15%
now only **£34**

Unitary method

The new price is 85% of the original price.

85% of original	= 34
1% of original = 34 ÷ 85	= 0.4
Original amount (100%) = 100 × 0.4	= 40

So the original price was £40.

−15%

new price   original price

0%   85%   100%

▶ In the unitary method you find the value of 1%.

Inverse operations

New price
$$= 85\% \text{ of original price}$$
$$= \frac{85}{100} \times \text{original price}$$
$$= 0.85 \times \text{original price}$$

So   original price = new price ÷ 0.85

$$34 \div 0.85 = 40$$

The original price was £40.

× 0.85

Original price   New price

÷ 0.85

Using algebra

This method is similar to the inverse operations method.

Let the original price
(in pounds) $= N$

Then   85% of N $= 34$

$0.85N$ $= 34$

$N = \dfrac{34}{0.85}$

$N = £40$

▶ You must interpret the calculator display in the context of the problem.
For example, a display of 4.2 in pounds should be written as £4.20.

Exercise N2.5

1 Use a mental, written or calculator method to work out the new amount.
   a Increase £46 by 3%
   b Decrease 130 °C by 20%
   c Decrease 3.5 m by 1%
   d Increase 1 h 10 min by 5%
   e Decrease 12.3 s by 15%
   f Increase 70 cl by 4%
   g Decrease £3000 by 1.6%
   h Increase £9.30 by 26%

2 Mr. Smith increased all the prices in his sweet shop by 10%.
   Copy and complete this price list.

Item	Original price	New price
Bag of mints	40p	44p
Small assorted sweets	£1.20	
Large assorted sweets	£1.65	
Box of chocolates	£2.82	

3 15 300 people attended a pop concert. However this was only 73% of the attendance the previous night.
   Work out the previous night's attendance (to the nearest person).

4 Wendy is given an 8% pay rise each year. Her starting salary was £9500 per year. How many years will Wendy have to work before her salary is at least:
   a £11 000   b £13 000   c £15 000?

5 The weight of a three-month old baby is 6.08 kg.
   This is 190% of her weight at birth. Calculate the baby's birth weight.

6 Charlotte is saving her spending money to buy a new microwave oven for her Great Aunt Lucy.
   Charlotte has saved £87, but this is only 60% of the amount she needs.
   a How much does the microwave oven cost?
   The store manager agrees to reduce the price of the microwave by 15%.
   b How much more money does Charlotte need to save?

7 Puzzle
   Earl went to the bank and was pleasantly surprised to find that he had £66.55 in his savings account.
   He had opened his account three years ago and had left it untouched ever since. The bank added on 10% to the value at the end of each year.
   How much money did Earl put into the bank originally?
   Show your workings clearly.

8 a During the first few weeks of its life, a squid increases its body weight by 6% each day. A squid is born with a body weight of 180 g.
      i How much will it weigh after one day?
      ii How much will it weigh after three days?
      iii How many days will it take the squid to double its body weight?
   b Steve invests £1000 in SuperSquid Inc. Each year his money increases by 8.4%. After eight years what is the value of his investment?

Comparing proportions

This spread will show you how to:

▶▶ Recognise when fractions or percentages are needed to compare proportions and solve problems.

▶▶ Express one number as a percentage of another.

▶▶ Use percentage changes to solve problems.

KEYWORDS

Proportion   Decimal

Percentage

You can use percentages, fractions and decimals to describe proportions.

example

Fergus scored 34 out of 38 in a maths test.
Calculate the proportion of the total that Fergus scored:

a   as a fraction   **b**   as a decimal to 3 d.p.   **c**   as a percentage to 1 d.p.

a   Proportion $= \frac{34}{38}$ **b** $34 \div 38 = 0.894736\ldots$ **c** $(34 \div 38) \times 100$

$= \frac{17}{19}$ $= 0.895$ to 3 d.p. $= 89.5\%$ to 1 d.p.

You can use proportions to make simple comparisons.

example

The nutritional information for three brands of baked beans states that:

a   Hernie's Beanies are 4.7% protein.

b   Big Beanz contain 10 g of protein per 207 g serving.

c   Beenie Beans contain 21 g of protein in each 415 g tin.

Which brand of baked beans contains the most protein?

a   Hernie's Beanies $= 4.7\%$ protein

b   Big Beanz $= \frac{10}{207} \times 100\% = 4.8\%$ protein (1 d.p.)

c   Beenie Beans $= \frac{21}{415} \times 100\% = 5.1\%$ protein (1 d.p.)

Beenie Beans have the highest percentage of protein.

Percentage change compares the size of a change to the original amount.

example

A wide-screen television is reduced in a sale from £900 to £765.
What is the percentage reduction in price?

Reduction $= 900 - 765 = 135$

Percentage reduction $= \dfrac{\text{reduction}}{\text{original amount}} \times 100\%$

$= \frac{135}{900} \times 100\% = 15\%$

▶ **Percentage change in an amount** $= \dfrac{\text{change}}{\text{original amount}} \times 100\%$

Exercise N2.6

1 What fraction of:
  a 300 pupils is 46 pupils
  b £2.40 is 68p
  c 80 cm is 20 mm
  d €9 is €0.80
  e 140 CDs is 72 CDs
  f 10 000 apples is 3464 apples
  g 1 day is 1 minute
  h 6 days and 8 hours is 6 hours?
Express your answers as fractions in their simplest form.

2 What proportion of each of these shapes is shaded? Give your answer as
  i a fraction   **ii** a percentage.

a
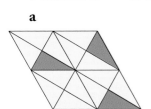

b
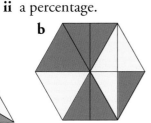

c
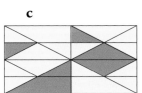

d
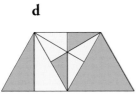

3 Barry, Jenny and Faye all work on Saturdays in the local supermarket. They have all been given a pay increase. The amounts are given as hourly rates:

BARRY
£3.10 to £4.60

JENNY
£3.30 to £4.80

FAYE
£3.00 to £4.50

  a Work out the percentage wage increase for each of these workers.
  b Is the pay rise fair? Comment on your answer.

4 Greengage School ran a campaign to encourage students to eat more vegetables in its canteen. The table shows the weight of each vegetable sold on one day both before and after the campaign.

	Before	After
Cabbage	12 kg	13 kg
Broccoli	5 kg	6 kg
Carrots	7.5 kg	8 kg
Cucumber	8 kg	9.4 kg
Onions	8.3 kg	9.2 kg
Lettuce	5.4 kg	7 kg

  a Work out the percentage increase in sales for each type of vegetable.
  b Is it fair to say that the vegetable with the greatest percentage increase is the more popular? Comment on your answer.

5 **a** To pass his maths exam, Joachim needs to score 45 marks out of 80. What percentage of the marks does he need to pass?
  b David earns £28 345 a year. He pays £7936 in tax. What percentage of his earnings does he pay in tax?

6 Copy and complete this table showing the yearly earnings of all five employees at Cheapo Clothes shop.

Employee	Earnings (£)	Percentage of total wage bill
Mark		18.75%
John	£8 000	12.5%
Richard	£7 400	
Roy	£12 800	20%
Carl		
Total	£64 000	100%

You should know how to ...

1 Use efficient methods to add, subtract, multiply and divide fractions.

2 Use proportional reasoning to solve a problem, choosing the correct numbers to take as 100%.

3 Solve substantial problems by breaking them into simpler tasks.

4 Give solutions to problems to an appropriate degree of accuracy.

Check out

1 Work out:

a $\frac{5}{11} - \frac{4}{5}$ **b** $\frac{7}{8} + \frac{12}{17}$

c $3\frac{1}{5} - 1\frac{7}{12}$ **d** $6\frac{2}{3} + 14\frac{6}{11}$

e $\frac{3}{7} \times \frac{4}{9}$ **f** $\frac{4}{21} \div \frac{3}{4}$

g $2\frac{1}{5} \times 3\frac{5}{9}$ **h** $5\frac{1}{4} \div 3\frac{4}{7}$

2 a In a local election 63% of the population of a village who were eligible to vote did so. This was 9135 people.

  i How many people were actually eligible to vote?

  ii How many of the eligible population did not vote?

b If a car travels 50 km in 40 minutes, how far would it travel in one hour?

3 A father wrote a will that shared out his £32 000 savings to each of his five children equally.
Each child spent 23% of their share and saved $\frac{2}{3}$.
They each gave the remainder to charity.

a What percentage of the £32 000 was
  i saved **ii** given to charity?

b If the saved amounts were invested at an interest rate of 5% how much would each child have saved at the end of one year?

4 The average amount of water drunk per day by each pupil in Year 8 is 3.68 litres.
Estimate the number of litres you would need to supply for a year if there are 143 pupils in Year 8.

2

Expressions and formulae

This unit will show you how to:

▶▶ Use index notation for integer powers and simple instances of the index laws.

▶▶ Simplify or transform algebraic expressions by taking out single-term common factors.

▶▶ Construct and solve linear equations with integer coefficients, using an appropriate method.

▶▶ Use formulae from mathematics and other subjects.

▶▶ Substitute numbers into expressions and formulae.

▶▶ Derive a formula and, in simple cases, change its subject.

▶▶ Solve increasingly demanding problems and evaluate solutions in the context of algebra.

▶▶ Represent problems and synthesise information in algebraic, geometric or graphical form.

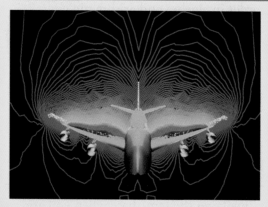

Air flow can be described using complex equations.

Before you start

You should know how to ...

1 Use the correct order of operations in arithmetic.

2 Reduce a fraction to its lowest form.

3 Find the highest common factor of three integers.

Check in

1 Find the calculations whose solution is 15:

$3 \times 4 + 3$ $3 + 2^2 \times 3$ $14 + 6 \div 3$

$2 + 3 \times 3$

$4 + (5 - 2)^2$ $5 - 2 \times 3$ $3^3 - 4 \times 3$

2 Find pairs of fractions which are equivalent.

$\frac{5}{10}$ $\frac{4}{14}$ $\frac{10}{35}$ $\frac{6}{9}$ $\frac{3}{13}$ $\frac{16}{40}$ $\frac{11}{22}$ $\frac{14}{21}$ $\frac{12}{52}$

3 a Write down all of the factors of these numbers: **i** 12 **ii** 30 **iii** 48

b Hence, find the highest common factor of:

i 12 and 30 **ii** 12 and 48 **iii** 30 and 48

iv 12, 30 and 48.

This spread will show you how to:
▶▶ Recognise that algebraic operations follow the same conventions and order as arithmetic operations.
▶▶ Apply simple instances of the index laws.
▶▶ Substitute integers into expressions involving powers.

KEYWORDS
Base
Index, indices
Order of operations
Expression

Index is another word for power.
It tells you how many times to multiply a number by itself.

2^3 means $2 \times 2 \times 2$ which equals 8.

2 is the **base**   3 is the **index**

The plural of index is 'indices', pronounced 'in de seas'.

Operations follow the same order in algebra and arithmetic.

If $a = 3$, $b = {}^-4$, $c = {}^-8$ and $d = \frac{1}{2}$, evaluate the expressions:

a $4a^2$

b $ac - b^2$

c d^4

....

a $4a^2 = 4 \times 3^2$
$= 4 \times 9$
$= 36$

b $ac - b^2 = 3 \times ({}^-8) - ({}^-4)^2$
$= 3 \times ({}^-8) - 16$
$= {}^-24 - 16$
$= {}^-40$

c $d^4 = \frac{1}{2} \times \frac{1}{2} \times \frac{1}{2} \times \frac{1}{2}$
$= \frac{1}{16}$

You can simplify expressions involving the same base when you are ...

... Multiplying

$3^2 \times 3^4$

$= (3 \times 3) \times (3 \times 3 \times 3 \times 3)$
$= 3^6$

You could just add the indices:
$3^2 \times 3^4 = 3^{2+4} = 3^6$

... Dividing

$$\frac{2^4}{2^3} = \frac{2 \times \cancel{2} \times \cancel{2} \times \cancel{2}}{\cancel{2} \times \cancel{2} \times \cancel{2}}$$

$= 2^1 (= 2)$

You could just subtract the indices:
$\frac{2^4}{2^3} = 2^{4-3} = 2^1$

... Using brackets

$(5^2)^3$

$= (5 \times 5) \times (5 \times 5) \times (5 \times 5)$
$= 5^6$

You could just multiply the indices:
$(5^2)^3 = 5^{2 \times 3} = 5^6$

These are the rules of indices ...

▶ $x^a \times x^b = x^{a+b}$

▶ $\dfrac{x^a}{x^b} = x^{a-b}$

▶ $(x^a)^b = x^{ab}$

For example:

$p^6 \times p^2 = p^{6+2} = p^8$

For example:

$5^{20} \div 5^{18} = 5^{20-18} = 5^2$ or 25

For example:

$(2a^3)^2 = 4a^{3 \times 2} = 4a^6$

Exercise A2.1

1 Evaluate these powers without a calculator.
  a 5^3 **b** 2^6 **c** 10^4 **d** 1^{20}
  e 0^6 **f** $(^-4)^2$ **g** $(^-3)^3$

2 a Rearrange these expressions in ascending order of size, where $n = 3$.

A   B   C   D $(n-4)^2$ E $(3n+2)^2$

  A n^4 B $2n^2$ C $n^1 + n^3$ D $(n-4)^2$ E $(3n+2)^2$

  b Repeat for $n = ^-2$.

3 Is each expression true or false? Explain your answer.
  a $5^2 > 2^5$ **b** $2^n = n^2$
  c $(\frac{3}{5})^2 = \frac{9}{25}$ **d** $x^2 > x$ for all values of x
  e $^-4^3 = (^-4)^3$ **f** $1^p = p$

4 A triangle of straws is made like this:

If the triangle has R rows, the number of straws (s) needed is given by the formula:

$$s = \tfrac{1}{2}(3R^2 + 3R)$$

How many straws are needed if there are nine rows?

5 Puzzle
If $p = 10$, which of these expressions gives the biggest value?

 $\dfrac{3p^3}{2}$ $\dfrac{2p^2(p-3)}{7p}$ $\dfrac{p + p^2 + p^3}{20 - p}$

6 Simplify these expressions. Give your answer in index form.
  a $x^7 \times x^9$ **b** $w^6 \times w^{20}$
  c $p^7 \times p^{-2}$ **d** $3b^6 \times 2b^7$
  e $h^{11} \div h^4$ **f** $\dfrac{m^{14}}{m^6}$
  g $\dfrac{q^{15}}{q^{-3}}$ **h** $100p^6 \div 10p^4$
  i $(K^6)^3$ **j** $(R^7)^8$
  k $(n^{-2})^{-5}$ **l** $(3p^7)^3$

7 Copy and complete:
  a $5^{20} \times 5^{\square} = 5^{30}$
  b $(4^{\square})^5 = 4^{35}$
  c $8^{\square} \div 8^4 = 8^{10}$
  d $n^{\square} \times n = n^6$
  e $(2p^2)^{\square} = 8p^{\square}$
  f $(q^7)^{\square} \times q^6 = q^{20}$

8 Puzzle
Which expression generates the greatest index?

A   B $\dfrac{(q^7)^3 \times q^{-3}}{q^{-4}}$ C

  A $\dfrac{(q^6 \times q^4)^2}{q^2}$ B $\dfrac{(q^7)^3 \times q^{-3}}{q^{-4}}$ C $\left[\dfrac{q^6}{q^{-3}}\right]^2 \times q$

9 Find values to solve these index equations.
  a $m^2 = 2^m$ **b** $4^p = 2^{2p}$
  c $0^m = 0^n$ **d** $(\frac{1}{2})^p = \frac{1}{4p}$

10 Write down the coordinates of four points that would lie on the graph $y = 5^x$.

11 A bacterium reproduces by dividing into two once every hour:

  1 hour later   1 hour later

  a Copy and complete this table.

Time (t)	0	1	2	3	4	5	6
Number of bacteria (B)	1	2					

  b Display your results in a graph.
  c What is the equation of your graph?
  d Use the equation to work out:
    i how many bacteria there are at the end of one day
    ii when the number of bacteria reaches 1024.

Further indices

This spread will show you how to:
- ▶▶ Use index notation for small integer powers.
- ▶▶ Know how to use the x^y key on a calculator.

KEYWORDS

Index notation   Positive

Index, indices   Negative

Reciprocal   Zero index

Here is a 'power line' for powers of 3:

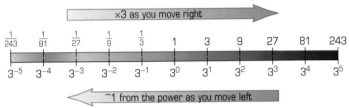

×3 as you move right

| $\frac{1}{243}$ | $\frac{1}{81}$ | $\frac{1}{27}$ | $\frac{1}{9}$ | $\frac{1}{3}$ | 1 | 3 | 9 | 27 | 81 | 243 |
| 3^{-5} | 3^{-4} | 3^{-3} | 3^{-2} | 3^{-1} | 3^0 | 3^1 | 3^2 | 3^3 | 3^4 | 3^5 |

$^-1$ from the power as you move left

▶ If you raise any number to a zero index, the answer will be 1.
$$x^0 = 1 \qquad (3^0 = 1, 4^0 = 1, 100^0 = 1 \ldots)$$

To evaluate a negative index: (for example, 5^{-2}):
- ▶ first evaluate the positive index: $5^2 = 25$
- ▶ then find the **reciprocal**: $5^{-2} = \frac{1}{25}$

$\frac{1}{25}$ is the reciprocal of 25.
25 is the reciprocal of $\frac{1}{25}$.

▶ $x^{-n} = \dfrac{1}{x^n}$ $(5^{-3} = \frac{1}{5^3}, 3^{-2} = \frac{1}{3^2} \ldots)$

example

Evaluate these indices using a mental method.

a 17^0 **b** 6^{-2} **c** 2^{-4} **d** $\left(\dfrac{2}{3}\right)^{-3}$

....

a $17^0 = 1$ **b** $6^2 = 36$ **c** $2^4 = 16$ **d** $\left(\dfrac{2}{3}\right)^3 = \dfrac{8}{27}$

     so $6^{-2} = \frac{1}{36}$ so $2^{-4} = \frac{1}{16}$ so $\left(\dfrac{2}{3}\right)^{-3} = \frac{27}{8} = 3\frac{3}{8}$

You can check your results on a calculator, using the power or index key $\boxed{x^y}$.
For example, you would input 2^{-4} as:

$\boxed{2}$ $\boxed{x^y}$ $\boxed{\pm}$ $\boxed{4}$ $\boxed{=}$ The display should read 0.0625 $(= \frac{1}{16})$.

If you use a calculator you will usually get a decimal answer, not a fraction.

Exercise A2.2

1 Match an index expression in A with a solution in B:

A

$\left(\frac{2}{5}\right)^{-2}$ 2^{-3} 4^{-2}

6^{-2}

3^0 $\left(\frac{1}{2}\right)^{-2}$ 10^{-3} 8^0

B

1 $\frac{1}{4}$ $\frac{1}{1000}$ $\frac{25}{4}$

$\frac{1}{16}$ $\frac{1}{8}$ $\frac{1}{36}$ 1

2 a Evaluate these indices. Use the rules of indices where appropriate.

i 7^{-2} **ii** 11^0

iii 5^{-3} **iv** $4^4 \div 4^6$

v $12^6 \times 12^{-6}$ **vi** $(3^2)^{-2}$

b Use the index or power key on your calculator to check your results.

3 Evaluate these expressions where $x = 2$, putting your results in ascending order:

 5^x x^{-2} $(-x)^3$ x^0 x^{-3}

4 Decide, giving reasons, if the following statements are true or false.

a $5^{-2} = 2^{-5}$ **b** $x^0 = y^0$

c $6^{-2} < 6^{-3}$ **d** $p^7 \times p^{-7} = 0$

e $\dfrac{10^6}{10^8} = 0.01$ **f** $n^{-3} = \dfrac{1}{n^3}$

g $h^{-2} = {}^-h^2$ **h** $\left(\dfrac{x}{y}\right)^{-2} = \dfrac{y^2}{x^2}$

5 Find the value of p in each case:

a $5^p = \frac{1}{125}$ **b** $6^p = 0$

c $\left(\frac{1}{2}\right)^p = 8$ **d** $7^{-p} = 49$

6 a Write as many expressions involving indices with the answer $\frac{1}{64}$ as you can.

b Repreat for a number of your choice.

7 Evaluate k, without using a calculator, if $p = 3$.

$$k = p^0 + p^{-2} + p^{-3}$$

8 a Use your calculator to evaluate these fractional powers. (You can use the fraction key $\left[\boxed{a^{b/c}}\right]$.)

i $25^{1/2}$ **ii** $36^{1/2}$

iii $100^{1/2}$ **iv** $144^{1/2}$

v $49^{1/2}$ **vi** $8^{1/3}$

vii $27^{1/3}$ **viii** $64^{1/3}$

ix $1000^{1/3}$

b i What does a power of $\frac{1}{2}$ do?

ii What does a power of $\frac{1}{3}$ do?

iii Test your predictions from **i** and **ii** on these, then use your calculator to check.

$16^{\frac{1}{2}}$ $125^{\frac{1}{3}}$

9 Use your findings from question 5 to evaluate these indices.

a $121^{1/2}$ **b** $169^{0.5}$

c $216^{1/3}$ **d** $8^{0.3}$

e $\left(\frac{4}{49}\right)^{1/2}$ **f** $\left(\frac{8}{27}\right)^{1/3}$

10 Challenge

You can combine negative and fractional powers.

Look at these examples:

$25^{-1/2} \longrightarrow$ reciprocal of $25^{1/2} \longrightarrow \frac{1}{5}$

$64^{-1/3} \longrightarrow$ reciprocal of $64^{1/3} \longrightarrow \frac{1}{4}$

a Evaluate these:

i $49^{-1/2}$ **ii** $64^{-1/2}$

iii $1000^{-1/3}$ **iv** $125^{-1/3}$

b Check on your calculator.

Simplifying expressions

This spread will show you how to:
- ▶▶ Simplify linear expressions by collecting like terms.
- ▶▶ Apply the index laws for multiplication and division of small integer powers.

You should try to simplify algebra expressions.
This can help you to work with formulae and equations.

Addition and subtraction

This pot contains seven terms, and only some are like terms.

An algebra expression is: $\qquad 3x + 2x^2 + 4 + 3y + x^2 + 8y + 4x$
- ▶ Put the like terms together: $\quad = \quad 3x + 4x + 3y + 8y + 2x^2 + x^2 + 4$
- ▶ Collect the like terms: $\quad = \quad 7x + 11y + 3x^2 + 4$

This pot contains four terms, two of which are negative.

An algebra expression is: $\qquad {}^-8q + 5p - 4p + 10q$
- ▶ Put the like terms together: $\quad = \quad {}^-8q + 10q + 5p - 4p$
- ▶ Collect the like terms: $\quad = \quad 2q + p$

Multiplication and division

Here is an algebra multiplication: $\qquad 3 \times p \times p \times p \times 2$

- ▶ Separate the numbers from the letters: $\quad = \quad 3 \times 2 \times p \times p \times p$
- ▶ Simplify to form a p^3 term: $\quad = \quad 6p^3$

In the term $6p^3$, 6 is the **coefficient**.

Here is an algebra division: $\qquad 4p \div 2q$

- ▶ Rewrite it as a fraction: $\quad = \quad \dfrac{4p}{2q}$
- ▶ Cancel common factors: $\quad = \quad \dfrac{2p}{q}$

The index laws often come in handy.

---

example

Simplify:

a $\quad 3p^2 \times 4p^3$ $\qquad\qquad\qquad\qquad$ **b** $\quad 15p^8 \div 3p^5$

....

a $\quad 3p^2 \times 4p^3 = 3 \times 4 \times p^2 \times p^3$

$\qquad\qquad = 12p^5$

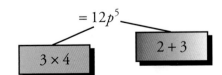

b $\quad 15p^8 \div 3p^5 = \dfrac{15p^8}{3p^5}$

$\qquad\qquad\qquad = 5p^3$

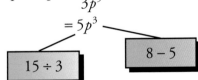

Exercise A2.3

1 Simplify these expressions by collecting like terms.

a $3a + 4b + 6a - 2b$ **b** $6x + 9y - 8x + y$ **c** $11x^2 + 6 + 3x^2 - 8$

d $5x^2 + 6x + 3x^2$ **e** $7ab - 4ba$ **f** $6mn - 2nm + 5mn$

g $pqrs + srqp$ **h** $9y + 4x - 11x^2 + 16x$

2 Simplify these expressions involving multiplication or division.

a $p \times w$ **b** $3p \times 4q$ **c** $11z \times 12z$ **d** $5m \times 6m$ **e** $c \div 6$ **f** $36p \div q$

g $\dfrac{12a}{4b}$ **h** $\dfrac{9abc}{3c}$ **i** $4p^6 \times 2p^3$ **j** $(10p^3)^2$ **k** $\dfrac{15p^6}{3p^2}$ **l** $\dfrac{545x^3}{5x}$

3 Here are twelve algebra 'snap' cards.

   a Find five matching pairs.

   b Hence, identify the pair that is not a match.

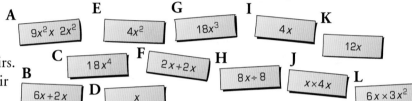

A $9x^2 x \; 2x^2$ E $4x^2$ G $18x^3$ I $4x$ K $12x$

C $18x^4$ F $2x + 2x$ H $8x \div 8$ J $x \times 4x$ L $6x \times 3x^2$

B $6x + 2x$ D x

4 Draw 'True' and 'False' pots and put these simplified algebra statements in them.

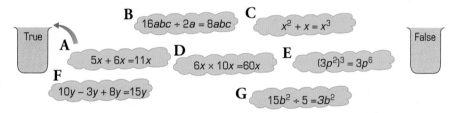

True

A $5x + 6x = 11x$

B $16abc \div 2a = 8abc$

C $x^2 + x = x^3$

D $6x \times 10x = 60x$

E $(3p^2)^3 = 3p^6$

F $10y - 3y + 8y = 15y$

G $15b^2 \div 5 = 3b^2$

False

5 Copy and complete these algebra grids.
The operation is shown in the top left-hand corner:

i

+	1st	
	$3x$	$6y$
2nd $6x$	?	?
^-4y	?	?

ii

×	1st		
	$3x$	$6y$	^-2x
2nd $6x$	?	?	?
^-4y	?	?	?

iii

−	1st		
	$11m$	$2n$	$^-3m^2$
2nd m^2	?	?	?
^-2m	?	?	?

iv

÷	1st	
	$18ab$	$9b^3$
2nd $3a$	?	?
$9b$	?	?

v

+	1st	
	$3x + 2x^2$	$10x^2 - x$
2nd $5x^2 + 3x$	?	?
$6x - 2x^2$	?	?

vi

×	1st		
	$6x$	$2y$	?
2nd $3x$	?	?	$27x^3y$
	?	$12xz$	?

6 Write a simplified formula for the required quantity.

a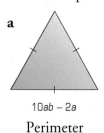

$10ab - 2a$

Perimeter

b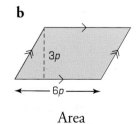

$3p$

$6p$

Area

c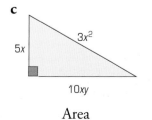

$5x$

$3x^2$

$10xy$

Area

d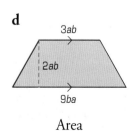

$3ab$

$2ab$

$9ba$

Area

Expanding brackets

This spread will show you how to:
- ▶▶ Multiply a single term over a bracket.
- ▶▶ Take out single-term common factors.
- ▶▶ Derive algebraic expressions and formulae.

KEYWORDS

Factor   Expand
Formula   Factorise
Expression

Brackets are useful when you want to multiply a whole expression.
You could write the formula for the area of this rectangle using a bracket.

8
$x + 2$

Area of rectangle = length × width
$= 8(x + 2)$

All of $x + 2$ has been multiplied by 8.

Sometimes you may need to remove, or **expand** brackets.

| Area = 2 × x | Area = 8 × 2 | 2 |
| x | 8 | |

Area of rectangle $= 2 \times x + 2 \times 8$
$= 2x + 16$
So $2(x + 8)$ $= 2x + 16$

▶ **To expand a bracket, multiply each term inside by the term outside the bracket.**

For example, $5(x - 3) = 5x - 15$

Be careful with negative terms outside a bracket.

example

Write an expression for the difference in area between these two rectangles.

← 4 →
$x - 1$ A

←3→
$x - 3$ B

Area $A = 4(x - 1)$ Area $B = 3(x - 3)$

Difference $= 4(x - 1) - 3(x - 3)$
$= 4x - 4 - 3x + 9$
$= 4x - 3x - 4 + 9$
$= x + 5$

$^-3 \times ^-3 = +9$

▶ **You factorise an expression by putting brackets into it.**

You can factorise $24x + 12$ in various ways:

Expanding and factorising are opposites:
If you expand each of the brackets, you will get $24x + 12$.

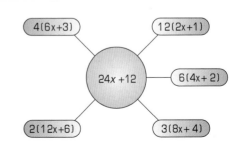
$4(6x+3)$ $12(2x+1)$
$24x + 12$ $6(4x+2)$
$2(12x+6)$ $3(8x+4)$

Exercise A2.4

1 Expand these expressions.

  a $5(2x+3)$ **b** $16(3-2y)$ **c** $p(p-3)$ **d** $2x(3x+y)$

  e $^-6(3x+1)$ **f** $^-7(10-3x)$ **g** $^-q(q-4)$ **h** $^-2m(^-m+n)$

2 Expand and simplify these expressions. Hence, select the odd one out.

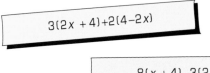

$$3(2x+4)+2(4-2x)$$

$$(3x+30)-(x-10)$$

$$8(x+4)-3(2x+4)$$

$$20+x(8x+4)-2(4x^2+x)$$

3 Copy and complete:

  a $8(a-6)-?(2a+?)=2a-60$ **b** $2k(?+4)-(?-k)=k^2+9k$

4 **a** Use brackets to write a formula for the required quantity.

    i Area   **ii** Volume   **iii** Difference between nth terms:

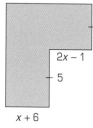 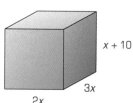

                                                        1, 7, 17, 31, 49 ...

                                                        2, 5, 10, 17, 26 ...

  b For each of part **a(i)**, **(ii)** and **(iii)** expand your brackets and simplify your answer where possible.

5 Show that all of these expressions simplify to give $3x+4$.

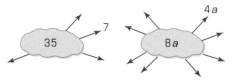

$$\frac{3(x+4)+4(3x+2)}{5}$$

$$\frac{2(5x-6)-4(x-5)}{2}$$

$$\frac{(5x+15)-(3-4x)}{3}$$

6 Copy and complete these factor diagrams.

  35 7 $4a$ $8a$ $7ab$ $6a^2b$

7 Find all of the possible factorisations of these expressions.

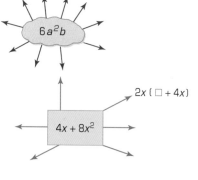

$12y+6$ $2(6y+\square)$

$4x+8x^2$ $2x(\square+4x)$

8 Expand $(x+2)(x+3)$.

  Check your answer by substituting $x=5$.

Factorising

This spread will show you how to:
▶▶ Simplify expressions by taking out single-term common factors.
▶▶ Derive algebraic expressions and formulae.

KEYWORDS
Simplify   Power
Transform   HCF
Expression

The opposite of expanding is factorising.

Expanding involves multiplication ...   and   ... factorising involves division.
$4(2x + 3)$ $=$ $8x + 12$ $12x + 24$ $=$ $6(2x + 4)$

Multiply both terms by 4   **Divide** both terms by 6

There are various ways to factorise $12x + 24$.

The highest common factor of $12x$ and 24 is 12.
$\Rightarrow$ To **fully factorise** the expression:
$12x + 24 = 12(x + 2)$

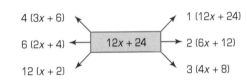

4 (3x + 6)   1 (12x + 24)
6 (2x + 4) ← 12x + 24 → 2 (6x + 12)
12 (x + 2)   3 (4x + 8)

▶ You fully factorise an expression by:
  ▶ finding the HCF of its terms and writing it outside a bracket
  ▶ dividing each term by the HCF and writing them inside the bracket.

$16 + 20y$
$= 4(4 + 5y)$

You can factorise harder expressions involving powers.
A Venn diagram might help.

example

a   Show all of the factors of $3x^2$ and $9xy$ in a Venn diagram.
b   Use your answer to **a** to fully factorise $3x^2 + 9xy$.

a
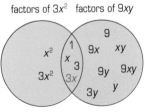
factors of $3x^2$ factors of $9xy$

x^2 1 $9x$ xy
       x
$3x^2$ 3 $9y$ $9xy$
       $3x$
       $3y$ y

b $3x^2 + 9xy = 3x(x + 3y)$

$3x$ is the highest common factor.

With practice, you will not need to show all this working.

▶ $8mp + 4n = 4(2mp + n)$ ▶ $16x - 8xy = 8x(2 - y)$
▶ $4mp + 8m^2 = 4m(p + 2m)$ ▶ $4k + 8k^2 = 4k(1 + 2k)$

You can factorise a formula.
$S = \frac{1}{2}vt - \frac{1}{2}ut$
$\quad = \frac{1}{2}t(v - u)$

$\frac{1}{2}$ and t are both common factors.

Exercise A2.5

1 Copy and complete these Venn diagrams for the factors of each term given.

   a HCF ($6x$ and $8y$) = __   **b** HCF ($4x^2$ and $8x$) = __   **c** HCF ($5x$, $10y$ and $15z$) = __

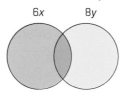
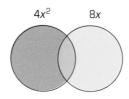
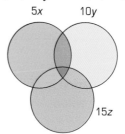

2 Factorise these expressions completely.
Check your solutions by expanding.

  a $8x + 10y$ **b** $12p + 36q$ **c** $6z + 12m - 18k$ **d** $8x^2 + 10x$

  e $pq - 2p$ **f** $a^2 + ab - 6a$ **g** $12ab + 18b^2$ **h** $4m^2 - 8mn$

  i $15u^2 - 5uv + 20u^2v$ **j** $6ab + 12ab^2$ **k** $14m^2 - 7m$ **l** $5a^2b^3 - 10a^2b^2 + a^2b$

3 Each student has made an error in the factorisation. Explain what it is and put it right.

$10x + 20y$
$= 2(5x + 18y)$

Elaine

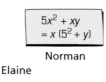

$5x^2 + xy$
$= x(5^2 + y)$

Norman

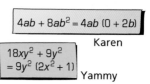

$4ab + 8ab^2 = 4ab(0 + 2b)$

Karen

$18xy^2 + 9y^2$
$= 9y^2(2x^2 + 1)$

Yammy

4 Clare and Jason were arguing about the formulae they had come up with for the number of crosses (C) in a square of side l.
Clare said '$C = 4l - 8$' but Jason said '$C = 4(l - 2)$'.

  a Who is right, or are they both right?

  b Justify how Clare came up with her formula.
    Justify how Jason got his formula.

5 Kushdip notices that whenever she adds three consecutive numbers, the answer is always a multiple of 3.
For example, $17 + 18 + 19 = 54$ $54 = 18 \times 3$

  a Try some numbers of your own to see if this is correct.

  b Use algebra to convince Kushdip that this is always true.

6 Prove, algebraically, that these statements are true.
Try some numerical examples first to convince yourself.

> The sum of five consecutive numbers is a multiple of 5.

> The product of two even numbers is even.

> If you take three consecutive numbers the difference between the product of the second and third, and the first and second is always even.

7 Investigation
The sum of an even and an odd number is always odd.
Prove this using algebra.

Solving equations

KEYWORDS

Equation   Term

Inverse   Solution

This spread will show you how to:

▶▶ Construct and solve linear equations.

▶ An equation is:

an expression	equal to	a number or expression.	
$6x + 2$	$=$	17	(one-sided equation)
$3x + 4$	$=$	$10 - 5x$	(two-sided equation)

One-sided equations

To solve a one-sided equation, you should:

▶ Read the equation, layer by layer

▶ Do the inverse of each layer, in reverse order.

> Solving an equation is like 'Pass the parcel': the first layer to go on will become the last layer to be undone.

example

Solve the equation: $\dfrac{6x - 2}{7} = 4$

▶ Read the equation: $\dfrac{6x - 2}{7} = 4$

> I think of a number, multiply it by 6, subtract 2 and divide by 7.

▶ Do the inverse:
  - ▶ Multiply by 7: $6x - 2 = 28$
  - ▶ Add 2: $6x = 30$
  - ▶ Divide by 6: $x = 5$

Two-sided equations

To solve a two-sided equation, you should:

▶ Subtract the smallest algebraic term from both sides

▶ Solve as a one-sided equation.

> You can use **SS** to remember 'subtract the smallest'

example

Solve these equations.

a $3x + 4 = 5x - 10$ **b** $10 - 2x = 9 - 5x$

Note:
$^-(^-5x) = +5x$

a $3x + 4 = 5x - 10$

    Subtract $3x$ from both sides.

$4 = 2x - 10$

    $+10$

$14 = 2x$

    $\div 2$

$7 = x$

b $10 - 2x = 9 - 5x$

    Subtract ^-5x from both sides

$10 + 3x = 9$

    $^-10$

$3x = ^-1$

    $\div 3$

$x = ^-\frac{1}{3}$

Exercise A2.6

1 Solve these equations.

a $\dfrac{3x-5}{2} = 10$

b $4(x+3) = 40$

c $2\left(\dfrac{x+1}{2} - 3\right) = 8$

d $5x - 5 = 3x + 5$

e $10 - 2x = 5x + 3$

f $3(x+1) = 9(x-4)$

2 **a** Arrange all of these expressions to make an equation and its solution.

   b Make a set of your own equation cards. Swap yours with a friend and solve each other's equation.

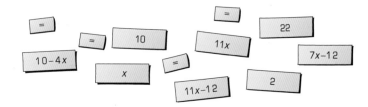

3 Copy and complete this crossword by solving the equations given in the clues.

Across
1 $2(x+2) = 30$
3 $2(x+10) = \frac{1}{2}(3x+80)$
4 $\dfrac{3x-11}{2} = 71$
6 $\dfrac{2x+50}{3} = \dfrac{x+175}{2}$

Down
1 $4(x-50) = 3x - 95$
2 $60 - 2x = 80 - 3x$
5 $x^2 = 196$

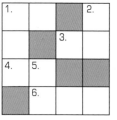

4 **a** This triangle is known to be isosceles. Use this information to find x.

   b Is the triangle equilateral?

5 What number must the $*$ represent in each case?

a $3x + * = 6x - 8$
   $* = 3x - 8$
   $12 = 3x$
   $* = x$

b $10 - *x = *x - 20$
   $x = 6$

c $*(10 - *x) = *x - 6$
   $* = x$

6 **Puzzle**

In each puzzle, the sum of the horizontal squares equals the sum of the vertical squares. What numbers should be in each square?

a

	$4 - 3x$	
$3x + 12$	$5 + 3x$	$7 - 8x$
	$10x + 6$	

b

	$11a + 5$	
$10a - ab$	$ab - 3$	$2ab + 6$
	$4x - ab + 3a$	

You should know how to ...

1 Use indices and apply the index laws:

2 Simplify algebraic expressions, including those with brackets.

3 Transform expressions by removing common factors.

4 Construct and solve linear equations with integer coefficients, using an appropriate method.

Check out

1 a Evaluate these indices:

i 2^5 **ii** $(^-3)^3$ **iii** $(\frac{1}{4})^2$ **iv** $18°$ **v** 5^{-2} **vi** $100^{1/2}$

b Simplify these expressions:

i $x^6 \times x^8$ **ii** $\dfrac{y^{10}}{y^2}$ **iii** $(z^2)^3$ **iv** $x^{-2} \times x^{-3}$

v $(2x^3)^2$

c True or False? $\dfrac{a^6 \times a^{-4}}{a^3} = a^1$

2 Simplify these expressions fully:

a $3x^2 + 12x + 4x^2 - 5x$
b $10ab - 3ba$
c $5x \times 2y \times 3z$
d $15p^2 \div 5p$
e $5x^3 \times 4x^4$
f $3a - 4b + 6a - 6b$
g $x(x + 2) + x(5 - x)$
h $3(x + 2) - 2(x - 4)$
i $2x \times 3x \times 4x$

3 Factorise these expressions fully by removing common factors:

a $9x + 18$
b $25y - 15$
c $3b + 9ab$
d $10xy + 5x^2 - 15x$

4 a Solve these equations.

i $5(x - 4) = 3(2 - 3x)$ **ii** $\dfrac{3x + 2}{4} = \dfrac{2x + 8}{5}$

b The areas of these rectangles are equal.

$x + 3$, 5 ; 10 , $x - 1$

Find x.

2

Measures and measurements

This unit will show you how to:

▶▶ Use units of measurement to calculate, estimate, measure and solve problems in a variety of contexts.

▶▶ Convert between area measures and between volume measures.

▶▶ Know and use the formulae for the circumference and area of a circle.

▶▶ Calculate surface area and volume of prisms.

▶▶ Use formulae from mathematics and other subjects.

▶▶ Solve increasingly demanding problems and evaluate solutions.

▶▶ Solve substantial problems by breaking them into simpler tasks.

▶▶ Give solutions to problems to an appropriate degree of accuracy.

You've got a head start!

You get to run around a smaller track!

Running tracks contain semicircles at either end.

Before you start

You should know how to ...

1 Convert between metric measures of length.

2 Use of formula to calculate the area of a:
- rectangle
- triangle
- parallelogram
- trapezium.

3 Calculate the volume of a cuboid.

4 Round decimals to one or two decimal places.

Check in

1 Copy and complete.

  a 1 cm = _____ mm   **b** 56 cm = _____ m

2 Find the area of these shapes.

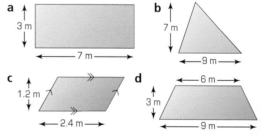

3 Calculate the volume of this cuboid.

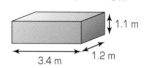

4 Round these numbers to the accuracy given.

  a 42.35 (1 d.p.)   **b** 27.93   (1 d.p.)

  c 4.255 (2 d.p.)   **d** 115.999 (1 d.p.)

S2.1 Metric units of area

This spread will show you how to:
- ▶▶ Use units of measurement to calculate, estimate and solve problems in the context of area.
- ▶▶ Convert between metric units of area.
- ▶▶ Use formulae for area.

KEYWORDS
Hectare
Estimate
Square metre

You could measure the area of ...

... the tip of a pencil in square millimetres (mm²)

... a mouse mat in square centimetres (cm²)

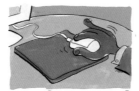

... your classroom in square metres (m²)

... your school field in hectares (ha)

... a town in square kilometres (km²)

Sometimes you need to convert between metric units.

$1 \text{ cm}^2 \qquad = 1 \text{ cm} \times 1 \text{ cm} \qquad = 10 \text{ mm} \times 10 \text{ mm}$

So $1 \text{ cm}^2 \qquad = 100 \text{ mm}^2$
Similarly, $1 \text{ m}^2 = 100 \text{ cm} \times 100 \text{ cm} = 10\,000 \text{ cm}^2$

Note:
$1 \text{ ha} = 10\,000 \text{ m}^2$

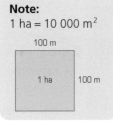

You should always estimate before calculating areas of shapes.

example

a   Estimate the area of the triangle.

b   Calculate its exact area in
   i cm²
   ii m²

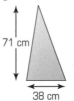

71 cm

38 cm

a   **Area** $A = \frac{1}{2} bh$
   Estimate: $\quad A \approx \frac{1}{2} \times 40 \times 70$
            $= 20 \times 70 = 1400 \text{ cm}^2$

b   **i** $\qquad A = \frac{1}{2} \times 38 \times 71$
            $= 1349 \text{ cm}^2$

   ii $\qquad 1 \text{ m}^2 = 10\,000 \text{ cm}^2$
   so $1349 \text{ cm}^2 = (1349 \div 10\,000) \text{ m}^2$
            $= 0.1349 \text{ m}^2$

Exercise S2.1

1 Find the areas of these shapes in the units given in brackets.

a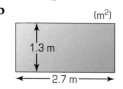
(m²)
2.1 m
4.2 m

b
(m²)
1.3 m
2.7 m

c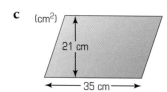
(cm²)
21 cm
35 cm

d
(cm²)
8 cm
6 cm
12 cm

e (mm²)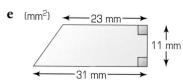
23 mm
11 mm
31 mm

2 Find the areas of these compound shapes.

a
15 cm
12 cm
10 cm

b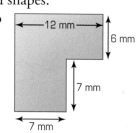
12 mm
6 mm
7 mm
7 mm

3 **Estimate** the areas of these fields.

a
35 m
42 m

b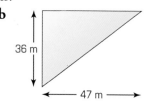
36 m
47 m

c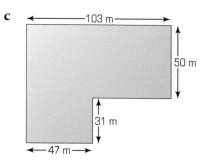
103 m
50 m
31 m
47 m

4 Calculate the exact area of the fields in question 3.

5 How many square metres (m²) are there in 1 km²?
Show your working.

6 Tom has a rectangular piece of land 200 m by 100 m.
   a How much is this in hectares?
   Sam has a rectangular piece of land 150 m by 190 m.
   b How much is this in hectares?
   c Sally owns this triangular piece of land.
      Calculate its area in hectares.
   d Who has the most land: Tom, Sam or Sally?

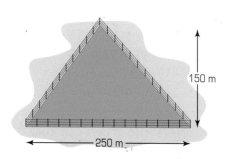
150 m
250 m

Investigation

7 What is the largest area that can be enclosed by a
fence 100 m long?

More metric units

This spread will show you how to:
⏩ Use units of measurement to calculate, estimate and solve problems in the context of volume.
⏩ Convert between metric units of volume, capacity and mass.
⏩ Use formulae for volume.

KEYWORDS
cubic millimetre
cubic centimetre
cubic metre   capacity
mass   tonne

You can use your knowledge of metric lengths to convert between units of volume.

$$1 \text{ cm}^3 = 1 \text{ cm} \times 1 \text{ cm} \times 1 \text{ cm}$$
$$= 10 \text{ mm} \times 10 \text{ mm} \times 10 \text{ mm}$$
$$= 1000 \text{ mm}^3$$

Similarly, 1 m^3
$$= 100 \text{ cm} \times 100 \text{ cm} \times 100 \text{ cm}$$
$$= 1\,000\,000 \text{ cm}^3$$

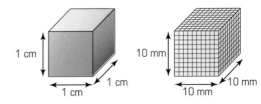

You should know the formula for the volume of a cuboid.

▶ Volume of cuboid $V = lbh$

Find the volume of the cuboid
a in mm^3
b in cm^3.

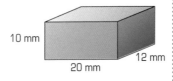

a $V = lbh = 20 \text{ mm} \times 12 \text{ mm} \times 10 \text{ mm}$
$$= 2400 \text{ mm}^3$$
b $1 \text{ cm}^3 = 1000 \text{ mm}^3$
So 2400 mm^3
$$= (2400 \div 1000) \text{ cm}^3 = 2.4 \text{ cm}^3$$

You can express other measures using metric units.

▶ Capacity is the amount of a 3-D shape can hold.
You measure capacity using litres (l), centilitres(cl) or millilitres (ml).
100 cl = 1 l   1000 ml = 1 l   1 ml = 1 cm^3

Note:
Volume is the amount of **space** a 3-D shape occupies.

▶ Mass is a measure of the weight of an object.
You measure mass using grams (g), kilograms (kg) and tonnes (t).
1000 g = 1 kg   1000 kg = 1 t

More exactly, mass is a measure of the amount of **matter** in a 3-D object.

A large bottle of cola can hold 2.5 litres. How much is this in cubic centimetres?

$$2.5 \text{ l} = 2.5 \times 1000 \text{ ml} = 2500 \text{ ml} \qquad 1 \text{ ml} = 1 \text{ cm}^3, \text{ so } 2.5 \text{ l} = 2500 \text{ cm}^3$$

Exercise S2.2

1 The volume of a cube is 125 mm^3.
What is the length of one side?

2 The volume of a cuboid is 240 cm^3, its length is 30 cm, and its width is 2 cm.
  a What is its height?
  b Can you find a cuboid with this volume whose base is square?

3 A cuboid has a square top and bottom.
Its volume is 2880 mm^3 and its height is 20 mm.
What are the dimension of its square faces?

4 Sani received this parcel. Find its volume in
  a mm^3
  b cm^3
  c m^3.

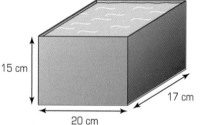

125 mm
0.4 m
15 cm

5 A tin is full of water.

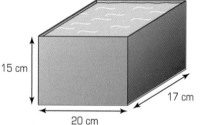

15 cm
17 cm
20 cm

  a Find its volume in **i** cm^3 **ii** m^3
  b What is the capacity of liquid it will hold?

6 Will the canister of oil fit in the oil tray?
Explain your answer.

Oil
5 litres
30 cm
8.5 cm
20 cm

7 A lift holds a maximum of 0.5 tonnes.
Will it hold these six people:
Zaina 90 kg, Ben 80 kg, Adebola 72 kg, Sarah 77 kg, Beth 64 kg, Tom 63 kg?
Explain your answer.

8 Packets of butter are cuboids with dimensions 4 cm by 5 cm by 3 cm.
How many packets will fit into a box measuring 80 cm by 1 m by 90 cm?

Circumference of a circle

This spread will show you how to:
- ▶▶ Know and use the formula for the circumference of a circle.
- ▶▶ Calculate the circumference of a circle.

KEYWORDS

Circumference   Similar

Diameter   Pi (π)

Radius

All circles are **similar** shapes. This means that their diameters and circumferences are in the same proportion.

The ratio $\dfrac{\text{circumference}}{\text{diameter}}$ is the same for all circles.

This ratio is an important number, and is known by the Greek letter π, or *pi*.

You pronounce π as 'pie'.

▶ $\dfrac{C}{d} = \pi$ for all circles   where C = circumference and d = diameter

▶ As a decimal, $\pi = 3.141592\ldots$, which rounds to **3.14** to 2 decimal places.
π cannot be expressed exactly as a fraction, but $\frac{22}{7}$ is close.

You can rearrange the formula $\dfrac{C}{d} = \pi$:

$d = 2 \times r$, so $C = \pi d$
becomes $C = \pi \times 2 \times r$
$= 2\pi r$

▶ $C = \pi d$, or $C = 2\pi r$ for all circles.

You can use the formulae to calculate the radius, diameter or circumference of a circle.

example

a   The diameter of a circle is 5 cm. Find its circumference.

b   The circumference of a circle is 8.2 m. Find its radius to 2 decimal places.

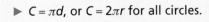

a $C = \pi d = 3.14 \times 5$
          $= 15.7$ cm

b $C = 2\pi r$

So $8.2 = 2 \times 3.14 \times r$

Then $r = \dfrac{8.2}{2 \times 3.14} = 1.3057$

So $r = 1.31$ m, correct to 2 d.p.

Exercise S2.3

Take $\pi = 3.14$ in this exercise, or use the π key on your calculator.

1 Measure the diameters of these circles and hence calculate their circumferences.

a

b

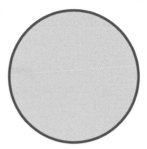

c

2 Find the circumference of a circle with radius:
    a 4.2 m   **b** 3.9 cm   **c** 21 mm   **d** 32 km

3 Find the circumference of a circle with diameter:
    a 24 mm   **b** 3.2 cm   **c** 2.15 mm   **d** 4 km

4 Find the perimeters of these shapes.

a

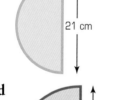

21 cm

b

2.3 m

c

4.3 mm

d

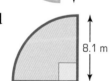

8.1 m

e

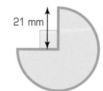

21 mm

5 The distance around a circular pool is 10 m.
Find the diameter of the pool correct to 1 decimal place.

6 This diagram shows the inner and outer track of a running field.

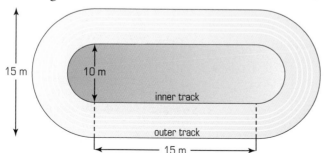

15 m

10 m

inner track

outer track

15 m

How much further would an athelete run on the outside track compared to the inside track?

S2.4 Area of a circle

This spread will show you how to:
▶▶ Know and use the formula for the area of a circle.

KEYWORDS

Sector   Circumference

Diameter   Radius

Imagine dividing a circle into tiny sectors ...

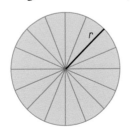

... and rearranging the sectors into a rectangular shape.

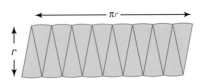

The length of the 'rectangle' is πr because it is half of the circumference.

The area of the rectangle $\approx \pi r \times r = \pi r^2$.
This leads to the formula for the area of a circle.

The smaller you make the sectors, the closer the shape becomes to a rectangle.

▶ $A = \pi r^2$ for any circle.

---

example

Find to one decimal place the area of a circle:

a with radius 2.3 m   **b** with diameter 14 cm.

....

a $A = \pi r^2$
     $= 3.14 \times 2.3 \times 2.3$
     $= 16.6106$
     $A = 16.6$ m correct to 1 d.p.

b $d = 14$ cm, so $r = 14$ cm $\div 2 = 7$ cm
     $A = \pi r^2$
     $= 3.14 \times 7 \times 7$
     $= 153.9$ cm correct to 1 d.p.

You can use the formula $A = \pi r^2$ to solve problems.

---

example

A semicircular window has an area of 1.2 m^2.
Find the radius of the window to the nearest centimetre.

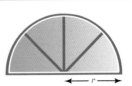

....

For the whole circle, $A = 2 \times 1.2$ m$^2 = 2.4$ m^2
$A = \pi r^2$, so $2.4 = 3.14 \times r^2$

$$r^2 = \frac{2.4}{3.14} = 0.7643 \dots$$

Remember:
The opposite of **square** is **square root**.

$$r = \sqrt{0.764331} = 0.8742 \dots$$

So the radius of the window is 0.8742 m, or 87 cm to the nearest centimetre.

Exercise S2.4

Take $\pi = 3.14$ in this exercise, or use the π key on your calculator.

1 Find the area of a circle with:

   a radius   **i** 4 cm   **ii** 5 mm   **iii** 10 m   **iv** 6.2 km

   b diameter   **i** 5.3 mm   **ii** 4.1 cm   **iii** 27 m   **iv** 82 km

   Give your answers to an appropriate degree of accuracy.

2 Find the area of each shape.

a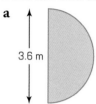

3.6 m

b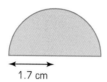

1.7 cm

c

27 mm

d

4.2 km

1.7 km

e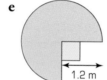

1.2 m

3 Sam has two circles.
One is blue with area 20 cm².
One is pink with circumference 20 cm. Which is bigger?

4 Which shape is biggest,
A, B or C?

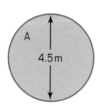

A   4.5m

B   = 4 m

C   5.5m

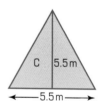

5.5m

5 Mary makes jam tarts.
Her pastry is rolled out to a perfect rectangle 12 cm by 16 cm.
Each tart is 4 cm in diameter.
How much pastry is wasted?

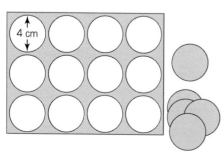

4 cm

This spread will show you how to:

▶▶ Calculate the volume of a right prism.

KEYWORDS
Cross-section
Right prism

▶ A **prism** is a solid with a uniform cross-section.

Uniform cross-section means that you can cut the solid anywhere throughout its length and get the same shape inside.

Here are three prisms:

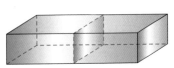

A rectangular prism (cuboid)

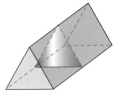

A triangular prism

A hexagonal prism

The ends of these prisms are all different shapes, but they are all examples of **right prisms**. A right prism has rectangles making up its other faces.

▶ **Volume of a prism = area of cross-section × length**

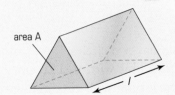

area A

l

Find the volumes of these prisms.

a

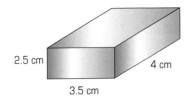

2.5 cm

4 cm

3.5 cm

b

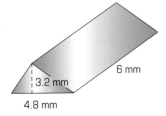

6 mm

3.2 mm

4.8 mm

a Cross-sectional area $= 2.5 \text{ cm} \times 3.5 \text{ cm}$
$= 8.75 \text{ cm}^2$
Volume $= 8.75 \text{ cm}^2 \times 4 \text{ cm}$
$= 35 \text{ cm}^3$

b Area of cross-section $= \frac{1}{2} bh$
$= \frac{4.8 \times 3.2}{2} \text{ mm}$
$= 7.68 \text{ mm}$
Volume $= 7.68 \text{ mm}^2 \times 6 \text{ mm}$
$= 46.08 \text{ mm}^3$

Exercise S2.5

1 Find the volumes of these cuboids.

a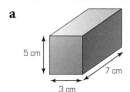

b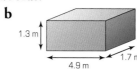

Use appropriate units for your answers.

2 Find the volumes of these shapes. (Hint for **c** and **d**: split the shapes up into separate cuboids.)

a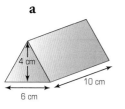

b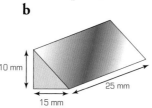

c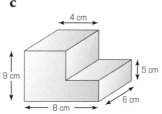

d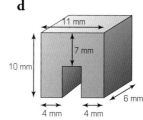

3 Find the volumes of these compound shapes (you may use a calculator).

a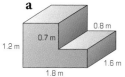

b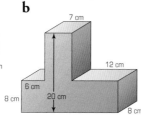

c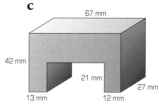

d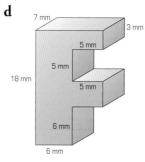

4 Which box holds most?

Give reasons for your answer.

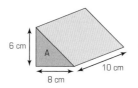

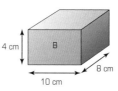

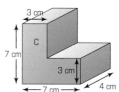

5 Here is a sketch of a swimming pool.
Calculate the volume of water the swimming pool holds.

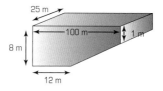

6 **a** Find the volume of this cylinder by finding the area of the cross-section, using $A = \pi r^2$, and multiplying by the length.

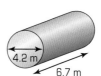

b What is the formula for the volume of a cylinder radius r and height h?

Surface area

This spread will show you how to:
▶▶ Calculate the surface area of a right prism.

KEYWORDS
Net
Surface area
Triangular prism

The **surface area** of a 3-D shape is a measure of the space occupied by its faces.
You can find the surface area of a prism by considering its **net**.

example

Find the surface area of this cuboid measuring 5.2 m by 4.8 m by 3.5 m.

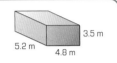

1 First sketch the net.
  Note that all the faces are rectangles.

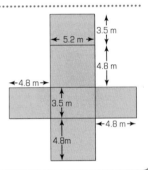

2 Now add the areas – note that they come in pairs:
  $2 \times (4.8 \times 5.2) + 2 \times (3.5 \times 5.2) + 2 \times (4.8 \times 3.5) = 119.92$

  Surface area of cuboid = 119.92 m^2.

▶ The surface area of a prism is the total area of its faces.

You can use your knowledge of the area of a triangle to calculate the surface areas of more
complicated prisms.

example

Find the total surface area of this triangular prism.

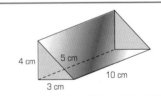

1 First sketch the net.
  Note that there are two identical triangles and three rectangles.

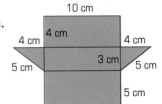

2 Calculate the area of the triangles:
  Area of each triangle $= \frac{1}{2} bh$
  $= \frac{1}{2} \times 4 \times 3 = 6$

3 Calculate the area of the rectangles:
  Area $= (4 \times 10) + (3 \times 10) + (5 \times 10) = 120$

4 Now add the areas together: $2 \times 6 + 120 = 132$
  So the total surface area of the prism = 132 cm^2.

Exercise S2.6

1 Find the surface areas of these cuboids.

a
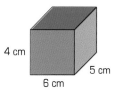
4 cm
5 cm
6 cm

b
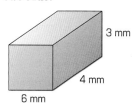
3 mm
4 mm
6 mm

c
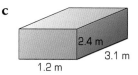
2.4 m
3.1 m
1.2 m

2 Find the surface area of this cuboid.

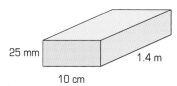
25 mm
1.4 m
10 cm

Give your answer in **a** mm^2 **b** cm^2 **c** m^2

3 Find the surface area of this triangular prism.
0.3 m
0.5 m
2.4 m
0.4 m

4 This cuboid has a surface area of
$(2 \times 8)cm^2 + (2 \times 6)cm^2 + (2 \times 12)cm^2 = (16 + 12 + 24)cm^2 = 52 \ cm^2$
Find a different cuboid with the same surface area.

3 cm
2 cm
4 cm

5 Here is a cylinder.
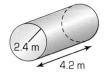
2.4 m
4.2 m

It is made up of two circles and a rectangle.
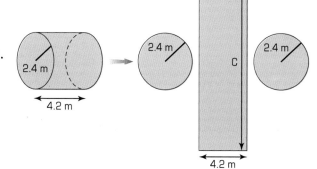
2.4 m
4.2 m
2.4 m
C
2.4 m
4.2 m

a Find the surface area of the cylinder.
b Find a general formula for the surface area of a cylinder.

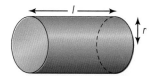
l
r
l = length
r = radius

83

Summary

You should know how to ...

1 Know and use the formulae for the circumference and area of a circle.

2 Solve substantial problems by breaking them into simpler tasks.

3 Give solutions to problems to an appropriate degree of accuracy.

Check out

1 Find:

   a the circumference

   b the area of this circle.

4.2 cm

2 Find the surface area of this prism.

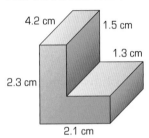

4.2 cm   1.5 cm

1.3 cm

2.3 cm

2.1 cm

3 Find the volume of this cuboid, giving your answer to an appropriate accuracy.

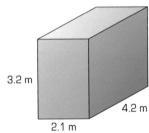

3.2 m

4.2 m

2.1 m

Functions and graphs

This unit will show you how to:

▶▶ Generate points and plot graphs of linear functions.

▶▶ Given values for m and c, find the gradient of lines given by equations of the form $y = mx + c$.

▶▶ Construct functions arising from real-life problems and plot their corresponding graphs.

▶▶ Interpret graphs arising from real situations, including distance-time graphs.

▶▶ Solve increasingly demanding problems and evaluate solutions.

▶▶ Represent problems and synthesise. information in algebraic or graphical form.

▶▶ Solve substantial problems by breaking them into simpler tasks.

Road signs often tell you the steepness of gradient of a hill.

Before you start

You should know how to ...

1 Substitute values into an expression.

2 Plot points on a coordinate grid.

3 Rearrange a linear function to make y the subject.

For example, if $4y + 2x = 8$.

Then $4y = 8 - 2x$

And $y = 2 - \frac{1}{2}x$

Check in

1 If $a = 3$, $b = {}^{-}2$ and $c = 5$, place these expressions in ascending order:

2 a On a grid labelled ⁻8 to 8, plot and join these points in order.

(6, 4), (⁻2, 4), (⁻2, 8), (⁻8, 1), (⁻2, ⁻2), (⁻2, 1), (6, 1),(6, 4).

b What do you see?

What is its mathematical name?

3 Make y the subject of these formulae:

a $y + x = 10$ **b** $y - 4 = 2x$ **c** $2y = 6x + 7$

d $2y - x = 14$ **e** $3y + 5x = 12$

Straight-line graphs

This spread will show you how to:
- ▶▶ Generate points and plot graphs of linear functions.
- ▶▶ Recognise that equations of the form $y = mx + c$ correspond to straight line graphs.
- ▶▶ Find the inverse of a linear function.

KEYWORDS

Graph	Parallel
Gradient	Intercept
Axes	

A graph is a set of points that follows a rule.
There are two main types of linear graph.

Horizontal and vertical lines

▶ Horizontal lines have equation $y =$ a number.　　▶ Vertical lines have equation $x =$ a number.

All the points have y equal to 4. The equation is $y = 4$.

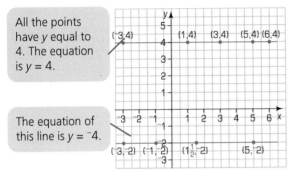

The equation of this line is $y = ^-4$.

All the points have x equal to $^-3$. The equation is $x = ^-3$.

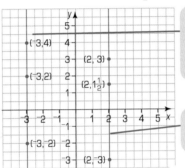

The equation of this line is $x = 2$.

Diagonal lines

As you go along a diagonal line, you move both across and up.
Therefore the equation must involve both x and y.

Graph 1

$y = 3x + 2$

x	0	1	2
y	2	5	8

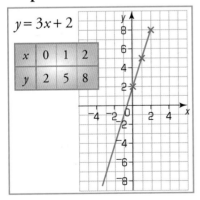

Graph 2

$y = 2x - 2$

x	0	1	2
y	$^-2$	0	2

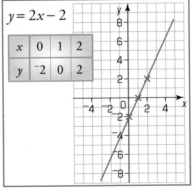

Graph 3

$2x + y = 4$

x	0	1	2
y	4	2	0

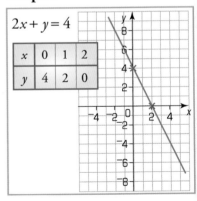

Diagonal lines vary in:
- ▶ Direction　　　Graphs 1 and 2 slope in a positive direction, whereas graph 3 slopes negatively.
- ▶ Steepness (or **gradient**)　　　Graph 1 is steeper than graph 2.
- ▶ Where they cut the y-axis (or y-axis **intercept**)　　　Graph 3 cuts the y-axis higher up than graph 2.

Exercise A3.1

1 a Copy and complete the table, sorting the equations into the correct column.

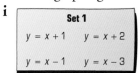

Horizontal	Vertical	Diagonal	Neither

Equation cards:
$y = 5$ $x = 4$ $2x + y = 8$ $y = x^2 + 1$ $y = 3x + 7$ $x = ^-2$ $y = ^-1$

b Add an example of your own equation in each column.

2 Produce a table of values for each equation. Use this to plot the graphs.
  a $y = 2$ **b** $x = 1$ **c** $y = 2x - 1$ **d** $y = 7 - 3x$ **e** $x + 3y = 9$

3 a Plot the graphs given in each set on a single pair of axes:

i Set 1
$y = x + 1$ $y = x + 2$
$y = x - 1$ $y = x - 3$

ii Set 2
$y = x + 1$ $y = 2x + 1$
$y = 3x + 1$ $y = \frac{1}{2}x + 1$

iii Set 3
$y = x$ $y = ^-x$
$y = x + 2$ $y = ^-x + 2$

iv Set 4
$y = 3x + 1$
$y = 2x - 1$
$y = ^-5x + 2$

b For sets **i–iii**, comment on the similarities and differences between the graphs.
   You should use the words: steepness, direction, y-axis intercept
c Do the graphs in set **iv** support your comments? Explain your answer.

4 You can write the equation $y = 2x + 1$ as a mapping:
$x \rightarrow 2x + 1$
  a Copy and complete the mapping diagram for $x \rightarrow 2x + 1$.
   Choose values of x from 0 to 4, including halves.

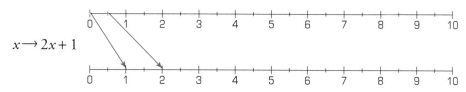

$x \rightarrow 2x + 1$

The function $x \rightarrow 2x + 1$ has an inverse function which reverses the mapping.
  b Find the inverse function of $x \rightarrow 2x + 1$.
  c Plot the graphs of $y = 2x + 1$ and its inverse function on the same axes.

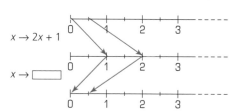

$x \rightarrow 2x + 1$

$x \rightarrow \boxed{}$

5 True or False?
  a $y = 3x + 2$ and $y = 4x + 2$ could be equations of opposite sides of a parallelogram.
  b $y = 5$ and $x = 4$ are perpendicular lines.
  c $y = 10 - 3x$ and $3x + y = 6$ are parallel lines.
  d $2y = 6x + 4$ and $y + 3x - 2 = 0$ are reflections of each other in the line $x = 0$.

Gradient of diagonal lines

This spread will show you how to:

▶▶ Find the gradient of lines given by equations of the form $y = mx + c$.

KEYWORDS
Gradient
Parallel
Coefficient

You can describe a diagonal line by its steepness, or **gradient**.
Here are three related diagonal graphs:

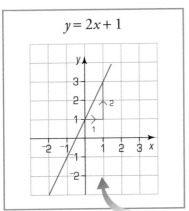

$y = 2x + 1$

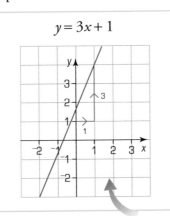

$y = 3x + 1$

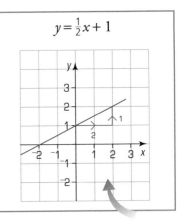

$y = \frac{1}{2}x + 1$

For every 1 you go across, you go 2 up. The gradient is 2.

For every 1 you go across, you go 3 up. The gradient is 3.

For every 2 you go across, you go 1 up. The gradient is $\frac{1}{2}$.

You can find the gradient of a line segment without having to draw a graph.

example

Find the gradient of the line joining $(2, 3)$ to $(4, 10)$.

$$\text{Gradient} = \frac{10 - 3}{4 - 2} = \frac{7}{2} \text{ or } 3\frac{1}{2}$$

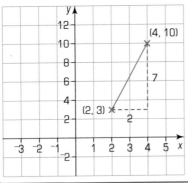

An easy way to remember gradient is 'TUBA':

$\dfrac{7}{2}$

T	The **T**op of the fraction
U	Is how far you go **U**p
B	The **B**ottom of the fraction
A	Is how far you go **A**cross

▶ In general, the gradient m of a straight line joining (x_1, y_1) to (x_2, y_2) is:

$$m = \frac{y_2 - y_1}{x_2 - x_1}$$

Exercise A3.2

1 On a squared grid, draw lines with these gradients:

  a Line A = $\frac{1}{3}$ **b** Line B = 4   **c** Line C = $^-\frac{1}{2}$ **d** Line D = $\frac{3}{5}$

  e Line E = $1\frac{1}{2}$ **f** Line F = $^-2\frac{1}{4}$

2 For each straight line on the graph, complete the row in the table:

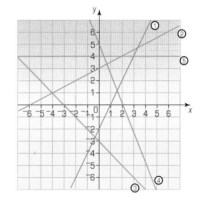

Line:	Gradient	y-axis intercept	Direction (positive or neg.)	Equation
1				
2				
3				
4				
5				
Your own				

3 Puzzles   Is each statement True or False?

  a Any two lines with the same steepness have the same gradient.

  b A gradient of $^-2$ is less steep than a gradient of zero.

  c A kite will have two pairs of sides with equal gradient.

  d A gradient of $\frac{10}{4}$ is steeper than a gradient of 2.

  e All sides of a square have equal gradient.

  f The line $y = 5$ has gradient of 5.

4 Find the gradients of these line segments.

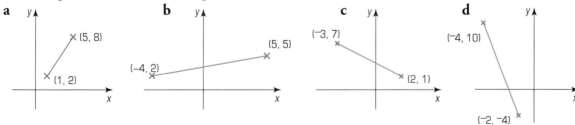

5 Puzzle   Find pairs of parallel lines.

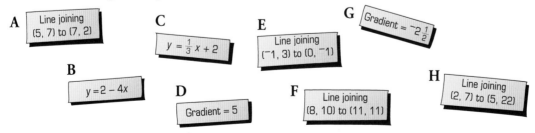

A   Line joining (5, 7) to (7, 2)

B $y = 2 - 4x$

C $y = \frac{1}{3}x + 2$

D   Gradient = 5

E   Line joining ($^-1$, 3) to (0, $^-1$)

F   Line joining (8, 10) to (11, 11)

G   Gradient = $^-2\frac{1}{2}$

H   Line joining (2, 7) to (5, 22)

6 A line with gradient 5 goes through the point (13, 24).
Name the next integer point it will pass through.

This spread will show you how to:

▶▶ Find the gradient of lines given by equations of the form $y = mx + c$.

KEYWORDS

Gradient   Constant

Intercept   Coefficient

▶ You can write the equation of a diagonal line in the form:

$$y = mx + c$$

y is the **subject** of the equation.

m is the **coefficient** of *x*. It represents the gradient.

c is a **constant**. It represents the *y*-axis intercept.

▶ If the gradient *m* is positive, the line slopes in a positive direction.

▶ If *m* is negative, the line slopes in a negative direction.

▶ The coordinates of the *y*-axis intercept are (0, *c*).

You can deduce the equation of a straight line from its graph.

example

Find the equation of each of these graphs.

a

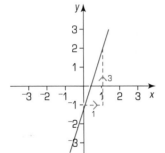

b

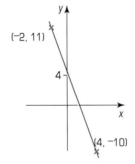

a $m = +3$

The graph cuts the *y*-axis at $(0, {}^-1)$

$\Rightarrow c = {}^-1$

So $y = 3x - 1$

b   Choose $(x_1, y_1) = ({}^-2, 11)$
and $(x_2, y_2) = (4, {}^-10)$

$$m = \frac{y_2 - y_1}{x_2 - x_1} = \frac{({}^-10) - 11}{4 - ({}^-2)}$$

$$= \frac{-21}{6} = \frac{-7}{2} = {}^-3\tfrac{1}{2}$$

The graph cuts the *y*-axis at $(0, 4)$ so $c = 4$.

$$y = {}^-3\tfrac{1}{2}x + 4 \qquad \text{or} \qquad y = 4 - 3\tfrac{1}{2}x$$

Exercise A3.3

1 True or False?
  a $y = 5x + 3$ is the equation of the line with gradient 5 that cuts the y-axis at $(0, 3)$.
  b $y = 10 - 2x$ is the equation of the line with gradient 10 that cuts the y-axis at $(0, {}^-2)$.
  c $3y = 6x - 18$ is the equation of the line with gradient 6 that cuts the y-axis at $(0, {}^-18)$.
  d $y = 10x + 1$ and $y = 10x - 2$ slope in opposite directions to each other.

2 **a** $y = 4x + 3$ **b** $y = {}^-2x + 5$ Fill in the required information for each equation.
   c $y = 10x - 2$ **d** $y = 7 - 3x$
   e $2y = 5x + 4$ **f** $y + 2x = 9$
   g $3y + 2x = 7$ **h** $y + px = q$

EQUATION	GRADIENT	DIRECTON	Y-AXIS INTERCEPT
$y = 5x + 1$	5	Positive	$(0, 1)$

3 From the given equations, find graphs that:
  a are parallel to each other
  b are steeper than $2y = x + 3$
  c have the same steepness, but different directions
  d intersect the y-axis at $(0, {}^-1)$
  e are mirror images of each other in the line $x = 0$.

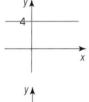
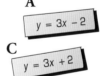

A $y = 4x + 3$
B $y + 1 = 3x$
C $y = 2 - 5x$
D $y = 5x - 1$
E $2y + 6x - 2 = 0$
F $2y = 8x + 4$

4 Match the equations with the sketches:

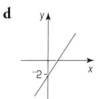

A $y = 3x - 2$
B $y = 4$
C $y = 3x + 2$
D $y = 4 - 3x$
E $y + 3x = 0$
F $y + 3x + 2 = 0$

5 Find the equations of the graphs **a** to **f**:

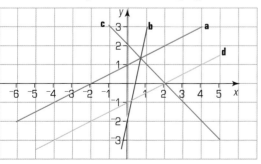
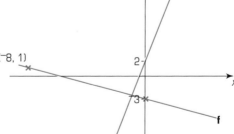

6 The graph $y = mx + 3$ goes through $(8, 7)$. What is m?

Parallel and perpendicular lines

This spread will show you how to:

▶▶ Investigate the gradients of parallel and perpendicular lines.

KEYWORDS

Parallel   Perpendicular
Gradient   Reciprocal

These graphs cut the y-axis at different heights.
However they all have the same gradient.
The graphs are **parallel**.

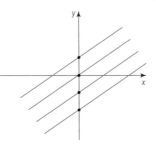

These three equations look different.
However they all have the same value of m.
The graphs of these equations all have gradient 3.
They are parallel.

$$y = 3x + 2 \Longrightarrow y = 3x + 2$$
$$y = 12 + 3x \Longrightarrow y = 3x + 12$$
$$3y = 9x - 2 \Longrightarrow y = 3x - \tfrac{2}{3}$$

▶ Two lines are parallel if they have the same gradient.
  Their equations will both have the same value of m.

▶ **Perpendicular** lines are lines that are 90° to each other.

Lines A and B are perpendicular.
They have gradients m_A and m_B respectively.

The gradient of A (3 across and 1 down) $= \tfrac{-1}{3} \Longrightarrow m_A = \tfrac{-1}{3}$
The gradient of B (1 across and 3 up) $= \tfrac{3}{1} \Longrightarrow m_B = \tfrac{3}{1}(= 3)$

Notice that m_A is the **negative reciprocal** of m_B.

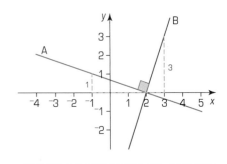

$$m_A \qquad\qquad m_B$$
$$\tfrac{-1}{3} \qquad\qquad \tfrac{3}{1}$$

Change the sign and invert the fraction.

Remember: the reciprocal of $\tfrac{3}{4}$ is $\tfrac{4}{3}$.
The reciprocal of 5 is $\tfrac{1}{5}$.

▶ Two lines are perpendicular if their gradients are the negative reciprocals of each other.
  A line with gradient $\tfrac{2}{3}$ will be perpendicular to a line with gradient $\tfrac{-3}{2}$.

Exercise A3.4

1 For each value of m, find the gradient of a line that is

    i parallel   **ii** perpendicular.

    a 4 **b** $\frac{1}{5}$ **c** $\frac{2}{3}$ **d** $1\frac{1}{2}$ **e** $^{-}1\frac{1}{4}$ **f** m

2 Copy this line on a square grid.

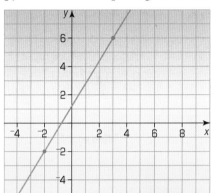

On the same grid, draw a line that is perpendicular to it.

3 True or False?
    a Two parallel lines never meet each other.
    b Two perpendicular lines always meet each other.
    c The lines $y = 3x + 2$ and $y = \frac{1}{3}x + 2$ are perpendicular.
    d The lines $y = 5x - 1$ and $2y = 10(x + 2)$ are parallel.

4 Copy and complete this table:

Equation of a parallel line	Equation	Equation of a perpendicular line
	$y = 4x + 1$	
	$y = 2\frac{1}{2}x - 3$	
	$2y = 7x + 4$	
	$2x + 3y = 9$	
	your own	

5 Under what circumstances could a pair of perpendicular lines be mirror images of each other in the y-axis?

6 Give the equation of each line used to construct these diagrams.

    a

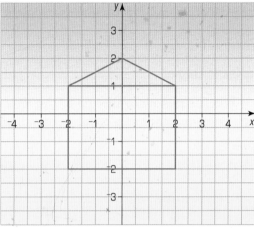

    b

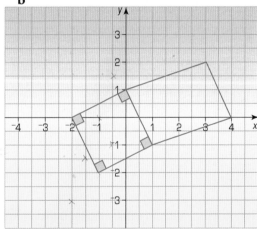

7 Give possible equations that could be plotted to construct:
    a a parallelogram
    b a rhombus
    c a right-angled triangle with no horizontal or vertical lines
    d a kite.

8 Construct your own coordinate picture with instructions on which equations to plot.

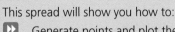

This spread will show you how to:

▶▶ Generate points and plot the graphs of simple quadratic or cubic functions

KEYWORDS

Cubic   Curve

Quadratic   Parabola

Not all graphs are straight.
The path of a shot putt being thrown might look like this.

Here are two types of curved graph.

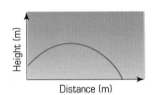

Distance (m)

Quadratic curves

Quadratic graphs are connected to the square numbers.
Their equations contain a term in x^2 as the highest power.

---

example

Plot the graph of $y = x^2$ for values of x from $^-3$ to 3.

First construct a table of values:

x	$^-3$	$^-2$	$^-1$	0	1	2	3
y	9	4	1	0	1	4	9

Plot the graph, choosing sensible axes:

The shape of a quadratic curve is called a **parabola**.

Cubic graphs

Cubic graphs contain an x^3 term as the highest power.

---

example

Plot the graph of $y = x^3$ for values of x from $^-3$ to 3.

x	$^-3$	$^-2$	$^-1$	0	1	2	3
y	$^-27$	$^-8$	$^-1$	0	1	8	27

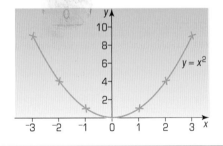

Cubic graphs are always roughly S-shaped.

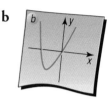

1 For each equation given:
  i predict the shape of the graph
  ii complete the table of values
  iii plot the graph on appropriately scaled axes.

  a $y = x^2 + 3$

x	-4	-3	-2	-1	0	1	2	3	4
x^2	16	9					4		
+3	+3	+3	+3	+3	+3	+3	+3	+3	+3
y	19	12					7		

  b $y = x^3 - x$

x	-4	-3	-2	-1	0	1	2	3	4
x^2	-64	-27					8		
-x	+4	+3					-2		
y	-60	-24					6		

  c $y = x^2 + x - 6$

y	-5	-4	-3	-2	-1	0	1	2	3
x^2	25							4	
x	-5							+2	
-6	-6							-6	
y	14							0	

  d $y = 3x^2 + 1$

y	-3	-2	-1	0	1	2	3	4
x^2								
$3x^2$								
+1								
y								

2 Devise your own table and plot the graphs over the range of values given.
  a $y = 2x^2 - 3$ $-3 \leqslant x \leqslant 3$
  b $y = 10 - x^2$ $-2 \leqslant x \leqslant 3$
  c $y = x^3 - x^2 + x$ $-2 \leqslant x \leqslant 3$

3 Use your graph in question 2a to find
  a the value of y when $x = 2.5$
  b the values of x when $y = 6$.

4 Match these shape and equation cards:

  a
  b

  A $y = {}^-x^2$ **B** $y = x^2 + 2x$

  c
  d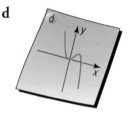

  C $y = x(x^2 + 4)$ **D** $y = x^2 - x^3$

5 **a** Use one set of axes, taking x from -5 to 5, to draw each graph group. Comment on how the change in equation causes the graph to change.

Group 1
$y = x^2$; $y = x^2 + 1$
$y = x^2 + 3$; $y = x^2 - 2$

Group 2
$y = x^2$; $y = (x + 1)^2$
$y = (x + 2)^2$; $y = (x + 2)^2$

  b Use your findings to sketch:
  i $y = x^2 + 10$ **ii** $y = (x - 4)^2$
  iii $y = (x + 5)^2 - 2$

6 Use your findings from question 5 to sketch the graph $y = (x - 2)^2 + 4$. What is the equation of its line of symmetry?

This spread will show you how to:
▶▶ Construct functions arising from real-life problems and plot their corresponding graphs.
▶▶ Interpret graphs arising from real situations, including distance-time graphs.

KEYWORDS

Distance   Velocity
Acceleration   Interpret

Graphs can often tell a story ...

1 Dan leaves home at 11 am to cycle slowly to his uncle's house, 5 km away.

2 Dan enjoys the last stretch, as it is downhill!

3 Dan stays at his uncle's house, where his brother Carl is waiting for him.

4 Carl needs to be home by 2:30 pm, so Dan lends him his bike.

5 At 2.30 pm Dan starts walking home.

You can use a **distance-time graph** to deduce information.

▶ The gradient of a distance-time graph represents the **speed**.

Use the distance-time graph of Dan's journey to answer these questions.

a At what speed did Dan cycle downhill?
b How long did Dan stay at his uncle's house?
c How much later than Carl did Dan arrive home?

Gradient = $\dfrac{vertical}{horizontal}$

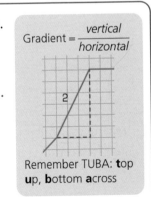

Remember TUBA: **t**op **u**p, **b**ottom **a**cross

a In the downhill section, Dan covers 3 km in $\frac{3}{4}$ of an hour.
$3 \div \frac{3}{4} = 3 \times \frac{4}{3}$
     $= 4 \Rightarrow$ Dan cycled downhill at a speed of 4 km/hour.

b The graph is flat between 12:45 and 14:30.
Dan stayed for $1\frac{3}{4}$ hours.

c Carl arrives home at 14:30 (point A), and Dan arrives home at 16:00 (point B).
Dan arrived home $1\frac{1}{2}$ hours after Carl.

Exercise A3.6

1 Match each distance-time graph with a description.

a
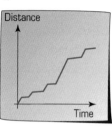

b
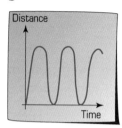

c
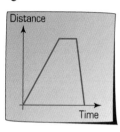

d
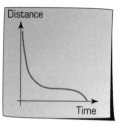

A: A parachute jump from a plane.
B: A pendulum on a clock.
C: A woman walking to and from the shops.
D: A car stuck in motorway traffic.

2 a Construct a distance-time graph to represent the journeys of these two trains between London and Liverpool.

London to Liverpool train
Left London at 10 am, reaching Birmingham 100 miles away at 11 am. Stopped for 15 min. Reached Crewe, 200 miles from London, after travelling for $\frac{3}{4}$ hour. Held up for 1 hour. Continued the last 100 miles to Liverpool at 50 m.p.h.

Liverpool to London (express)
Left Liverpool at 11:30 a.m. Travelled non-stop to London at 90 miles per hour.

---

b i At what time did the trains pass each other?

ii Roughly where was this?

c Which train finished its journey first and by how much?

3 The graph shows two sisters, Jo and Vicky, having a run from home and back.

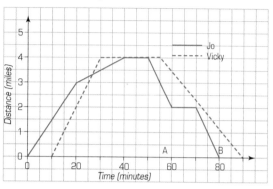

Explain whether these statements are true or false:

a Vicky stopped for $\frac{1}{2}$ hour.

b The sisters were away from home for the same length of time.

c Jo's starting speed was 3 miles per hour.

d The sisters saw each other twice on their run.

e Vicky ran faster on the way out than on the way home.

f After 70 minutes, Jo was nearer home than Vicky.

g Jo's speed between 20 and 40 minutes was 6 miles per hour.

h Vicky's average speed for the whole journey was 6 miles per hour.

4 Water flows at a constant rate into this vessel. Complete the sketch graph.

a

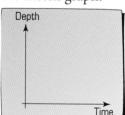

b Draw the vessel that this sketch graph might describe.

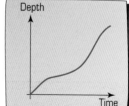

You should know how to ...

1 Given the values for *m* and *c*, find the gradient of lines with equations of the form $y = mx + c$.

2 Construct and interpret graphs arising from real situations.

Check out

1 a Find the gradient of each line:

   i $y = 3x + 2$ **ii** $3y = 4x + 9$

   iii A line connecting (3, 11) to (10, 18).

b Give the gradient of lines perpendicular to those in part **a**.

2 a i Describe what is happening to this car in each point of its journey (A, B, C, D).

   ii Is the speed of the car greater over A or B? Find its greatest speed.

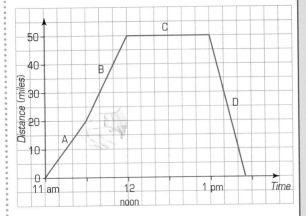

b Describe what is happening in each graph.

i

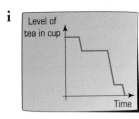

ii

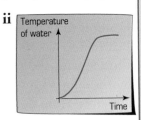

iii

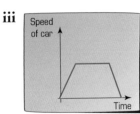

13 Multiplicative reasoning

This unit will show you how to:

- Extend knowledge of integer powers of 10.
- Use rounding to make estimates.
- Round numbers to the nearest whole number or to one or two decimal places.
- Use proportional reasoning to solve a problem.
- Compare two ratios.
- Interpret and use ratio in a range of contexts, including solving word problems.
- Understand the effects of multiplying and dividing by numbers between 0 and 1.
- Solve word problems mentally.

- Make and justify estimates and approximations of calculations.
- Use standard column procedures to add and subtract integers and decimals.
- Multiply and divide by decimals.
- Solve increasingly demanding problems and evaluate solutions.
- Explore connections in mathematics across a range of contexts.
- Give solutions to problems to an appropriate degree of accuracy.

It says 50 ml of cream for 4 people, so for 6 people ... $50 \times 1\frac{1}{2} = 75$

You use multiplication or division to scale quantities.

Before you start

You should know how to ...

1 Round numbers to the nearest integer.

2 Use standard column procedures for multiplication and division of integers.

3 Convert between fractions, decimals and percentages.

Check in

1 Round each of these numbers to the nearest integer:
   a 2.634   b ⁻0.024
   c 100.99999 d 6.9876

2 Work out:
   a 473 × 29   b 83 × 427
   c 965 ÷ 9   d 2163 ÷ 14

3 Copy and complete the table:

Fraction	Decimal	Percentage
$\frac{7}{12}$		
$3\frac{1}{4}$		
	2.7	
	0.01	
		35%
		16.5%

Multiplying by powers of 10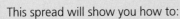

This spread will show you how to:

▶▶ Extend your knowledge of integer powers of 10.

▶▶ Multiply and divide by any integer power of 10.

▶▶ Understand the effects of multiplying and dividing by numbers between 0 and 1.

KEYWORDS

Power of 10

Place value

You can write numbers like 0.01 and 1000 as powers of 10.

Numbers divided by 10

On a calculator, you could input 10^3 like this:

[1] [0] [x^y] [3]

Number		Power of 10
1000	$10 \times 10 \times 10$	10^3
100	10×10	10^2
10	10	10^1
1	1	10^0
0.1	$\frac{1}{10}$	10^{-1}
0.01	$\frac{1}{10 \times 10}$	10^{-2}

Powers decreasing by 1

You can use powers of 10 in a place value table.

10^3(Th)	10^2(H)	10^1(T)	10^0(U)	.	10^{-1}(t)	10^{-2}(h)	10^{-3}(th)
3	9	2	7	.	4	7	3

The digit 9 stands for 9 hundreds, or 9×10^2.

The digit 7 stands for 7 hundredths, or 7×10^{-2}.

Place value helps you to multiply or divide by powers of 10 mentally.

example

Calculate mentally: **a** 500 kg × 0.1   **b** 30 m ÷ 0.01

a × 0.1 is the same as × $\frac{1}{10}$ ...
... is the same as ÷10:

$\Rightarrow$ 500 kg × 0.1 = 500 kg × $\frac{1}{10}$
= 500 kg ÷ 10
= 50 kg

Remember (from page 48):

▶ × $\frac{1}{10}$ = ÷10

▶ ÷ $\frac{1}{10}$ = ×10

b ÷ 0.01 is the same as ÷ $\frac{1}{100}$ ...
... is the same as ×100:

$\Rightarrow$ 30 m ÷ 0.01 = 30 m ÷ $\frac{1}{100}$
= 30 m × 100
= 3000 m (= 3 km)

To put decimals in order, you need to compare digits working from left to right.

example

Place these numbers in ascending order: 1.76, ⁻2.46, ⁻0.4535, 1.756, ⁻0.5

Compare the first digits: ⁻2.46, ⁻0.4535, ⁻0.5, 1.76, 1.756
Now compare the second digits: ⁻2.46, ⁻0.5, ⁻0.4535, 1.76, 1.756
(be careful with the negative sign)
Finally compare the third digits: ⁻2.46, ⁻0.5, ⁻0.4535, 1.756, 1.76

Exercise N3.1

1 Calculate, using a mental method:

  a $46 \div 100$ **b** 3.2×1000

  c $29 \div 1000$ **d** $0.2 \div 10$

  e $0.031 \times 10\,000$ **f** 1.3×10^2

2 Calculate, using a mental method:

  a 43×0.1 **b** $4.5 \div 0.01$

  c 234.6×0.01 **d** $0.06 \div 0.1$

  e 5.7×0.001 **f** $345 \div 0.01$

  g 0.006×0.1 **h** $7.44 \div 0.001$

3 Work these out without using a calculator.

  a 5×10^1 **b** $3 \div 10^3$

  c 98×10^5 **d** $^-7 \div 0.1$

  e $^-6 \times 10^{-2}$ **f** $19 \div 1000$

  g 217×10^2 **h** $^-287 \div 10^2$

4 On a map the scale is $1 : 100\,000$.

  a A field shown on the map has a real length of 2 km.
  What is its length on the map in centimetres?

  b What would be the actual length of an object that was 3 mm on the map? Give you answer in metres.

5 Use the facts in the shaded box to convert these areas into the units shown in brackets.

> $1 \text{ m}^2 = 10\,000 \text{ cm}^2$
> $1 \text{ cm}^2 = 100 \text{ mm}^2$

  a 2.74 m^2 (cm^2)

  b 4000 cm^2 (m^2)

  c $800\,000 \text{ mm}^2$ (cm^2)

  d 0.006 m^2 (cm^2)

  e 0.56 cm^2 (mm^2)

6 Arrange each of these sets of numbers from smallest to largest.

  a $^-10.49,\ 10.49,\ ^-0.49,\ 1.049,\ 14.09$

  b $^-0.6,\ 0.\dot{6},\ ^-0.062,\ 0.162,\ ^-0.006$

  c $5.6472,\ 5.648,\ 0.98276,\ ^-5.2,\ 5.7,\ ^-60$

  d $\frac{7}{8},\ 0.72,\ 0.8171,\ \frac{2}{3},\ \frac{11}{14},\ ^-0.63417$

7 Investigation

Ivor Sum uses his calculator to divide the number 10 by each of the numbers, 0.1, 0.2, 0.3, ... 0.9, 1 and records his results

$10 \div 0.1$	$10 \div 0.2$	$10 \div 0.3$	etc.	$10 \div 1$
			etc.	10

  a Copy and complete Ivor's table of results and comment on the answers in the table.

  b Ivor continues the investigation by multiplying 10 by 0, 0.1, 0.2 etc. Set up another table similar to the one above and comment on the answers you get.

  c Copy and complete these sentences.
  ▸ *Multiplying by a number between 0 and 1 ...*
  ▸ *Dividing by a number between 0 and 1 ...*

8 Use your calculator to decide whether these are true or false.

  a $9.0 \times 10^4 = 90 \times 10^2$

  b $0.8 \times 10^{-3} = 800 \times 10^{-6}$

  c $4.0 \times 10^7 = 0.04 \times 10^9$

  d $0.006 = 0.6 \times 10^2$

  e $0.721 \times 10^3 = 721$

  f $0.84 = 0.840 \times 10^0$

9 The three numbers in each row are equivalent. Fill in the boxes in the table.

a	6×10^2	$\square \times 10^3$	0.06×10^4
b	$\square \times 10^4$	$0.1 \times \square^5$	0.01×10^6
c	$12 \times \square^6$	1.2×10^7	$0.12 \times 10^{\square}$
d	0.5	$\square \times 10^{-1}$	$0.05 \times 10^{\square}$
e	1.63	$163 \times 10^{\square}$	$16300 \times 10^{\square}$
f	$300 \times 10^{\square}$	0.03	$0.3 \times \square^{-1}$
g	10	$10^{\square}$	$0.01 \times 10^{\square}$
h	$10^{\square}$	1	$1000 \times 10^{\square}$

Rounding

This spread will show you how to:
▶▶ Use rounding to make estimates.
▶▶ Round numbers to the nearest whole number or to one or two decimal places.
▶▶ Make and justify estimates and approximations of calculations.

KEYWORDS
Round   Estimate
Degree of accuracy
Decimal place

There are many practical situations where you round a number to make an estimate.

> **example**
>
> The average weight of a Yonda ZTT motorbike is 182.7 kg.
> Find an estimate for the total weight of 15 of these motorbikes:
> **a** in kilograms   **b** in tonnes
>
>
>
> **a**   Approximate weight of 15 motorbikes = 180 kg × 15
>   = 2700 kg
> **b**   1000 kg = 1 t $\Rightarrow$ 2700 kg = (2700 ÷ 1000) t = 2.7 t

You can round numbers to any given power of 10.

> **example**
>
> Round 13.617482 to 3 decimal places.
>
> The third decimal place is the **thousandths** (10^{-3}) digit.
>
> You need to look at the **ten-thousandths** (10^{-4}) digit. 13.617482
>
> 13.617 |————|————————————| 13.618
>
> 13.617482 is nearer to 13.617 than it is to 13.618.
> 13.617482 ≃ 13.617   (to 3 decimal places).

When you use a written method or a calculator, you should only round when you have worked out the final result.

> **example**
>
> Calculate the circumference of a circle with a diameter of 31 cm:
>
> **a**   using the value of π on a calculator   **b**   using $\pi = 3.14$.
>   Give your answers to 1 decimal place.
> **c**   Looking at your answers to parts **a** and **b**, which gives the
>   greater degree of accuracy, and why?
>
> **Remember:**
> The circumference of a circle is its perimeter.
>
>
>
> **a** $C = \pi d$ **b** $C = \pi d$
>   = 3.1415926 ... × 31 cm   = 3.14 × 31 cm
>   = 97.389372 ... cm   = 97.34 cm
>   = 97.4 cm (to 1 d.p.)   = 97.3 cm (to 1 d.p.)
> **c**   Part **a** is more accurate because it uses a more accurate value of π.

Exercise N3.2

1 Round each of these decimals to the number of decimal places indicated in brackets.
   a 3.142 (2 d.p.)   **b** 0.9876 (3 d.p.)
   c 0.09 (1 d.p.)   **d** 0.003 (2 d.p.)
   e 5.8696 (2 d.p.)   **f** 6.997 (1 d.p.)
   g 7.936281 (4 d.p.)   **h** 762.199 (2 d.p.)

2 Convert each fraction to a decimal, giving your answer
   i   to 2 d.p.   **ii** to 1 d.p.
   iii to the nearest whole number.
   a $11\frac{4}{9}$ **b** $3\frac{5}{11}$ **c** $39\frac{7}{13}$ **d** $46\frac{3}{8}$

3 Ahmed has £1628 in his bank account. Ahmed says that he has nearly £2000. His father says that Ahmed has over £1500.
   a Explain how Ahmed and his father have different answers.
   b Who is the more accurate, Ahmed or his father?

4 Work these out using a calculator. Give your answer correct to 3 decimal places.
   a $\dfrac{34 \times 78}{16}$ **b** $\dfrac{14.6 \times 9.81}{14.8 \times 7.4}$

5 **a** Work out an approximate answer to:
       $\dfrac{45.611 \times 12.845}{3.923}$
   b Now use a calculator to work out the answer, giving your answer:
       i to 3 d.p.
       ii to the nearest whole number.

6 The weight of a footballer is given as 80 kg to the nearest 10 kg. Which one of these five weights could he **not** possibly be?
   78.5 kg, 84.3 kg, 74.9 kg, 80 kg, 81.053 kg

7 **Puzzle**
   Box A contains a set of exact measurements.
   Box B contains the same measurements, rounded to 1 decimal place.

Box A	
7.302 cm	14.90 m
14.99 m	25.06 ℓ
17.009 mm	182.33 s

Box B	
7.3 cm	15.0 m
	17.0 mm
182.3 s	25.1 ℓ

   Pair each length in Box A with its rounded equivalent in Box B.
   Hence find the odd one out.

8 **Investigation**
   Harry is trying to work out the circumference of a circle.
   He uses the formula $C = \pi \times$ diameter.
   He uses three different values for π: 3.1, 3.14 and $\frac{22}{7}$.

   Investigate how the different values for π would affect Harry's final answer for different sized circles.

9 Calculate the value of each of these amounts to the accuracy stated in brackets:
   a $\frac{4}{9}$ of $\frac{1}{2}$ of €100 (to the nearest cent)
   b $\frac{2}{3}$ of $\frac{1}{3}$ of $\frac{3}{8}$ of 1 m (to the nearest cm)
   c 40% of $\frac{8}{11}$ of $\frac{1}{2}$ of 500 (to 3 d.p.)
   d $\frac{7}{13}$ of $\frac{6}{12} \times$ 32% of 620 (to 2 d.p.)
   e The answers to **c** and **d** multiplied together and rounded to 1 d.p.

Adding and subtracting

This spread will show you how to:
- ▶▶ Consolidate and extend mental methods of addition and subtraction.
- ▶▶ Use a standard column procedure for addition and subtraction of numbers of any size, including decimals.
- ▶▶ Make and justify estimates and approximations of calculations.

You can often do addition and subtraction problems mentally.
There is a range of mental strategies that you can use.

Partitioning

Partitioning involves breaking a number into parts that are easier to calculate in your head.

$$^-7.4 - {}^-2.8 = {}^-7.4 + 2.8$$
$$= {}^-7.4 + 2 + 0.8$$

```
        +2          +0.8
    ┌────────┐ ┌──────────┐
────┼────────┼─┼──────────┼──
   ‾7.4     ‾5.4        ‾4.6
```

$$= {}^-4.6$$

Compensation

Compensation involves rounding a number up or down and then compensating by adding or subtracting the extra amount.

$$0.47 + {}^-0.29 = 0.47 - 0.29$$
$$= 0.47 - 0.3 + 0.01$$

```
              +0.01
          ┌──────────┐
──────┼───┼──────────┼────
    0.17 0.18       0.47
```

$$= 0.17 + 0.01$$
$$= 0.18$$

When numbers are too difficult to calculate in your head you need to use a written method.

Work out $5.928 + 4.7 - 7.79 - 1.245 + 0.069$

Approximate first: 6   + 5   − 8   − 1   + 0   = 2

Rearrange: $(5.928 + 4.7 + 0.069) - (7.79 + 1.245)$

Add separately:
$$\begin{array}{r} 5.928 \\ 4.7 \\ +\ 0.069 \\ \hline \mathbf{10.697} \end{array}$$

$$\begin{array}{r} 7.79 \\ +\ 1.245 \\ \hline \mathbf{9.035} \end{array}$$

A number line helps to show the calculation:

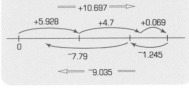

Combine the answers:
$$\begin{array}{r} 10.697 \\ -\ \ 9.035 \\ \hline \mathbf{1.662} \end{array}$$

Check:
1.662 rounds to 2, which is the value of the estimate.

Exercise N3.3

1 Work out these using a mental method.
  a $43 + {}^-100$ **b** ${}^-5.0 - {}^-20 + 2.3$ **c** ${}^-8.9 + 79 - 69$ **d** $60 + 7.2 - 80 - 3$
  e $100 - 256 + 7.3$ **f** $62 - 71 + 3$ **g** ${}^-4.7 + 2 - 89$ **h** ${}^-8.2 - 9.6 + 1.7$

2 a Work out the missing value for each of the four people's bank accounts:

	Start balance	Transactions	Final balance
Bill	£1321.47	${}^-$£14.40, +£10.60, ${}^-$£80.24	
Jenny	£96.28	£14.87, , ${}^-$£24.00	${}^-$£20.36
Harry	£364.90	, ${}^-$£700.23, +£84.00	£500.60
Louise	£941.40	£26.41, ${}^-$£836.18,	£37.10

  b Work out the total of the final balances.

3 Puzzle
Two numbers have a sum of ${}^-5.86$ and a difference of 3.74 when the smaller is subtracted from the larger.
Work out the two numbers.

4 Place the digits in the clouds in the correct boxes.

  a

  b

  c

  d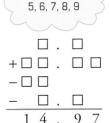

5 In this number pyramid, each number is the sum of the two numbers directly above it.
Copy and complete the pyramid.

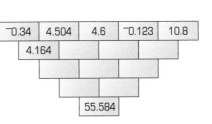

6 Puzzle
Work out the next three numbers in each sequence.
Explain the pattern in each case.
  a $0.1, \quad 0.2, \quad 0.15, \quad 0.175, \quad 0.1625, \quad 0.16875$
  b $0.1, \quad 0.2, \quad {}^-0.05, \quad 0.125, \quad {}^-0.0875, \quad 0.10625$

7 Puzzle
The difference between two numbers is 7.055.
The number exactly halfway between the same two numbers is ${}^-1.1875$.
  a What are the two numbers?
  b Explain clearly the method you have used to solve the problem.

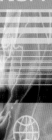 **Mental multiplication and division**

This spread will show you how to:
▶▶ Consolidate and extend mental methods of multiplication and division.
▶▶ Apply mental skills to solving simple word problems.

KEYWORDS

Factor   Product
Partitioning   Equivalence
Sum

You should always see if a multiplication or a division can be done in your head.
Here are some strategies for multiplying and dividing mentally.

Using factors

This method involves splitting a number into a **product**.

example

Calculate $2 \div 0.04$ mentally.

$$
\begin{aligned}
2 \div 0.04 &= 2 \div (4 \times 0.01) \\
&= 2 \div 4 \div 0.01 \\
2 \div 4 &= 0.5 \\
0.5 \div 0.01 &= 0.5 \times 100 \\
&= 50 \\
\text{So } 2 \div 0.04 &= 50
\end{aligned}
$$

Using partitioning

This method involves splitting a number into a **sum**.

example

Calculate 12% of 31 m, using a mental method.

$$
\begin{aligned}
12\% \text{ of } 31 &= 12\% \times 31 \\
&= 0.12 \times 31 \\
&= 0.12 \times (30 + 1) \\
&= (0.12 \times 30) + (0.12 \times 1) \\
&= (0.12 \times 10 \times 3) + 0.12 \\
&= (1.2 \times 3) + 0.12 \\
&= 3.6 + 0.12 \\
&= 3.72
\end{aligned}
$$

So 12% of 31 m is 3.72 m.

Using near 10s

This method involves multiplying by a convenient multiple of 10.

example

Calculate the value of $19x$ when $x = 0.7$

$$
\begin{aligned}
19x = 19 \times 0.7 &= 0.7 \times 19 \\
&= 0.7 \times 20 - 0.7 \\
&= 14 - 0.7 \\
&= 13.3
\end{aligned}
$$

Using equivalence

This method involves converting between decimals and fractions.

example

Calculate the volume of a box that measures 3.5 cm by 4.5 cm by 16 cm.

$$
\begin{aligned}
\text{Volume} &= 3.5 \times 4.5 \times 16 \text{ cm} \\
\text{Convert to fractions: } &\tfrac{7}{2} \times \tfrac{9}{2} \times 16 \\
&= \frac{7 \times 9 \times 16}{2 \times 2} \\
&= 7 \times 9 \times 4 \\
&= 252
\end{aligned}
$$

So the volume is 252 cm^3.

Exercise N3.4

1 Calculate using an appropriate mental method:

  a 23×11 **b** $\frac{1}{8} \times 96$

  c 0.1×50 **d** $12.4 \div 0.1$

  e $0.36 \div 0.01$ **f** 16×0.01

  g 0.1×0.1 **h** $12 \times \frac{1}{6}$

2 Calculate using an appropriate mental method:

  a 19×2.1 **b** $^-2.3 \times 11$

  c 6.7×31 **d** $^-3.4 \div 0.2$

  e 2.6×2.5 **f** 29×6.7

3 **a** Work out the cost of a 'Giant Sweet Bag' weighing 3.6 kg, if sweets cost £1.20 per kg.

  b Work out the cost of a week's supply for Kevin if he eats 5% of a bag per day. (Give your answer to the nearest penny.)

4 **Puzzle**

The diameter of a 2 pence piece is 2.6 cm. Use this information to answer these questions.

  a Henry receives a 2p coin from his grandmother each day. He lays them side by side in the hope of making a '1 km line of copper'.
How many weeks will it take him?

  b Henry has a friend Gary who receives one 2p coin from his grandmother in week 1, two 2p coins in week 2, four in week 3, eight in week 4 and so on. Will Gary make the '1 km line of copper' before Henry or not? Show your working to justify your answer.

5 Calculate the area of the rectangles with the dimensions given. Use a mental method.

  a $2.3 \text{ m} \times 1.5 \text{ m}$ **b** $250 \text{ cm} \times 30 \text{ cm}$

  c $0.06 \text{ m} \times 0.14 \text{ m}$

6 Work out the value of the expression $\dfrac{x^2}{2y}$ when x and y take these values:

  a $x = 0.02$ $y = {}^-0.1$

  b $x = {}^-50$ $y = \frac{1}{100}$

  c $x = 3.2$ $y = ({}^-0.2)^2$

7 **Puzzle**

Work out the value of each letter in the grid using this rule:

4	A	18
B	7.2	C
5	D	E

Multiply the first two numbers in each row or column to produce the third number, for example $4 \times A = 18$, $A \times 7.2 = D$.

8 In each multiplication trail you must choose numbers, one from each row, which multiply together to give the target number.

3.2	3.4	3.5
3	5	2
4	6	5

96

Example $3.2 \times 5 = 16$
            $16 \times 6 = 96$

a

1.3	1.4	1.5
5	10	15
9	8	7

49

b

2.4	1.2	0.6
10	15	30
6	8	7

84

This spread will show you how to:
- ▶▶ Use a standard column procedure for multiplication involving decimals.
- ▶▶ Understand where to put the decimal point for the answer.
- ▶▶ Make and justify estimates and approximations of calculations.

KEYWORDS

Approximate	Estimate
Integer	Equivalent
Round	Justify

When numbers become too difficult to calculate using mental strategies you could try using a written method.

example

Work out 74.3×0.32, giving your answer to 1 decimal place.

▶ First approximate: $75 \times \frac{1}{3} = 25$ (because 0.32 is approximately $\frac{1}{3}$)

▶ Convert to an equivalent calculation: 74.3×0.32
   (without decimals)

You should always make and justify estimates to difficult calculations.

$$= 743 \div 10 \quad \times \quad 32 \div 100$$
$$= 743 \times 32 \div 1000$$

▶ Work out 743×32:

$$\begin{array}{r} 743 \\ \times \quad 32 \\ \hline 22290 \\ 1486 \\ \hline 23776 \end{array}$$

▶ Divide by 1000:
   $23\,776 \div 1000 = 23.776$
   $= 23.8$ to 1 d.p.

An exact answer is not always required but you should take care when rounding.

example

a Estimate the area of carpet needed for a rectangular room, 5.32 m by 3.9 m.
b Calculate the exact area of the floor.
c Was your estimate useful in this context?
   If not, how could you have produced a better estimate?

a Approximate area (rounding to the nearest integer) $= 4 \text{ m} \times 5 \text{ m}$
$$= 20 \text{ m}^2$$

b Exact area
of the floor $= 3.9 \text{ m} \times 5.32 \text{ m}$
$3.9 \times 5.32 = 39 \times 532 \div 1000$

$$\begin{array}{r} 532 \\ \times \quad 39 \\ \hline 4788 \\ 15960 \\ \hline 20748 \end{array} \Longrightarrow 3.9 \times 5.32 = 20\,748 \div 1000 = 20.748$$

So the area of floor is 20.748 m^2.

c If you use the estimate, you will not have enough carpet.
It makes more sense to round up (say to the nearest 0.5 m):
Approximate area $= 4 \text{ m} \times 5.5 \text{ m} = 22 \text{ m}^2$
This would cover the floor with carpet to spare.

Exercise N3.5

1 Calculate using a mental or written method:

a 39×54 **b** 48×25

c 397×47 **d** 860×21

e 109×708 **f** 16.8×53

g 859×3.8 **h** 12.3×4.6

i 47.1×2.8

2 a Which is larger: 64% of £0.81 or 81% of £0.64?
Show working to justify your answer and comment on your results.

b A runner estimates that on average it will take him 72.3 seconds to run each lap of a 400 m track in a 5 km race. Calculate

  i how long it will take him to run the race

  ii his time if he improves his average lap time to 68.3 seconds.

c A tin of paint states that the contents will cover 8.3 m². Mary buys 14 of these tins and estimates that she will lose 2.5% of the paint washing out the brush each evening. What area will she be able to cover?

d Work out the volume in m³ of a cuboid that measures 0.03 m × 0.12 m × 0.036 m.

3 The manual for Janet's car contains this table for fuel consumption:

> 30 mph = 9.3 miles per litre
> 56 mph = 12.5 miles per litre
> 70 mph = 6.7 miles per litre

The tank will hold 47 litres of fuel.
The current price of fuel for her car is 73p per litre.

a How much would it cost her to fill the tank?

b How far could she travel on a full tank at each of the three speeds listed?

4 Calculate using a written method:

a 84.2×6.3 **b** 113×2.7

c 15.6×8.2 **d** 56×4.3

e 6.3×882 **f** 0.57×345

5 Estimate each answer by rounding each number to an appropriate degree of accuracy. You do not need to work out the exact answer.

a $(3075 \times 498) + 289$ **b** $32^2 \times 469$

c $\dfrac{97 \times 0.53}{\sqrt{390}}$ **d** $1.31 \times (6.4 + 2.76)$

6 Calculate these products using a written or calculator method.
Estimate the answer to each question before you begin.

a $^-0.2 \times 0.3214$ **b** $^-0.505 \times 0.120$

c $2.3 \times (0.12)^2$ **d** $^-16.1 \times 0.032$

e $(^-0.4)^3 \times 1.7$ **f** $0.00024 \times {}^-0.0316$

g $570\,000 \times 1\frac{1}{5}$ **h** $20.4 \times 0.4 \times {}^-0.006$

7 a The spinner shown is spun three times.

The three numbers are then multiplied together.

Number 1	Number 2	Number 3	Product

Copy and complete the table to show all the possible products that could be achieved. The order of the numbers does not matter.

b The numbers on the spinner use the digits 1, 2, 3, 4, 5 and 6.
Place these digits in the boxes to achieve

  i the highest possible product

  ii the lowest possible product.

    $0.\square\square \times 0.\square\square \times 0.\square\square$

This spread will show you how to:

⏩ Use a standard written procedure for divisions involving decimals.

⏩ Make and justify estimates and approximations of calculations.

⏩ Use the context of a problem to check whether an answer is sensible.

KEYWORDS

Decimal   Integer

Equivalent   Estimate

Justify

You can divide decimals by converting to an equivalent calculation involving integers.

example

Work out $163.8 \div 0.7$, showing your working clearly on paper.
Give an estimate first.

1 Approximate by changing to numbers that can be divided easily:

$$160 \div 0.8 = 1600 \div 8$$
$$= 200$$

2 Now convert to an equivalent calculation:

$$\overset{\times 10}{\underset{\times 10}{\frac{163.8}{0.7} = \frac{1638}{7}}}$$

3 Now use the **repeated subtraction method** for division:

$$
\begin{array}{r}
7)\overline{1638} \\
- \quad 1400 \quad 7 \times 200 \\
\hline
238 \\
- \quad 210 \quad 7 \times 30 \\
\hline
28 \\
- \quad 28 \quad 7 \times 4 \\
\hline
0 \quad 7 \times \mathbf{234} = 1638
\end{array}
$$

So $1638 \div 7 = 234$,
and $163.8 \div 0.7 = 234$

You will not always get an exact answer when you divide decimals.

example

Calculate $0.067 \div 0.0028$, giving your answer to 1 decimal place.

First approximate: $660 \div 30 = 22$

Multiply by 10 000 (10^4): $\dfrac{0.067}{0.0028} = \dfrac{670}{28}$

$$
\begin{array}{r}
28)\overline{670} \\
- \quad 560 \quad 28 \times 20 \\
\hline
110 \\
- \quad 84 \quad 28 \times 3 \\
\hline
26.0 \\
- \quad 25.2 \quad 28 \times 0.9 \\
\hline
0.80 \\
- \quad 0.56 \quad 28 \times 0.02 \\
\hline
0.24
\end{array}
$$

$\Rightarrow 0.067 \div 0.0028 = 23.92$ remainder 0.24
$= 23.9$ to 1 d.p.

Exercise N3.6

1 Work out each of thse divisions using either a mental or a written method.

a $2710 \div 5$ **b** $232 \div 4$

c $2583 \div 3$ **d** $644 \div 14$

e $442 \div 17$ **f** $4256 \div 28$

g $1089 \div 99$ **h** $10\ 197 \div 11$

2 Answer each of these problems, showing your working out.

a A cinema has 26 rows of seats with an equal number of seats in each row. The total number of seats in the cinema is 1274. How many seats are there in each row?

b Akil's football team has 18 players in its squad. Their total weight is 1422 kg. What is the mean weight of the players?

c Jenny's car travelled 255 miles and used 17 litres of fuel. How far could she travel with 1 litre?

d George wanted to share his £37 728 lottery winnings equally between the 24 families in the street. How much should he give to each family?

3 Work out the remainder from each of these divisions.

a $190 \div 4.3$ **b** $70.6 \div 2.2$

c $4.83 \div 0.4$ **d** $35.26 \div 1.3$

e $40\ 568 \div 0.13$ **f** $0.0236 \div 0.00018$

g What length of string would be left over if lengths of 1.21 m were cut from a 12 m ball of string?

4 Work out each of these divisions using the repeated subtraction method. Give your answers to 2 decimal places.

a $140 \div 9$ **b** $270 \div 17$

c $354 \div 11$ **d** $1552 \div 3$

e $6410 \div 6$ **f** $7302 \div 7$

5 Work out the missing side of each of these shapes.

Give your answers to 1 d.p.

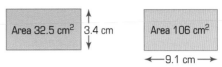

a rectangle, area $= 32.5\ \text{cm}^2$, width $= 3.4$ cm

b rectangle, area $= 106\ \text{cm}^2$, length $= 9.1$ cm

c triangle, area $= 50.3\ \text{cm}^2$, base $= 8.4$ cm

d triangle, area $= 210.5\ \text{cm}^2$, vertical height $= 12.7$ cm

6 The table shows the areas of six countries and their population.

Country	Area (thousand km²)	Population (millions)
Czech Republic	78.866	10.264
Greenland	2175.6	0.05635
Bangladesh	144.0	131.270
UK	244.82	59.648
Australia	7686.85	19.358
Jamaica	10.99	2.666

Calculate the average number of people per square kilometre for each country.

7 Work out each of these divisions, giving your answer to 4 decimal places.

a $^-0.056 \div 0.11$ **b** $0.00003 \div ^-0.07$

c $0.01 \div 9$ **d** $^-0.0004 \div ^-0.03$

e $^-1.19 \div 0.0019$ **f** $0.1 \div ^-72$

This spread will show you how to:
▶▶ Simplify a ratio expressed in fractions or decimals.
▶▶ Interpret and use ratio in a range of contexts.

KEYWORDS
Ratio   Scale factor
Simplify

You use a ratio to compare two or more quantities.

▶ Ratios can be simplified in the same way as fractions.

$10 : 25 = 2 : 5$ $\frac{10}{25} = \frac{2}{5}$

▶ Ratios are often written in whole-number form.

$3.4 : \frac{8}{10}$
$= 34 : 8 = 17 : 4$

Leon is eight years old and his sister Naomi is 20.
The ratio of their ages is $8 : 20 = 2 : 5$

Leon is ...
... $\frac{2}{5}$ of Naomi's age
... 0.4 × Naomi's age
... 40% of Naomi's age

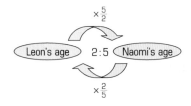

Naomi is ...
... $\frac{5}{2}$ × Leon's age
... 2.5 × Leon's age
... 250% of Leon's age

▶ You can use a ratio to divide a quantity into different-sized parts.

example

You can make green paint by mixing blue, yellow and white paint in the ratio $2 : 7 : 1$.
How much blue paint is needed to make 64 litres of green paint?

$2 + 7 + 1 = 10 \Rightarrow 10$ parts in total = 64 litres
$\Rightarrow$ 1 part = 64 litres ÷ 10 = 6.4 litres
$\Rightarrow$ The amount of **blue** paint needed = 2 parts × 6.4 = 12.8 litres

example

a A metal alloy is made in the ratio three parts tin to five parts lead.
How much tin needs to be mixed with 22 kg of lead?
b A real distance of 8 km is shown by 3.2 cm on a map. What is the map scale?

a Ratio of tin : lead = $3 : 5 \Rightarrow$ amount of tin = $\frac{3}{5}$ × amount of lead
$= \frac{3}{5} × 22$ kg = 13.2 kg
b Ratio of map distance : real distance = 3.2 cm : 8 km
3.2 cm : 800 000 cm = 32 : 8 000 000
$= 1 : 250\,000$

The numbers in a ratio must be in the same units so that they can be compared.

Exercise N3.7

1 Write each of these ratios both in its whole number form and in its simplest form.
   a 0.5 : 6   **b** $\frac{1}{4}$: 3   **c** 4.2 : 0.7
   d 130 : 17.5   **e** 5 : 6.2   **f** 6 : 3.21
   g 7 : $\frac{1}{8}$ **h** $2\frac{4}{5}$: 5.7

2 Maximum growth of a particular type of sunflower is achieved by mixing three plant food chemicals A, B and C in the ratio 2 : 6 : 7.
   Use this information to solve these problems:
   a How many grams of chemical A and chemical B would be needed to mix with 30 g of chemical C?
   b What is the weight of each chemical in a tub of plant food containing 80 g of the mixture?

3 The angles of a quadrilateral are in the ratio 3 : 7 : 4 : 10.
   Work out the size of each angle of the quadrilateral.

4 **Puzzle**
   Dion, Esther and Francis earn £18 000, £25 000 and £32 000 respectively.
   They each receive a 30% pay rise.
   Are their salaries in the same ratios as they were before the pay rise?

5 **Investigation**
   A map has a scale of 1 : 30 000.
   a What would be the real area corresponding to a square on the map measuring 2.5 cm by 2.5 cm?
   b Repeat part **a** for a map scale of:
      i 1 : 10 000   **ii** 1 : 200
   c Investigate the actual area of a map square measuring 2.5 cm × 2.5 cm for different scales. Write down what you notice.

6 Change these ratios to the forms 1 : m or m : 1.
   a 25 : 40   **b** 8 : 7   **c** 4 cm : 2 m
   d 340 g : 2.5 kg   **e** $\frac{1}{6}$: 3   **f** 5.2 : 0.5
   g 56 : 0.7   **h** $\frac{1}{10}$: 3.2   **i** $1\frac{4}{5}$: 0.6

7 A copper-lead alloy is in the ratio of four parts copper to seven parts lead.
   a If a block of this alloy contains 21 kg of copper, how much lead is there?
   Another block of the alloy weighs 2.64 kg.
   b How much lead is in this block?

8 William and Wilma both like blackcurrant cordial drink. William likes the blackcurrant and water to be mixed in a ratio 3 : 20 but Wilma likes the mixture to be in the ratio 4 : 25.
   a Who prefers the 'stronger' mix (a higher proportion of blackcurrant)?
   b If both children are given a litre of water how much blackcurrant can they make?

9 By converting each ratio in the cloud to the form 1 : m decide which ratio is

   a the smallest
   b the largest
   c the closest to 13 : 120

10 **Investigation**
   Here are some common map scales,
   1 : 2 000 000; 1 : 200 000; 1 : 25 000;
   1 : 500 and 1 : 200.
   a What distance does 4 cm on the map represent in real life using each of these scales?
   b Investigate some other distances. What kind of map should each scale be used for? Explain and justify your answer.

This spread will show you how to:
- ▶▶ Interpret and use ratio in a range of contexts.
- ▶▶ Use percentage changes to solve problems.

KEYWORDS
Multiplicative inverse
Proportion   Ratio

Clare and Jenny share £800 between them in the ratio 9 : 7.

- ▶ The ratio contains 16 equal parts. $(9 + 7 = 16)$
- ▶ Clare's proportion of the total is $\frac{9}{16}$ of £800. $(= £450)$
- ▶ Jenny's proportion of the total is $\frac{7}{16}$ of £800. $(= £350)$

You can compare Clare's and Jenny's amounts using a **scale factor**:

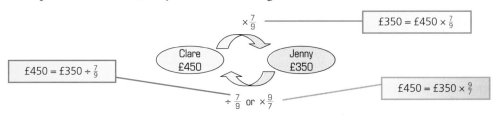

$£350 = £450 \times \frac{7}{9}$

$£450 = £350 \div \frac{7}{9}$

$£450 = £350 \times \frac{9}{7}$

$\div \frac{7}{9}$ or $\times \frac{9}{7}$

- ▶ A scale factor has a **multiplicative inverse**.
  The multiplicative inverse of ... $\times 3$ is $\times \frac{1}{3}$ ... $\times \frac{3}{4}$ is $\times \frac{4}{3}$ ... $\times 2.5$ is $\times \frac{1}{2.5} = 0.4$

example

a Joey spends $2\frac{1}{4}$ times as much as he saves.
    If he spends £270 per week, how much does he save?
b A shirt is decreased in price by 15% to £12.75. Calculate the original price.

a $\times \frac{9}{4} (= \times 2\frac{1}{4})$

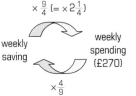

weekly saving   weekly spending (£270)

$\times \frac{4}{9}$

Weekly saving $= £270 \times \frac{4}{9}$
$= £120$

b $\times \frac{85}{100}$

Original price   New price (£12.75)

$\times \frac{100}{85}$

Original price $= £12.75 \times \frac{100}{85}$
$= £15$

The new price is
100% − 15% = 85%
of the original price.

Check: 85% of
£15 = £12.75

- ▶ You can express a scale factor as a fraction, a decimal or a percentage.

$\times 78\%$

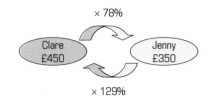

Clare £450   Jenny £350

$\times 129\%$

Clare's share is ...
... $\frac{9}{7} \times$ Jenny's share
... 1.29 × Jenny's share
... 129% of Jenny's share

Jenny's share is ...
... $\frac{7}{9} \times$ Clare's share
... 0.78 × Clare's share
... 78% of Clare's share

Exercise N3.8

1 Calculate

a $\frac{2}{7}$ of 420 kg **b** 23% of £110

c $1\frac{1}{3} \times €520$ **d** $5\frac{1}{8}$ lots of 72 g

e 16% of 120 litres **f** $53 \times \frac{9}{16}$

g 20 cm $\times 8\frac{2}{5}$ **h** 81% of 2.4 cm

2 Express the first quantity in each pair:
i as a fraction of the second quantity, in its simplest form
ii as a percentage.

a 180, 150 **b** 150, 180

c 2 hours, $1\frac{1}{4}$ hours **d** 2.5 kg, 120 g

e 38 cm, 0.912 m

3 At Mixenmatch High school there are 320 boys and 280 girls.
Copy and complete this spider diagram.

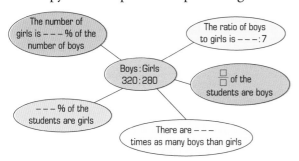

Make up some statements of your own.

4 Callum's wage was £8000 per annum until his boss gave him a £3000 per year increase.
Calculate the percentage increase that Callum received.

5 The table shows the original and sale prices of three Play Station games.

Game	Original price	Sale price
Scooby Doo	£24.99	£18.99
Jet Racer	£19.99	£16.99
FIFA Soccer	£23.99	£19.99

For each game calculate the percentage decrease (give your answers to the nearest whole numbers).

6 The table shows information about students in Motley High School.

Year	Boys	Girls
7	87	68
8	70	87
9	78	69
10	60	69
11	72	69

a What proportion of Motley High's population are:
i girls **ii** boys
iii Year 8 pupils?

b What is the ratio of boys to girls in each year group?

c In which year group is the proportion of girls the highest?

7 A window blind comes in three different sizes. 'Super size' and 'Supermax' size are enlargements of the 'Original' size (this means that the length and width have been increased by the same scale factor).

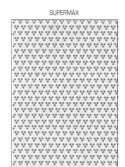

	Original	Super	Supermax
Length	120 cm	150 cm	195 cm
Width		112.5 cm	

a Copy and complete this table.
b What is the ratio of the length of the 'Supermax' : length of the 'Original'?
c What percentage of the width of the 'Supermax' is the width of the 'Original'?

This spread will show you how to:

⏩ Identify when proportional reasoning is needed to solve a problem.

KEYWORDS
Direct proportion
Scale factor
Unitary method

Hannah is cooking apple pie for six.

Her recipe book says that for four people she needs 220g of apples.

Hannah needs to scale the recipe up:

$\times 1\frac{1}{2}$
4 people   220 g
6 people   330 g
$\times 1\frac{1}{2}$

The weight of apples is **directly proportional** to the number of people.

You can use direct proportion to solve problems.

---

example

With eight gallons of petrol Hamid's car travels 248 miles. How far will it travel with 11 gallons of petrol?

Unitary method
Find the number of miles covered by 1 gallon:

$\times \frac{1}{8}$ 8 gallons   for   248 miles $\times \frac{1}{8}$
     1 gallons   for   31 miles
$\times 11$ 11 gallons   for   **341** miles $\times 11$

Scaling method
Calculate the scale factor:

$$\text{Scale factor} = \frac{11 \text{ gallons}}{8 \text{ gallons}} = \frac{11}{8} (= 1.375) \implies$$

8 gallons for 248 miles
$\times \frac{11}{8}$ 11 gallons for **341** miles $\times \frac{11}{8}$

Ratio method
Calculate the ratio between the two quantities:
Gallons : miles $= 8 : 248 = 1 : 31$

$\times 31$

Number of gallons   Number of miles

$\times \frac{1}{31}$

The ratio 'number of miles : number of gallons' is a **rate** and should be read as: '31 miles per gallon'.

$\implies$ 11 gallons for 11×31 miles $= $ **341** miles

Exercise N3.9

1 Solve these direct proportion problems.
   a If 12 tickets cost £9 what do five tickets cost?
   b If a car travels 60 miles in 5 hours how far does it travel in $3\frac{1}{2}$ hours?
   c If ribbon costs £0.80 for 2.5 m what does it cost for 32 m?
   d If a meal for nine people costs £62.91 what would a meal for seven people cost?

2 A fruit stall sells produce at these prices.

Apples £1.20 for 3 kg   **Bananas** £1.80 for 5 kg   **Pears** 3 kg for £1.10

Calculate the price of
   a 8 kg of pears
   b 2 kg of bananas and 5 kg of pears
   c A bag of fruit with 6 kg of apples containing apples, bananas and pears in the ratio 1 : 2 : 3.

3 Fred says 'I swam 10 lengths in 350 seconds. I must have swum each length in 35 seconds'.
   a Comment on Fred's statement.
   b Is the number of lengths that Fred swims proportional to the time taken? Explain your answer.

4 Kofi pays £16.99 for five reams of A4 paper.
   a How many reams could he buy for £75 and how much change would he receive?
   b If the price was reduced to $\frac{2}{3}$ of its original price what would the answers to **a** be?

5 A car hire firm charges £30 fixed fee and £42 per day for a family saloon car. A family is charged £366 for the hire period.
   a How many days did the family hire the car for?
   Another family hires the same car for half the number of days, but the cost is not half of £366.
   b Have the company made a mistake? Explain and justify your answer.

6 Triangles ABC and ADE are similar. This means their sides are in proportion to each other.

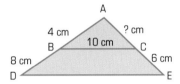

   a What is the scale factor that links the sides of triangle ABC to those of triangle ADE?
   b Write the ratio of the side AB : side AD in its simplest form.
   c Work out the lengths of AC and DE.

7 The table shows the conversions for gallons to litres.

Gallons	Litres
3.$\dot{7}$	17
1.$\dot{5}$	7
0.$\dot{6}$	3
2.$\dot{2}$	10

   a Express as a ratio in the form 1 : n
      i gallons : litres
      ii litres : gallons
   b Calculate the number of litres in 200 gallons.
   c Construct a conversion graph for gallons to litres
      (use x-axis for litres 0 $\rightarrow$ 50
      y-axis for gallons 0 $\rightarrow$ 12)
   d Use the graph to work out the number of litres in nine gallons.

You should know how to ...

1 Use proportional reasoning to solve a problem, choosing the correct numbers to take as 100% or as a whole.

2 Make and justify estimates and approximations of calculations.

3 Give solutions to problems to an appropriate degree of accuracy.

Check out

1 a Copy and complete the 'sale tickets':

> **Was** ☐
> **5% off**
> **Now £15.60**

> **Was £18**
> ☐ **off**
> **Now £12.99**

b Work out the original height of a tree that grew by 20% and is now 11.4 m high.

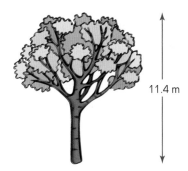

11.4 m

2 Estimate these calculations, giving a reason for the estimates you make:

a $(3612 + 430) \div 6$

b $\dfrac{172 \div 36}{\sqrt{80}}$

3 Give two examples of situations where it would be satisfactory to round a calculation to a problem and two where it would not.

Transformations and congruence

This unit will show you how to:

- ▶▶ Understand congruence.
- ▶▶ Transform 2-D shapes by combinations of translations, rotations and reflections.
- ▶▶ Know that translations, rotations and reflections preserve length and angle.
- ▶▶ Identify reflection symmetry in 3-D shapes.

- ▶▶ Enlarge 2-D shapes, given a centre of enlargement and a whole-number scale factor.
- ▶▶ Recognise that enlargements preserve angle but not length.
- ▶▶ Use ratio and proportion to solve problems.
- ▶▶ Solve increasingly demanding problems and evaluate solutions.

Reflections can combine to produce fascinating effects.

Before you start

You should know how to ...

1 Transform 2-D shapes.

2 Recognise straight-line graphs parallel to the axes.

3 Recognise 3-D shapes.

4 Simplify ratios.

Check in

1 On a square grid, draw the triangle with coordinates (1, 1), (2, 1) and (2, 4).
  a Reflect it in the *y*-axis.
  b Rotate it through $^+90°$, centre the origin.
  c Translate it by a vector of $\begin{pmatrix} -3 \\ 2 \end{pmatrix}$.

2 Give the equations of lines A and B.

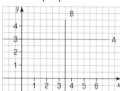

3 Name these 3-D shapes.

  a   **b**   **c**

4 Simplify these ratios.
  a 4 : 2 **b** 3 : 9 **c** 2 m : 10 cm **d** $2 : 3\frac{1}{2}$

Congruence and transformations

This spread will show you how to:
▶▶ Understand congruence.
▶▶ Know that translations, rotations and reflections preserve length and angle and map objects onto congruent images.

KEYWORDS

Congruence	Vector
Translation	Reflection
Mirror line	Rotation

▶ **Congruent** shapes have the same shape and size. For two congruent shapes, corresponding sides and angles are equal.

These two triangles are congruent. The corresponding sides and angles are indicated.

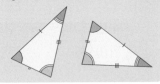

Congruent shapes can be mapped onto each other by a **translation**.

example

A and B are congruent triangles.
Describe how A maps to B.

Remember: You describe a translation by using a **vector**.

A maps to B by a translation with vector $\begin{pmatrix} 5 \\ 6 \end{pmatrix}$.

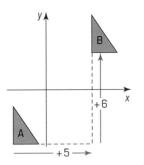

Congruent shapes can also be mapped onto each other by a **reflection**.

example

The quadrilateral A is mapped to the congruent image B by a transformation. Describe the transformation.

A maps to B by a reflection in the line with equation $x = 1$.

Remember: You describe a reflection by its **mirror line**.

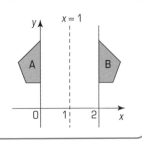

Another way that congruent shapes can be mapped onto each other is by a **rotation**.

example

The rectangle PQRS is mapped to P′Q′R′S′ by a transformation.

Describe the transformation that maps PQRS onto P′Q′R′S′.

PQRS maps to P′Q′R′S′ by a rotation of 90° clockwise, centre the origin.

Remember: You describe a rotation by its **centre** of rotation, its **angle**, and its **direction**.

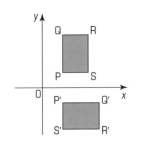

Exercise S3.1

1

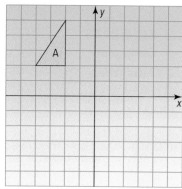

  a Reflect A in the *y*-axis.
  b Reflect A in the *x*-axis.

2

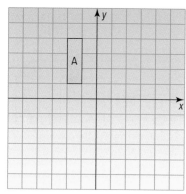

  a Rotate A about (0, 0) through 90° in a clockwise direction.
  b Rotate A about (0 ,0) through 90° in an anticlockwise direction.

3 Which shapes are congruent?

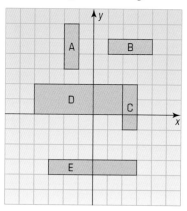

4 Translate the L-shape by these vectors:

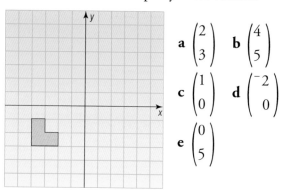

$$\mathbf{a} \begin{pmatrix} 2 \\ 3 \end{pmatrix} \quad \mathbf{b} \begin{pmatrix} 4 \\ 5 \end{pmatrix}$$

$$\mathbf{c} \begin{pmatrix} 1 \\ 0 \end{pmatrix} \quad \mathbf{d} \begin{pmatrix} ^-2 \\ 0 \end{pmatrix}$$

$$\mathbf{e} \begin{pmatrix} 0 \\ 5 \end{pmatrix}$$

5 What transformations map A to each of the other shapes?

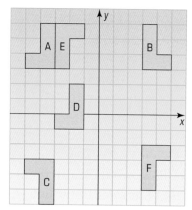

6 **a** Which shapes are congruent to A?
  b Describe the transformation that maps A to each of the **congruent** shapes.

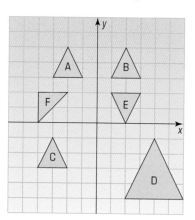

S3.2 Repeated transformations

This spread will show you how to:
▶▶ Transform 2-D shapes by repeated rotations and reflections.
▶▶ Know that rotations and reflections map objects onto congruent images.

KEYWORDS
Congruent
Tessellation

A tessellation is made up of congruent shapes.

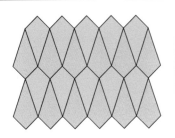

Remember: a tessellation is a repeated pattern that fits together without gaps or overlaps.

You can make a tessellation by repeating a reflection.

Reflect rectangle A in the line M_1 to get B.

Reflect AB in M_2 to get CD.

Reflect ABCD in line M_3 to get EFGH ...

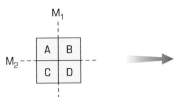

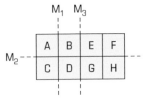

You can also make a tessellation by repeating a rotation.

example

The diagram shows an equilateral triangle A, with the midpoint O marked on one of its sides. Show how you can make a tessellation from this shape, starting with O as the centre of rotation.

Rotate A through 180° about O to get B.

Rotate B through 180° about O′ to get C.

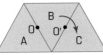

Rotate D 180° about O‴ to get E ...

Rotate C through 180° about O″ to get D.

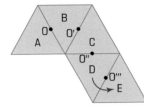

When you place the centre of rotation will determine where the image ends up.

▶ You can produce a tessellation by repeated reflections or rotations.

▶ A tessellation produces a pattern of congruent shapes.

Exercise S3.2

1

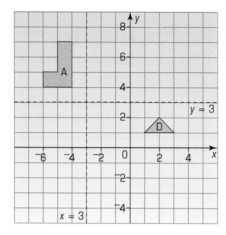

   a Reflect shape A in the line $x = {}^-3$.
   b Reflect A in the line $y = 3$. Label the new shape C.
   c Reflect D in the x-axis and label it E.
   d What reflection maps E back to D?

2

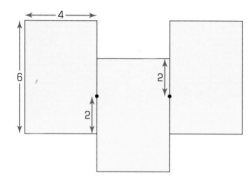

Investigate the effect of half-turns about different points on a 4 by 6 rectangle (as shown above). Use squared paper to display your results.

3

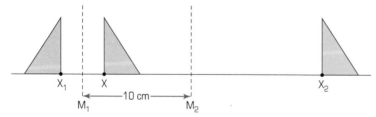

The triangle X is reflected in the mirror line M_1, and the image is X_1.
X_1 is then reflected in the mirror line M_2, and the image is X_2.

Mirror 1 (M_1) and mirror 2 (M_2) are 10 cm apart. $M_1X = 3$ cm. Copy the diagram and measure:

a M_1X_1
b XX_2
c X_1X_2
What do you notice? Investigate.

4 Make your own tessellation patterns using regular polygons.

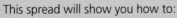
Combining transformations

This spread will show you how to:

▶▶ Transform 2-D shapes by combining translations, rotations and reflections.

KEYWORDS

Congruent

Image

Transformation

You can map congruent shapes by combining transformations.

▶ When two shapes are congruent, you can map one shape onto the other by a combination of translations, reflections and rotations.

example

The diagram shows a pentagon A on a grid.

a Reflect A in the line $x = 2$ and rotate the image by 90° anticlockwise about the origin. Label the final image B.

b Do you get the same image B if you do the rotation first?

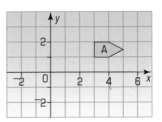

a Reflect A in $x = 2$.

Rotate the image by 90° anticlockwise about (0, 0).

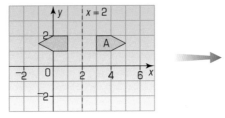

b Rotate A by 90° anticlockwise about (0, 0).

Reflect in the line $x = 2$.

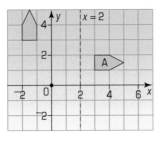

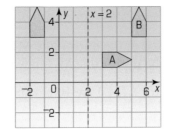

The image is different.

▶ When you combine two transformations, the image will depend on the order of combination.

Exercise S3.3

Copy the grids in this exercise onto squared paper.

1 A is transformed by a reflection in the x-axis followed by a reflection in the y-axis.

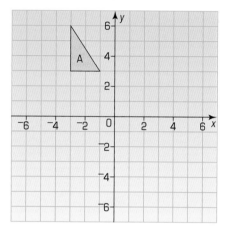

  a What single transformation has the same effect?

  b Do you get the same image if you do the reflections the other way round?

2 The diagram shows a shape A on a grid.

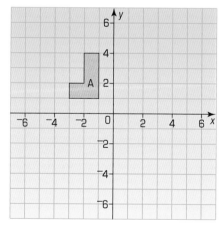

  a Rotate A by 90° clockwise about the origin.
     Label the image B.

  b Reflect B in the x-axis.
     Label the image C.

  c What single transformation maps A to C?

3 The diagram shows a shape P on a grid.

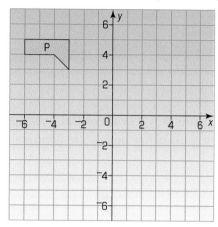

  a Reflect P in the y-axis.
     Label the image Q.

  b Translate Q by the vector $\begin{pmatrix} 0 \\ -3 \end{pmatrix}$.
     Label the image R.

  c Rotate R by 90° clockwise about the point (1, 2).
     Label the image S.

4 The diagram shows congruent shapes A to F on a grid.
Find a single transformation that will map:

  a A to C   **b** C to D
  c D to E   **d** E to F
  e A to D   **f** D to F
  g C to E.

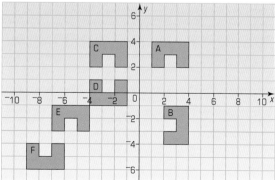

This spread will show you how to:
- ▶▶ Identify reflection symmetry in 3-D shapes.
- ▶▶ Visualise sections obtained by slicing in different planes.

KEYWORDS
Plane of symmetry
Cross-section

This pair of houses is symmetrical – the houses are identical on either side of the dividing wall.

You can cut a cuboid in half like this ... or like this ... or like this.

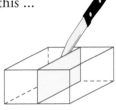 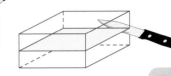

The cuboid has three **planes of symmetry**.

Remember:
A **line of symmetry** cuts a 2-D shape into two identical halves.

▶ A plane of symmetry divides a 3-D shape into two identical halves.

example

State the number of planes of symmetry of a square-based pyramid.

A square-based pyramid has four planes of symmetry.

A plane of symmetry is a cross-section through a solid shape.
Many cross-sections are **not** planes of symmetry.

example

Show how it is possible to slice a triangular prism so that the cross-section is:

a a triangle **b** a rectangle

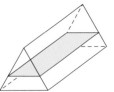

a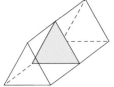

The cross-section is a triangle.

b

The cross-section is a rectangle.

Exercise S3.4

Draw sketches of these solids showing all their planes of symmetry.

1

2
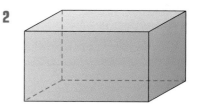

3

4
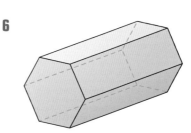

5
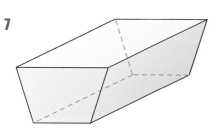

6
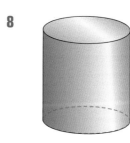

7

8
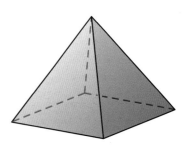

A cylinder has an infinite number of planes of symmetry. You need only show two of them.

9 A cube has nine planes of symmetry.
Try to identify them all, and illustrate your answers clearly.

10 Show how you can slice this square-based pyramid so that the cross-section is:
   a a square
   b an isosceles triangle
   c a trapezium
   d an equilateral triangle.

Enlargements

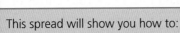

This spread will show you how to:

▶▶ Enlarge 2-D shapes given a negative whole-number scale factor.

▶▶ Identify scale factor as the ratio of corresponding lengths.

KEYWORDS

Enlargement	Scale factor
Object	Image

To enlarge a shape you need:

a centre of enlargement ...   ... and a scale factor

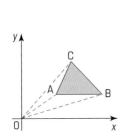

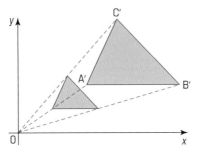

The centre of enlargement is O.   The scale factor is 2.

The scale factor is 2 because:
OA' = 2 × OA
OB' = 2 × OB
OC' = 2 × OC

The lengths of A′B′C′ are twice as long as the lengths of ABC.

▶ **The scale factor of an enlargement is the ratio of any two corresponding lengths.**

You can also enlarge shapes on the opposite side of the centre of enlargement.

▶ **The scale factor of an enlargement is negative if the image and object are on opposite sides of the centre of enlargement.**

example

The triangle PQR has coordinates P(1, 1), Q(4, 1) and R(1, 3).
Enlarge PQR by a scale factor ⁻2 with centre of enlargement the origin.

Draw lines from each of   Extend the lines twice the   Join the endpoints to form the
the vertices to the origin.   distance in the opposite direction.   image P′Q′R′.

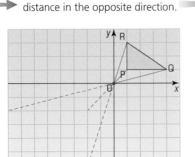

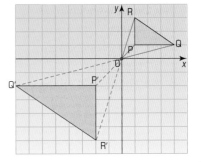

Exercise S3.5

1. On a pair of axes scaled from ⁻8 to +8 plot ABCD where A is (0, 0), B is (2, 0), C is (2, 4) and D is (0, 3). Enlarge ABCD
   a. centre (0, 0), scale factor 2
   b. centre (3, 3), scale factor 2.

2. Copy these figures and, using centre O, enlarge them by the scale factor stated (label the image carefully).

a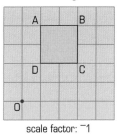
scale factor: ⁻1

b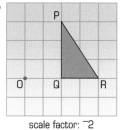
scale factor: ⁻2

c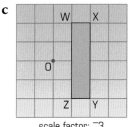
scale factor: ⁻3

d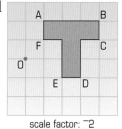
scale factor: ⁻2

e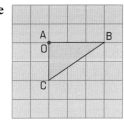
scale factor: ⁻2

f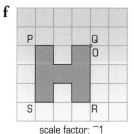
scale factor: ⁻1

g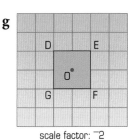
scale factor: ⁻2

h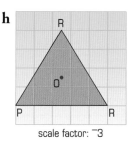
scale factor: ⁻3

3. Copy these diagrams, mark the centres of enlargement and state the scale factors.

a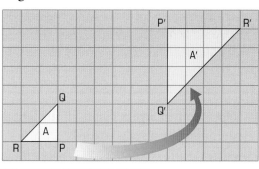

b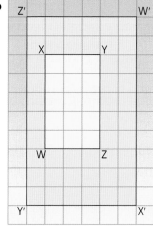

4. The diagram shows a shape T_1 on a grid.

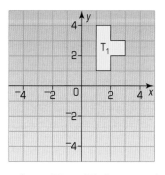

a. Transform T_1 to T_2 by an enlargement, centre (⁻1, 4), scale factor ⁻1.
b. What transformation maps T_2 to T_1?
c. What rotation maps T_1 to T_2?
d. What reflection maps T_1 to T_2?

This spread will show you how to:
▶▶ Identify the scale factor of an enlargement as the ratio of corresponding lengths.
▶▶ Recognise that enlargements preserve angle but not length.
▶▶ Understand the implications of enlargement for perimeter.

KEYWORDS

Enlargement   Image
Scale factor   Ratio
Perimeter

When you enlarge a shape, all the lengths are multiplied by a scale factor k.

The lengths in the image are in the same proportion as the object.
The angles in the image and the object are the same.

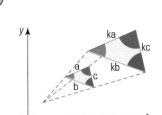

▶ Enlargements preserve angle but not length.

When you enlarge a shape its perimeter will increase as well.

---

example

Rectangle A′B′C′D′ is an enlargement of rectangle ABCD.
a Find the centre of enlargement and the scale factor.
b By what ratio has the perimeter increased?

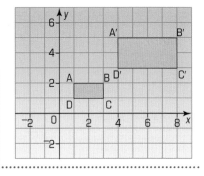

a Join the corresponding vertices and extend the lines backwards.
Where they intersect is the centre of enlargement, P, ($^-2$, $^-1$).
Find the ratio of corresponding sides:
A′B′ : AB = 4 : 2 = 2 : 1
⟹ the scale factor is 2.

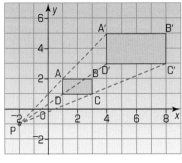

b Perimeter of ABCD
= 2 + 1 + 2 + 1 = 6
Perimeter of A′B′C′D′
= 4 + 2 + 4 + 2 = 12
The perimeter has increased by a ratio 12 : 6 = 2 : 1

▶ When you enlarge a shape by a scale factor k:
▶ All corresponding lengths are increased by a factor k.
▶ The perimeter is increased by a factor k.

---

example

A drawing of a shape is enlarged on a photocopier by 24%.
If the perimeter of the shape was originally 35 cm, what is the perimeter of the image?

24% of 35 cm $= \frac{24}{100} \times 35 = 8.4$ cm
New perimeter = 35 cm + 8.4 cm = 43.4 cm

Exercise S3.6

1 Stamp B is an enlargement of stamp A by a scale factor 3.

   a Calculate the dimensions p and q of stamp B.

   b Calculate the perimeter of

      i stamp A

      ii stamp B

   c Compare the ratio of perimeter A to perimeter B.

      What do you notice?

2 Photo B is an enlargement by scale factor 2 of photo A.

   a What are the lengths x and y?

   b Find the area of photo A and the area of photo B.

      What is the ratio, area A : area B?

   c Compare this with the ratio, perimeter A : perimeter B.

      What do you notice?

3 Triangle X is a scale factor +3 enlargement of triangle Y.

   a Calculate the area of each triangle and hence find the ratio of their areas.

   b Compare the ratio of the perimeters to the ratio of areas.

      What do you notice?

Area = $\frac{1}{2}$ × base × height.

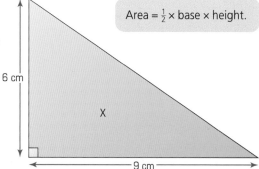

4 The ratio of the perimeters of two shapes is 1 : 5. What is the ratio of their areas?

You should know how to ...

1 Know that translations, rotations and reflections preserve length and angle and map objects onto congruent images.

2 Use proportional reasoning to solve a problem.

Check out

1 The diagram shows five shapes on a grid.

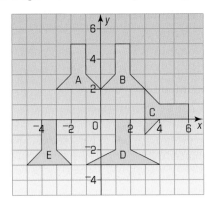

a Which shapes are congruent to A?

b Describe the transformations that map:

i A → B **ii** A → E **iii** B → C **iv** B → E

2 P is an enlargement of Q by a scale factor +6.

Find:

a lengths *a* and *b*

b the perimeter of P

c the perimeter of Q

d the ratio of lengths on Q to the lengths on P

e the ratio of area Q to area P.

This unit will show you how to:

▶▶ Distinguish the different roles played by letter symbols and equations, identities, formulae and functions.

▶▶ Add simple algebraic fractions.

▶▶ Construct and solve linear equations with integer coefficients, using an appropriate method.

▶▶ Use formulae from mathematics and other subjects.

▶▶ Substitute numbers into expressions and formulae.

▶▶ Derive a formula and, in simple cases, change its subject.

▶▶ Solve increasingly demanding problems and evaluate solutions.

▶▶ Explore connections in mathematics across a range of contexts.

▶▶ Represent problems and synthesise information in algebraic form.

▶▶ Solve substantial problems by breaking them into simpler tasks.

Computers allow you to substitute multiple values into a formula.

Before you start

You should know how to ...

1 Solve simple linear equations.

2 Substitute numbers into a formula.

3 Add and subtract numerical fractions.

Check in

1 Solve these equations:

   a $2x + 6 = 40$

   b $5y + 8 = 3y + 16$

   c $10 - 2z = 6z - 14$

2 a Which formula gives the biggest value of p when $r = 5$ and $t = {}^-2$?

     $p = 3r + 2t$ $p = 10 - t^2$ $p = rt - 4$

   b If $C = 2w + 2l$, what is t when $C = 22$ and $w = 6$?

3 a Evaluate:

    i $\frac{1}{5} + \frac{1}{9}$ **ii** $\frac{2}{3} - \frac{1}{7}$ **iii** $3\frac{1}{5} - 2\frac{1}{2}$

   b Find the perimeter of this shape:

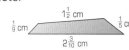

Solving linear equations

This spread will show you how to:

▶▶ Construct and solve linear equations with integer coefficients.

KEYWORDS
Linear equation   Solve
Cross-multiply

Jalina, Clare and Imran have all got their own way of solving the equation: $10 - 4x = 2$

Jalina says:

I like to think of this as a double-sided equation.
$10 - 4x = 2 + 0x$
I now add $4x$ to both sides.

Clare says:

I don't like subtracting from 10, so I add $4x$ to both sides:
$10 - 4x + 4x = 2 + 4x$

Imran says:

I find these tricky so I try to use my common sense.
$10 - \mathbf{8} = 2$, so $4x = 8$

Clare's method is a good strategy for dealing with negatives.

▶ **You can deal with a negative term by adding it to both sides of the equation.**

$$10 - 4x = 2$$
$$10 = 4x + 2$$
$$8 = 4x$$
$$2 = x$$

Jalina, Clare and Imran are now trying to solve the equation: $\frac{5}{x} + 3 = 7$
Jalina's method involves:

Clare says:

I would multiply all terms by x to get rid of the $\div x$.
$\frac{5}{x} + 3 = 7$
$5 + 3x = 7x$

Jalina says:

I would rearrange the equation. I get rid of the outer layer (+3), and then I don't like dividing x into 5 so I multiply by x.

Imran says:

I like cross-multiplying, so I aim to get a fraction on both sides.

$$\frac{5}{x} + 3 = 7$$
$$\frac{5}{x} = 4$$
$$5 = 4x$$
$$\frac{5}{4} = x$$
$$x = 1\tfrac{1}{4}$$

▶ reading the layers of the equation,
▶ and then reversing them.

You can solve some equations by **cross-multiplying.**

example

Solve the equation $\dfrac{x+3}{4} = \dfrac{x+2}{6}$

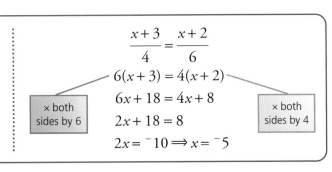

$$\frac{x+3}{4} = \frac{x+2}{6}$$
$$6(x+3) = 4(x+2)$$
$$6x + 18 = 4x + 8$$
$$2x + 18 = 8$$
$$2x = {}^{-}10 \implies x = {}^{-}5$$

× both sides by 6

× both sides by 4

Exercise A4.1

1 Solve these one-sided equations.

a $3x - 4 = 29$ **b** $\dfrac{y}{4} + 8 = 14$ **c** $2(a - 4) = 12$ **d** $\dfrac{p^2 - 9}{10} = 4$

e $3x + 2(x - 4) = 11$ **f** $\frac{2}{5}y - 2 = 12$

2 Solve these two-sided equations.

a $5x - 4 = 2x + 17$ **b** $5x - 4 = 3 - x$ **c** $7 - 3x = 5 - 2x$

d $2(3y - 1) = 3(y - 1)$ **e** $3(y + 2) + 5(y - 4) = 2(y + 5) - (y - 6)$

3 Solve these equations containing negative terms.

a $10 - 3x = 7$ **b** $5 - 8x = 1$ **c** $6 - 9x = 24$ **d** $^-x - 4 = {}^-3$

e $^-3 - y = {}^-5$ **f** $5a - 3(a - 1) = 39$

4 Solve these equations containing fractions.

a $\dfrac{2x - 1}{3} = \dfrac{x}{2}$ **b** $\dfrac{3y + 2}{4} = \dfrac{y - 5}{3}$ **c** $\dfrac{z + 3}{2} = \dfrac{z - 4}{5}$

d $\dfrac{5}{x} = 3$ **e** $^-4 = \dfrac{9}{y}$ **f** $2 = \dfrac{18}{x + 4}$

g $\dfrac{4}{x} + 5 = 3$ **h** $\dfrac{9}{y} - 2 = 8$ **i** $5 - \dfrac{6}{z} = {}^-1$

5 Find a pair of equations with matching solutions.

$15 - 3x = 9$ $\dfrac{x + 4}{2} = \dfrac{3x - 9}{3}$ $30 - 2x = 42$ $\dfrac{8}{x} = 4$

$15 - \dfrac{20}{x} = 13$ $\dfrac{30}{x} + 7 = 2$

6 Puzzle   In this triangular arithmagon, the number in a square is the sum of the two numbers either side. Use algebra to find k, l and m.

k is the number in the top circle. Write the other missing numbers in terms of k.

(Arithmagon: top circle k; squares 32 and 29; bottom circles l and m with square 21 between them.)

7 Quadratic equations can have two solutions.

For example, $x^2 = 25$ is satisfied by $x = 5$ or $x = {}^-5$, since $\sqrt{25} = {}^+5$ or $^-5$.

Can you find two solutions to these equations?

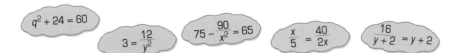

$q^2 + 24 = 60$ $3 = \dfrac{12}{y^2}$ $75 - \dfrac{90}{x^2} = 65$ $\dfrac{x}{5} = \dfrac{40}{2x}$ $\dfrac{16}{y + 2} = y + 2$

Adding and subtracting algebraic fractions

This spread will show you how to:

▶▶ Add and subtract simple algebraic fractions.

Algebra follows the same rules as arithmetic.
You can add algebraic fractions in the same way as you
would add numerical fractions.

example

a Work out $\frac{1}{3} + \frac{2}{7}$.

b Simplify $\frac{x}{3} + \frac{2y}{7}$.

Note: $\frac{2y}{7}$ is the same as $\frac{2}{7}y$ because of BIDMAS: It doesn't matter what order you do the ×2 and ÷7

a $\frac{1}{3} + \frac{2}{7}$

$= \frac{7}{21} + \frac{6}{21}$

$= \frac{13}{21}$

Make the
denominators equal

Add the numerators

b $\frac{x}{3} + \frac{2y}{7}$

$= \frac{7x}{21} + \frac{6y}{21}$

$= \frac{7x + 6y}{21}$

You cannot simplify this further, since $7x$ and $6y$ are not **like terms**.

Sometimes the algebra terms are in the denominators.

example

Simplify $\frac{3}{x} - \frac{4}{y}$.

$\frac{3}{x} - \frac{4}{y} = \frac{3 \times y}{x \times y} - \frac{4 \times x}{y \times x}$ make the denominators equal

$= \frac{3y - 4x}{xy}$ subtract the numerators

You can deal with mixed numbers by converting them to improper fractions.

example

Write $3\frac{1}{3}x + 2\frac{1}{9}x^2$ as a single fraction.

$3\frac{1}{3}x + 2\frac{1}{9}x^2 = \frac{10x}{3} + \frac{19x^2}{9}$ change to improper fractions

$= \frac{30x}{9} + \frac{19x^2}{9}$ make the denominators equal

$= \frac{30x + 19x^2}{9}$ add the numerators

Remember: $30x$ and $19x^2$ are not like terms.

▶ When you add/subtract algebraic fractions:
    ▶ make the denominators equal
    ▶ add/subtract the numerators.

Exercise A4.2

1 Calculate:

a $\frac{2}{5} + \frac{3}{4}$ **b** $\frac{2}{9} - \frac{1}{6}$ **c** $\frac{3}{4} \times \frac{1}{7}$ **d** $\frac{5}{6} \div \frac{1}{2}$ **e** $3\frac{1}{2} + 2\frac{1}{5}$ **f** $7\frac{1}{5} - 2\frac{1}{6}$

2 Simplify:

a $\frac{4}{x} + \frac{2}{x}$ **b** $\frac{x}{3} + \frac{2x}{3}$ **c** $\frac{x}{4} + \frac{x}{5}$ **d** $\frac{2x}{5} - \frac{x}{5}$ **e** $\frac{1}{5}x + \frac{3}{5}x$ **f** $\frac{4x}{5} + \frac{x}{4}$

g $\frac{x}{7} - \frac{x}{9}$ **h** $\frac{5}{x} + \frac{6}{y}$ **i** $\frac{7}{p} - \frac{2}{p}$ **j** $\frac{7}{p} - \frac{2}{q}$ **k** $5\frac{1}{5}x + 2\frac{1}{2}x$ **l** $1\frac{1}{9}x - \frac{2}{7}x$

3 This is what a student wrote.
Show that the student was wrong.

For all numbers a and b:
$$\frac{1}{a} + \frac{1}{b} = \frac{2}{a+b}$$

4 Find pairs of matching fraction cards.

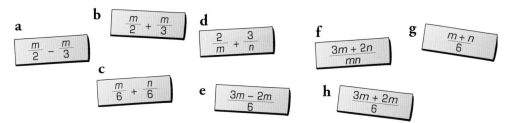

a $\frac{m}{2} - \frac{m}{3}$

b $\frac{m}{2} + \frac{m}{3}$

c $\frac{m}{6} + \frac{n}{6}$

d $\frac{2}{m} + \frac{3}{n}$

e $\frac{3m - 2m}{6}$

f $\frac{3m + 2n}{mn}$

g $\frac{m+n}{6}$

h $\frac{3m + 2m}{6}$

5 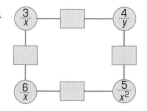 Two students each raised some money for charity.

Hint: use an equation.

a Write an expression to show the total money raised.

b If the total money raised was £115, how much did each student collect?

$\frac{2m}{5}$ $\frac{3}{4}m$

6 a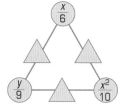

$\frac{3}{x}$ □ $\frac{4}{y}$

□ □

$\frac{6}{x}$ □ $\frac{5}{x^2}$

The expression in each square is the sum of the two expressions in circles either side. Copy and complete.

b

$\frac{x}{6}$

△ △

$\frac{y}{9}$ △ $\frac{x^2}{10}$

The expression in each triangle is the difference between the two expressions in circles either side. Copy and complete.

Solving problems with equations

This spread will show you how to:
▶▶ Construct and solve linear equations with integer coefficients.

KEYWORDS
Solve   Construct
Unknown   Equation
Variable

Algebra can be useful for solving problems.

example

Find the length of this rectangle.

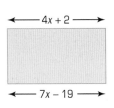

← 4x + 2 →

← 7x − 19 →

$$4x + 2 = 7x - 19$$
$$2 = 3x - 19$$
$$7 = x$$
$$\text{length} = 4x + 2$$
$$= 4 \times 7 + 2$$
$$= 30$$

When you write your own equations, begin by deciding what letter to use.

example

The perimeter of a rectangle is 48 cm.
The length is 8 cm more than the width. What are the rectangle's dimensions?

← x + 8 →

x

Choose a letter to represent the width: ⟹ Width = x
Write the length in terms of x as well: ⟹ Length = $x + 8$

Form your equation: ⟹ $x + (x + 8) + x + (x + 8) = 48$
Solve the equation: ⟹ $4x + 16 = 48$
$$4x = 32$$
$$x = 8$$

Check the solution:
16 + 8 + 16 + 8 = 48

Answer the question: ⟹ Width = 8 cm, length = 16 cm

Sometimes you need to use facts that are not given in the question.

example

One of the angles of this isosceles triangle is 40° more than the other two.
Find the angles of the triangle.

Let $\angle A = x$, so $\angle C = x$ as well   (isosceles triangles have two equal angles)
Then $\angle B = x + 40°$ (one of the angles is 40° more than the other two)

Now write the equation:

$$x + x + (x + 40) = 180$$ (angles in a triangle add up to 180°)
$$3x + 40 = 180$$ ⟹ $x = \frac{140}{3}$ or $46\frac{2}{3}$

Check:
$46\frac{2}{3}° + 86\frac{2}{3}° + 46\frac{2}{3}° = 180°$

So $\angle A = 46\frac{2}{3}°$, $\angle C = 46\frac{2}{3}°$ and $\angle B = 86\frac{2}{3}°$

Exercise A4.3

1 In a Hot Cross, the horizontal and vertical lines have the same total. Find the value of the unknown in these Hot Crosses.

a

	5	
‾11	x	2x
	6	

b

	7y	
‾4	3y	18
	‾6	

c

	7	
10z	‾5z	2z
	3	

d

	2	
3	10	‾6x
	5	

2 Try these 'Think of a number' problems by forming an equation.

a I think of a number. When I treble it and add 6 I get the same answer as when I multiply it by 7 and subtract 14.

b I think of a number. When I double it and subtract it *from* 15 I get the same answer as when I treble it and add 4.

c I think of a number. I get 30 when I subtract four lots of it from 50.

d I think of a number. When I divide 30 by this number I get 45.

e I think if a number. When I add 5 to its reciprocal I get 11.

3 Ben and Vicky have £250 between them. Ben gives Vicky £50. Vicky now has four times as much money as Ben. Use an equation to find how much money each person had to start with.

4 The area of the L-shape is equal to the area of the square that has been removed. What length square has been removed?

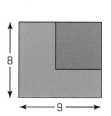

5

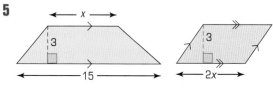

The areas of the shapes are equal. What is this area?

6 ∠BAC is three-quarters of ∠ACB. What are the angles of the triangle?

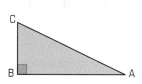

7

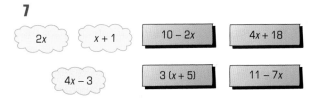

The mean of the expressions in the clouds is the same as the mean of the expressions in the boxes. What numbers are in each cloud and box?

8 Sarah is 11 years younger than Jan who, in turn, is eight years younger than Pauline. Between them, they have been alive 197 years.
How old is Jan?

9 The angle at the centre of a regular polygon is dependent on the number of sides.

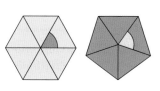

a Write an expression for the central angle in an *n*-sided polygon.

b If the central angle is 15°, how many sides does the polygon have?

10 a Six times the reciprocal of a number is 18.
What is the number?

b When 7 is added to 10 times the reciprocal of a number, you get 12.
What is the number?

c When 8 times the reciprocal of a number is subtracted from 13, you get 3.
What is the number?

Introducing inequalities

This spread will show you how to:
▶▶ Solve linear inequalities in one variable.
▶▶ Represent the solution set on a number line.

KEYWORDS
Inequality   Solution set
Integer

You often see descriptions containing the phrases 'at least' or 'at most'.

You could say: 'Height (cm) greater than or equal to 150'.
You could write: $h \geqslant 150$

You could say: 'Age (years) less than 16'.
You could write: $A < 16$

You can use **inequalities** to write statements in mathematics.

▶ < means 'less than'   ▶ > means 'greater than'

▶ ⩽ means 'less than or equal to'   ▶ ⩾ means 'greater than or equal to'

You can read inequalities from left to right, or vice versa.

| No more than 12 people allowed in this lift |

Number of people ⩽12
$p \leqslant 12$ or $12 \geqslant p$

12 is greater than or equal to p.

An inequality is rather like an equation, but it can have more solutions.
You can represent its **solution set** on a number line.

$x \leqslant 3$ $y > ^-4$ $2\frac{2}{5} < z \leqslant 5$

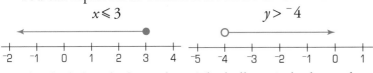

The shaded circle shows that 3 is part of the solution.

The hollow circle shows that $^-4$ is not part of the solution.

This shows that z is in between $2\frac{2}{5}$ and 5.
5 is part of the solution, but $2\frac{2}{5}$ is not.

You can solve a simple inequality rather like an equation.

example

Solve the inequality $3x + 2 > 47$.
Show the solution set on a number line.

$3x + 2 > 47$ ⟩ — Read this as: *'I think of a number, treble it, add 2 and my answer is over 47'.*

$3x > 45$

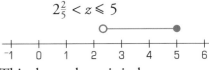

$x > 15$ — Read this as: *'My number must have been over 15'.*

Exercise A4.4

1 Use inequalities to write these statements.

a
> No more than
> 13 people can go in
> the minibus

let p be the
number of people

b
> SPEED
> LIMIT
> **30**

let s be the
speed of car

c
> A healthy heart
> rate is between
> 60 and 95
> beats per minute

let b be the
beats per minute

d
> POP GROUP
> Over 5000
> people applied for
> a new pop group

let a be the
number of applicants

2 Read the text in the box and answer the questions.

  a Bethan is 17. Could she have sat the exam?

  b Paul scored 70%. Did he pass?

  c Four people claimed they finished. Could this be true?

  d Miss Mann has marked 40 scripts. Does she have to do any more?

  e The exam was on Monday. Did all students have their results by Wednesday?

> **The age of the people who sat the exam**
>
> was $15 \leqslant a \leqslant 17$ and the pass mark was $> 70\%$
>
> It was a long exam, so, at the end, < 7 people had
>
> completed all questions. Each teacher had to mark
>
> > 40 scripts so the students would know their scores
>
> in $\leqslant 3$ days.

3 Match these number lines and inequalities. For any left over, write their match:

a

b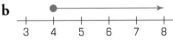

A $4 \leqslant p$

B $y > 4$

c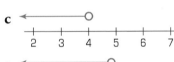

d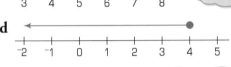

C $z \leqslant 4$

e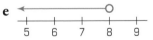

D $4 > q$

E $9 \leqslant w < 16$

4 Decide if each of these statements is true or false.

  a $2^5 > 5^2$

  b $25^{\frac{1}{2}} < 64^{\frac{1}{3}}$

  c 30% of 210 > 20% of 350

  d $5 < (^-2) \times (^-6) < 10$

  e an acute angle $\leqslant 90°$

5 **a** If p is prime, write all values of p such that $p \leqslant 37$.

  b If n is even, write all values of n such that $17 < n \leqslant 34$.

  c If s is square, write the largest value of s such that $63 < s < 100$.

  d If f is a fraction, write a value of f such that $\frac{1}{6} < f < \frac{1}{5}$.

  e If r is a factor of 200, find all values of r such that $r > 75$.

6 Solve these inequalities and represent your solutions on a number line:

  a $3x \leqslant 18$

  b $2x - 5 > 17$

  c $\dfrac{y}{5} + 1 \leqslant 6$

  d $\dfrac{3z + 1}{4} < 7$

  e $5x + 3 \leqslant 2x + 5$

  f $28 < 7z + 49$

7 **a** Investigate the $\boxed{n!}$ button on your calculator. What does it do?

  b $100 < n! < 10\,000$. What could n be?

This spread will show you how to:

▶▶ Distinguish the different roles played by letter symbols in formulae.

▶▶ Use formulae from mathematics and other subjects.

▶▶ Substitute numbers into expressions and formulae.

▶▶ Derive a formula and, in simple cases, change its subject.

KEYWORDS

Subject   Inverse

Formula   Evaluate

Rearrange

A **formula** describes the relationship between variables.

For example, the surface area of a cube is related to its length by the formula:

$$A = 6l^2 \qquad \text{where } A = \text{surface area}$$
$$l = \text{length of one edge}$$

A is the **subject** of the formula.

Sometimes you need to rearrange a formula to evaluate a variable. For example:

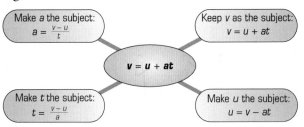

Make a the subject:
$$a = \frac{v - u}{t}$$

Keep v as the subject:
$$v = u + at$$

$$v = u + at$$

Make t the subject:
$$t = \frac{v - u}{a}$$

Make u the subject:
$$u = v - at$$

It is easy to rearrange a formula if you use inverse operations.

<table>
<tr><td>

example

</td><td>

a Find the surface area of a cube with length 3 cm.

b Find the length of a cube with surface area 294 cm².

....

a Area of one face $= l^2$, so $A = 6l^2$ where $l =$ length of edge and $A =$ surface area

$A = 6 \times 3 \times 3 = 54 \implies$ Surface area $= 54$ cm²

b $A = 6l^2$ Read this as:

building

squared   ×6

$l \implies l^2 \implies 6l^2 \qquad A = 6l^2$

square root   ÷6

$\sqrt{\dfrac{A}{6}} \impliedby \dfrac{A}{6} \impliedby A = 6l^2$

rearranging

$$l = \sqrt{\dfrac{A}{6}} \implies l = \sqrt{\dfrac{294}{6}} = \sqrt{49} = 7$$

So the length is 7 cm.

</td></tr>
</table>

Rearranging a formula is like 'Pass the Parcel': the last layer to go on is the first to come off.

Exercise A4.5

1 Use these formulae to find the required variable:

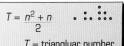

$T = \dfrac{n^2 + n}{2}$

T = triangluar number
n = position

Find the 12th triangular number

$F = \dfrac{9C}{5} + 32$

F = temp in °F
C = temp in °C

Find $^-15$°C in degrees Fahrenheit

$T = 6\sqrt{\dfrac{L}{g}}$

T = time L = length
g = gravity

Find T when $L = 10$ m and $g = 9.8$ m/s^2

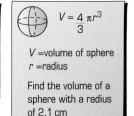

$V = \dfrac{4\,\pi r^3}{3}$

V = volume of sphere
r = radius

Find the volume of a sphere with a radius of 2.1 cm

2 Derive your own formulae for the variables described.

a The perimeter, p, of a rectangle whose length is twice its width.

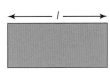

b The perimeter, p, of a semicircle, radius r.

c The surface area, s, of a cuboid with length l, width w, height h.

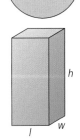

3 Evaluate the required variable from these formulae, without a calculator:

a $C = 5\left(\dfrac{F - 32}{9}\right)$ ... C when $F = 59$

b $T = 40 - 3d$ ... T when $d = ^-4$

c $v = lwh$ ... v when $l = 0.4$, $w = 0.2$, $h = 0.1$

d $P = \dfrac{1}{v} + \dfrac{1}{u}$ ... P when $v = 3$, $u = 5$

e $y = mx + c$ ... y when $m = \frac{1}{3}$, $x = 21$ and $c = ^-2$

4 Use algebra to explain why these formulae work.

a A = shaded area
$A = x(6 - y) + y(9 - x)$

b A = shaded area
$A = 4r^2 - \pi r^2$

c C = change from £50.
n = number of CDs bought.

$C = 50 - \dfrac{7n}{2}$

5 Rearrange these formulae to make the letter given in brackets become the subject.

a $A = lw$ $[w]$ **b** $P = a + b + c$ $[a]$

c $s = \dfrac{D}{T}$ $[D]$ **d** $R = lp - k$ $[l]$

e $S = \dfrac{v}{p} + k$ $[v]$ **f** $v^2 = u^2 + 2as$ $[a]$

g $A = 4\pi r^2$ $[r]$ **h** $v = lwh$ $[w]$

i $F = \dfrac{9(C + 40)}{5} - 40$ $[C]$

6

The number of faces you can see when n cubes are stuck together is given by:
$F = 4n + 2$

a Use the formula to work out the number of faces you can see when ten cubes are stuck together

b Rearrange the formula to make n the subject.

c Use the rearranged formula to work out how many cubes are stuck together if 54 faces are visible.

d Can you explain *why* the given formula works?

Rearranging harder formulae

This spread will show you how to:
- ▶▶ Use formulae from mathematics and other subjects.
- ▶▶ Derive a formula and change its subject.

You can rearrange formulae by using inverse operations.
Remember that you perform any operations on **both** sides of the formula.

---

example

Rearrange:

a $p = 2(l + w)$ to make w the subject.   **b** $R = 8l^3$ to make l the subject.

....

a $+l$ then $\times 2$

$\div 2$: $\frac{p}{2} = l + w$

^-l: $\frac{p}{2} - l = w$

$\frac{p}{2} - l$

b cube l, then $\times 8$

$\div 8$: $\frac{r}{8} = l^3$

cube root $\sqrt[3]{\dfrac{R}{8}} = l$

▶ **Read** the formula

▶ **Reverse** the operations

There are two types of inverse operations that you need to be careful with.

---

example

Rearrange the formulae to make x the subject.

a $V = p - qx$ **b** $k = \frac{p}{x}$

....

a $V = p - qx$ $\times q$ then **subtract from** p

▶ Make the formula easier to read:

$V + qx = p$ $\times q$ then $+ V$

▶ Now reverse:

$-V$: $qx = p - V$

$\div q$: $x = \frac{p - V}{q}$

b $k = \frac{p}{x}$ **divide into** p

▶ Make the formula easier to read:

$kx = p$ $\times k$

▶ Now reverse:

$\div k$: $x = \frac{p}{k}$

The operations 'subtract from' and 'divide into' may be part of a larger formula.

---

example

Rearrange each formula to make the letter in brackets become the subject.

a $B = \frac{R - 6y}{w}$ (y) **b** $R = \frac{S}{T} - U$ (T)

....

a Read the formula:

$\times 6$, then subtract from R, then divide by w

$\times w$: $wB = R - 6y$

Make the formula easier to read:

$+6y$: $wB + 6y = R$

$-wB$: $6y = R - wB$

$\div 6$: $y = \frac{R - wB}{6}$

b Read the formula:

Divide into S, then $-U$

$+U$: $R + U = \frac{S}{T}$

Make the formula easier to read:

$\times T$: $T(R + U) = S$

$\div(R + U)$: $T = \frac{S}{R + U}$

Exercise A4.6

1 Make the letter in brackets the subject of each formula.

a $p = s + r$ (s) **b** $z = qp + k$ (q) **c** $w = \dfrac{p}{x} - m$ (p)

d $z = \sqrt{x}$ (x) **e** $m = p^2 + 3$ (p) **f** $r = x^3 + z$ (x)

g $k = px^2 - q$ (x) **h** $m = p^4$ (p) **i** $p(x - r) = w$ (x)

2 These formulae involve negative terms. Rearrange them to make x the subject by first adding the inverse of the negative term to both sides.

a $p = w - x$ **b** $z = r - px$ **c** $q = z - x^2$ **d** $p - wx = r$

e $m = l - \sqrt{x}$ **f** $m = z - x^3$ **g** $w = r - mx^2$ **h** $m = p - \dfrac{x}{q}$

3 These formulae involve fraction terms. Rearrange them to make y the subject by first multiplying both sides by the denominator.

a $p = \dfrac{w}{y}$ **b** $z = \dfrac{m}{y}$ **c** $q = \dfrac{z}{3y}$ **d** $r = \dfrac{p}{y^2}$

e $k = \dfrac{1}{\sqrt{y}}$ **f** $w = \dfrac{m^2}{y^3}$ **g** $m = \dfrac{p}{my}$ **h** $t = \dfrac{s}{wy^2}$

4 Read the layers carefully to rearrange these formulae to make m the subject.

a $pm - q = x$ **b** $q - m = px$ **c** $\dfrac{z}{m} = q$ **d** $\dfrac{m^2}{p} - q = k$

e $q - m^2 = r$ **f** $\dfrac{q}{m^2} + 2 = p$ **g** $\dfrac{p - m}{q} = z$ **h** $k(q - m^2) = t$

5 Rearrange these formulae to show all given subjects:

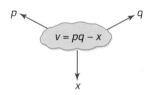

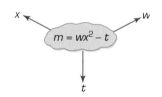

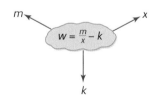

6 **Challenge**
Rearrange these formulae to make x the subject.

a $k = \dfrac{z(px + q)}{w} + c$

b $m = \dfrac{\left(\frac{x}{p} - q\right)}{w} + k$

c $w = \dfrac{px^2 - k + c}{z} \div m$

7 $m = p - \dfrac{w}{x}$ ... this formula involves a negative term and a fraction. How would you make x the subject?

8 $x = \dfrac{\sqrt{(b^2 - 4ac)} - b}{2a}$ This is a well-known formula in mathematics.
     a Can you make c the subject?
     b Find out what the formula is for and see if you can use it.

You should know how to …

1 Construct and solve linear equations with integer coefficients, using an appropriate method.

Check out

1 a Solve these equations:

   i $5(x + 2) = 3(x - 4)$ **ii** $10 - 4x = 5x + 7$

   iii $16 - 5x = 6$ **iv** $\frac{5}{x} + 7 = 11$

   v $\frac{x + 3}{4} = \frac{x - 5}{7}$

b Write an equation in each situation. Solve it to find x.

   i

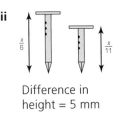

   ii

Difference in height = 5 mm

   iii

Perimeter = 20 cm

c

Claire thinks of a number, trebles it and adds 6. The answer is over 42.

   i Why can't you write an equation to represent this information? What can you write?

   ii What can you say about the number Claire is thinking of?

2 Solve substantial problems by breaking them into simpler tasks.

2 a i What is the formula for the area of this circle?

   ii Rearrange the formula to make r the subject.

b i Write a formula for the length of the shaded piece of wood.

   ii Rearrange the formula to make x the subject.

This unit will show you how to:

- ▶▶ Discuss how data relate to a problem.
- ▶▶ Identify possible sources of data, including primary and secondary sources.
- ▶▶ Find summary values that represent the raw data.
- ▶▶ Select, construct and modify suitable graphical representation.
- ▶▶ Identify key features present in the data.

- ▶▶ Have a basic understanding of correlation. Compare two or more distributions and make inferences.
- ▶▶ Communicate interpretations and results of a statistical enquiry.
- ▶▶ Solve increasingly demanding problems and evaluate solutions.
- ▶▶ Present a concise, reasoned argument, using symbols, diagrams, graphs and related explanatory text.

As you can see, 72% of customers use this train service between 5 and 6 pm.

We'd better provide a few more trains then ...

Displaying data can make it easier to understand.

Before you start

You should know how to ...

1 Draw bar charts and line graphs.

2 Calculate the mean, median, mode and range.

Check in

1 Draw a bar chart to represent this data:

Pet	Frequency
Cat	5
Dog	7
Rabbit	3

2 Find the mean, median, mode and range for this set of data:

3   5   4   8   8   7   1

Planning data collection

This spread will show you how to:
- ▶▶ Discuss how data relate to a problem that can be addressed by statistical methods.
- ▶▶ Identify possible sources of primary and secondary data.
- ▶▶ Plan how to collect the data.

Benford is a company that produce house numbers.
They are having a problem at their warehouse!

Some digits seem to occur more often than others. The company needs to do some research …

First they need to collect some data.

They consider using primary data.

They finally opt for primary data.

They consider using secondary data.

Benford have planned how they are going to collect the data.
They still need to work out how they are going to record it.

- ▶ When you discuss a problem that can be addressed by statistical methods there may be related questions you need to explore.
- ▶ You need to decide what data to collect and identify possible sources.
- ▶ You need to plan how you are going to collect and record the data.

Exercise D2.1

1 A survey of house numbers in five streets produced the following data.

Street	A	B	C	D	E
Even numbers	2 to 34	2 to 60	2 to 38	2 to 52	2 to 44
Odd numbers	1 to 33	1 to 45	1 to 55	1 to 51	1 to 59

Note:
Sometimes streets are curved so that there are more houses on one side than the other.

a Do you think this data is typical?
Give reasons for your answer.

b Using the data for street C complete a tally chart to show the distribution of all the digits that will be needed to number each house.

c Using the data for street C complete a tally chart to show the distribution of the **first** digit needed for each house.

d Compare the two tally charts and comment on your results.

e Do you think that the other streets will show similar results?
Give a reason for your answer.

2 a Choose one of streets A, B, D or E from the table in question 1 and draw two tally charts to show the distribution of: **i** all digits **ii** the first digits of house numbers.

b Compare the two tally charts and comment on your results.

c Compare your observations on house number digits for this street with your observations for street C. What do you notice?

3 A hospital radio station can only broadcast 15 minutes of sport each Saturday.
They can do this either in:
i three 5-minute slots
ii a 10-minute slot and a 5-minute slot, or
iii one 15-minute slot.
The sporting news they transmit is from the game played by the local football team.

a If they want to be on air when a goal is scored, which of the three options should they choose?

b Identify what data you would need to collect and where you might collect this data.

Displaying data

This spread will show you how to:
- ▶▶ Gather data from specified secondary sources.
- ▶▶ Construct pie charts for categorical data.
- ▶▶ Draw stem-and-leaf diagrams.

Frank surveyed the houses in his street and recorded the first digit of each house number.
He collated his results in a table.

First digit	1	2	3	4	5	6	7	8	9
Frequency	12	11	11	9	6	2	1	1	1

Frank constructed a pie chart to represent the data.

1 First find the **frequency total**.
In the table, this is 54.

2 Then find each angle as a **fraction** of **360°**.
So for first digits 1, 2, ...
$\frac{12}{54} \times 360° = 80°$, $\frac{11}{54} \times 360° = ...$

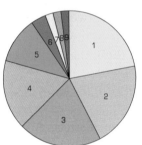

Frank found that he would need more of the lower digits to number each house in his street.

Benford needed to know if Frank's street was typical.
They collected data on the number of houses there were in each of 27 streets.

```
52   62   44   47   59   72   109   64    78
52   84   70   68   66   48    60   52   105
56   80   81   66   58   58    74   50   106
```

They drew a **stem-and-leaf diagram** to represent the data.

To draw a stem-and-leaf diagram:

1 Look at the data and decide what the **stem** should be. Most of the data are tens and units numbers.

2 The units are the leaves added to the stem. Organise the leaves in numerical order.

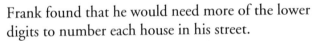

```
10 | 5 6 9
 9 |
 8 | 0 1 4
 7 | 0 2 4 8
 6 | 0 2 4 6 6 8
 5 | 0 2 2 2 6 8 8 9
 4 | 4 7 8
```

Key:
5 | 2 means 52

3 Write a key.

The diagram suggests that most streets have 50 to 70 houses.

▶ A stem-and-leaf diagram shows all the original data and gives you an overall picture of the trend.

Exercise D2.2

1 Here is part of the data from Exercise D2.1 on page 149, relating to house numbers on a street.

Street	Even numbers	Odd numbers
C	2 to 38	1 to 55

Use the data for street C to draw pie charts to show:
a the distribution of all the digits
b the distribution of the first digit of each house number.

2 The doors of the houses in street C are painted in the following colours:

Colour	Blue	Green	Red	White	Yellow
Frequency	12	8	6	18	3

Draw a pie chart to represent these data.

3 Gemma surveyed 27 streets in her area, counting the number of houses in each street. They were

```
47  54  68  39  32  57  54  44  60
56  53  48  62  38  58  38  46  58
36  48  62  54  64  66  42  44  50
```

Draw a stem-and-leaf diagram to represent these data.

4 The data shows the total points scored by the teams in the premier league division for the 2001/2002 season.

```
87  80  77  71  66  64  53  50  50  46  45  45  44  44  43  40  40  36  30  28
```

Draw a stem-and-leaf diagram to represent these data.

5 Draw a back to back stem-and-leaf diagram to show the overall points scored by Division One and Division Two in the Nationwide league for the 2001/2002 season.

Division One
```
99  89  86  77  76  75  75  72  67  66  66  64
60  59  55  54  53  51  50  50  49  49  48  26
```

Division Two
```
90  84  83  83  80  78  73  71  70  64  64  63
59  58  57  56  55  52  50  49  44  44  43  34
```

A **back-to-back** stem-and-leaf diagram looks like this:

```
      Boys         Girls
     9 5 2 | 8 | 0 5 9
   9 9 3 3 1 | 7 | 1 2 4 6 6 7
 9 5 4 4 4 2 | 6 | 2 3 3 8 9
   8 3 2 2 1 | 5 | 0 4 5 5 6
       7 5 0 | 4 | 2 3 7
       8 4 1 | 3 | 0 2
```

You can use it to **compare** two data sets.

This spread will show you how to:
▶▶ Interpret tables, graphs and diagrams.
▶▶ Draw inferences to support or cast doubt on initial conjectures.

KEYWORDS

Interpret	Infer
Mean	Median
Mode	Range
Stem-and-leaf diagram	

Benford want to analyse the results of their house number survey.
They can calculate statistics from their stem-and-leaf diagram.

```
10 | 5 6 9
 9 |
 8 | 0 1 4
 7 | 0 2 4 8
 6 | 0 2 4 6 6 8
 5 | 0 2 2 2 6 8 8 9
 4 | 4 7 8
```

Median: the 27 pieces of data are arranged in order so just count to find the middle (14th) value:
The median is 64 houses.

Mode: Just scan the rows to find the most frequent number:
The mode is 52 houses.

Mean: Add up all the values (1821) and divide by the number of values (27): $1821 \div 27 = 67.4$
The mean is 67.4 houses.

Key:
5 | 2 means 52

Range: Subtract the smallest number (44) from the largest (109):
The range is 65.

Benford need to interpret the statistics that they have calculated.

The mean is 67.4 houses

What's 0.4 of a house – a shed?

The part of the stem with most leaves is 50, and the mode supports this.

5 | 0 2 2 2 6 8 8 9

The mean is not necessarily a data value.

However, the median and mean are both in the sixties, suggesting a slightly higher average value for house numbers.

The shape of the diagram shows that most of the data is in the fifties and sixties. All three averages are within these values.

```
10 5 6 9
 9
 8 0 1 4
 7 0 2 4 8
 6 0 2 4 6 6 8
 5 0 2 2 2 6 8 8 9
 4 4 7 8
```

The range is 65, suggesting that there is a lot of variation in the number of houses in each street.

Three streets contained more than 100 houses.
Benford did not have enough data to decide whether streets with over 100 houses were **extreme** values, or were likely to be **typical**.

Exercise D2.3

1 The masses, in milligrams, of a sample of pebbles are:

169	178	164	182	194	204	186	192	201
182	164	175	179	173	182	172	180	171
168	172	169	185	182	200	166	198	170

  a Draw a stem-and-leaf diagram to represent these data.
  b Find the range, mean, median and mode of these data.
  c Comment on the shape of the diagram and your results in **b**.

2 The winning times, in hours, minutes and seconds, of the New York marathon from 1976 to 1992 for men are given in this set of data.

2 : 10 : 10	2 : 11 : 29	2 : 12 : 12	2 : 11 : 42	2 : 09 : 41
2 : 08 : 13	2 : 09 : 29	2 : 08 : 59	2 : 14 : 53	2 : 11 : 34
2 : 11 : 06	2 : 11 : 01	2 : 08 : 20	2 : 08 : 01	2 : 12 : 39
2 : 09 : 24	2 : 09 : 29			

  a Draw a stem-and-leaf diagram to represent these data.
  b Find the range, mean, median and mode of these data.
  c Comment on the shape of the diagram and your results in **b**.

3 The data shows the total points scored by the football teams in Division 1 and Division 2 at the end of the 1980/1981 season.

Division One

60	56	53	52	51	50	50	48	44	43	42
39	38	37	36	35	35	35	35	33	32	19

Division Two

66	53	50	50	48	45	45	43	43	42	42
40	40	39	39	38	38	38	36	36	30	23

  a Draw a back-to-back stem-and-leaf diagram to represent these data.
  b Find the mean, median and range of these data sets.
  c Comment on the shape of the diagram and your results in **b**.

This spread will show you how to:
▶▶ Construct scatter graphs.
▶▶ Identify scatter graphs.
▶▶ Develop basic understanding of correlation.

KEYWORDS

Scatter   Correlation
  graph   Trend
Variable

The table gives data about the number of vehicles wheel-clamped and towed away by London police.

All figures are given in thousands to the nearest thousand.

Year	1984	1985	1986	1987	1988	1989	1990	1991	1992	1993	1994
Wheel-clamps	44	35	34	114	130	153	163	128	100	55	21
Tows	48	45	47	46	102	117	136	138	123	81	31

Each column in the table shows a
pair of variables, linked by year,
for example (34, 47) in 1986.

1986
34
47

▶ You can show data containing two linked variables on a **scatter graph**.

The graph shows that generally as the
number of wheel-clamps increased, so did
the number of vehicles towed away.
The **trend** is generally increasing. There is a
relationship, or **correlation**, between wheel-
clamps and tows.

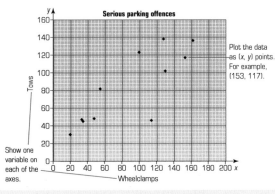

Plot the data
as (x, y) points.
For example,
(153, 117).

Show one
variable on
each of the
axes.

▶ You use a scatter graph to show if there is any **correlation** between two variables.

When the trend is increasing,
there is **positive correlation**
between the variables.

When the trend is decreasing,
there is **negative correlation**
between the variables.

When there is no apparent
trend, there is **no correlation**
between the variables.

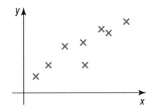

Exercise D2.4

1 The data shows the goals scored for and the goals scored against each team in the premier division in 2001/2002.

For	79	67	87	74	53	66	48	46	49	55	46	35	36	38	45	44	29	41	33	30
Against	36	30	45	52	37	38	57	47	53	51	54	47	44	49	57	62	51	64	63	64

a Draw a scatter graph to display this data.
b Comment on any trend shown by your graph.

2 The results of two tests X and Y, taken by 12 students are given in the table.

Test X	16	12	18	15	6	14	18	4	16	8	13	16
Test Y	14	13	15	15	8	12	19	6	17	5	11	19

a Draw a scatter diagram to show these results.
b What can you say about the performance of the students in each of the tests X and Y?

3 Josh was training hard to improve his 100 m sprint times.
He was timed, to the nearest tenth of a second, each Sunday morning over a period of ten weeks.

Week	1	2	3	4	5	6	7	8	9	10
Time (s)	34.6	33.9	33.0	32.2	31.5	31.8	31.0	30.6	30.2	29.6

a Draw a scatter diagram to show these results.
b Comment on the correlation shown by your graph.
c Use your graph to comment on what Josh's 100 m time might be after 50 weeks training. Is your answer sensible?

4 The table shows how long, in seconds, it took eight people to spell their name backwards.

Name	Hugh	Helen	Harry	Hannah	Hamish	Horatio	Heather	Henrietta
Number of letters in name	4	5	5	6	6	7	7	9
Time in (seconds)	3.3	5.4	4.9	3.6	6.2	7.8	7.6	9.6

a Plot a scatter diagram of these data.
b One of the points plotted does not seem to fit with the rest of the data. Circle this point and suggest a reason why it may not follow the trend.

The table gives data on vehicles wheel-clamped and towed away by London police, as shown on page 154. All figures are given in thousands, to the nearest thousand.

Year	1984	1985	1986	1987	1988	1989	1990	1991	1992	1993	1994
Wheel-clamps	44	35	34	114	130	153	163	128	100	55	21
Tows	48	45	47	46	102	117	136	138	123	81	31

You can use statistics to compare the data.

	Mean	Median	Range
Wheelclamps	88.8	100	142
Tows	83.1	81	107

The two means and medians suggest that there are more vehicles wheel-clamped than towed away.

The two ranges suggest that there is greater variation in numbers of vehicles clamped than towed away.

When people deal with large amounts of data, sometimes data can get lost or distorted.

▶ Minimal changes in data can affect graphs and statistical measures.

If data had been lost for 1987 to 1990, then the calculated statistics would be:

	Mean	Median	Range
Wheelclamps	59.6	44	107
Tows	73.3	48	107

The median number of wheel-clamps is more typical of the data.

The mean is distorted by the large values in 1991 and 1992.

These statistics suggest that on average more vehicles are towed away than clamped, and that there is no difference in variation.

▶ The average you choose for a data set is the one that should best represent all the data.

Statistics summarise the original data, or **raw data**.

When you calculate statistics, you lose some of the information in the raw data.

▶ Statistics can help compare data, but the original values are also important.

Exercise D2.5

1 For each of the following sets of data write down, with reasons:
i which average, mean, median or mode, is the most appropriate to find, and
ii find this average.
  a 14.6   19.3   12.0   15.7   31.7
  b 2003   2005   2008   2011   2006   2003   2008   2003
  c 101   102   102   102   108   108   108   109
  d 49   44   44   47   38   36   44   44   49   44   43

2 **a** Find the mean, median, mode and range of this set of data.
    7   7   24   5   2
  b One number is added to the data set. What could that number be if
    i the mode remains the same
    ii the median remains the same
    iii the mean remains the same
    iv the mean is increased by 2?
  c One number is removed from the data set. What could that number be if
    i the range and median remain unchanged
    ii the mean is increased by 1?

3 **a** Calculate the mean, median, mode and range of each of these two data sets.
    Set A: 0, 99, 99, 100, 100, 100, 100, 100, 101, 101, 200
    Set B: 0, 0, 99, 99, 100, 100, 100, 101, 101, 200, 200
  b Compare your results. What do the statistics suggest about the two data sets?

4 Find two sets of numbers that have the same mean, median, mode and range.
(Do not use the data in question 3.)

5 Find data sets with the following properties
  a Set A: Whatever number you remove, the mode remains the same.
  b Set B: When you remove one number, the mean stays the same.
  c Set C: When you remove one number, the mean is half the original value.
  d Set D: When you remove a number, the mean and range remain the same.

6 The table shows grouped data of heights of a sample of Year 8 pupils.

Height, h cm	$135 \leqslant h < 145$	$145 \leqslant h < 150$	$150 \leqslant h < 155$	$155 \leqslant h < 170$
Frequency	2	4	6	3

Find two different sets of raw data that:
  a could be grouped in this frequency table
  b have the same mean, median and range.

Statistical reports

This spread will show you how to:

▶▶ Communicate interpretations and results of a statistical enquiry.

▶▶ Select tables, graphs and diagrams to support findings.

Sharon conducted a survey into how air traffic had changed from 1984 to 1994.

The table shows the numbers of air terminal passengers in millions.

	Heathrow Airport	Gatwick Airport	Luton Airport	Stanstead Airport	Scheduled flight	Charter flight
1984	29.2	14.0	1.8	0.5	35.0	10.5
1985	31.3	14.9	1.6	0.5	38.0	10.4
1986	31.3	16.3	2.0	0.5	38.5	11.7
1987	34.7	19.4	2.6	0.7	43.8	13.7
1988	37.5	20.7	2.8	1.0	48.1	14.2
1989	39.6	21.2	2.8	1.3	51.9	13.3
1990	42.6	21.0	2.7	1.2	56.4	11.5
1991	40.2	18.7	2.0	1.7	52.2	10.6
1992	45.0	19.8	2.0	2.3	58.0	11.4
1993	47.6	20.1	1.8	2.7	61.0	11.5
1994	51.4	21.0	1.8	3.3	65.5	12.4

Sharon used statistics from the Department of Transport, which is secondary data. You should always state where the data has come from.

Sharon drew a line graph to show changes in passenger numbers at the airports.

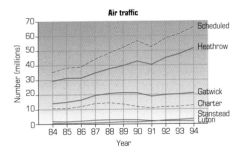

Sharon drew a **multiple bar chart** to show passenger numbers at Luton and Stanstead.

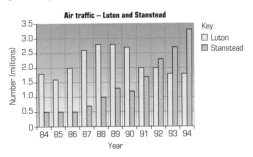

▶ Generally numbers were increasing.
▶ There was a drop in numbers in 1991 (an effect of the Gulf War).
▶ Stanstead had a rapid increase in passenger numbers after 1991 (a new terminal opened).

▶ The bar chart shows clearly how passenger numbers at Stanstead had overtaken passenger numbers at Luton.

In a statistical report you should
▶ **Explain how the data was collected**
▶ **Analyse the data**
▶ **Use graphs to highlight key points**
▶ **Look to see if there are other related questions to explore.**

Exercise D2.6

1 a Use the air traffic data on the opposite page to draw a line graph showing how scheduled flights and charter flights changed over the 11-year period.

b Comment on the changes in scheduled and charter flights from 1984–1994.

2 The numbers of people injured in road traffic accidents in a London borough over a three-year period sorted into male and female drivers are given in the table.

	Pedestrians	Car drivers	Car passengers	Pedal cyclists	Motorcyclists	Bus passengers	Goods vehicles	Other
Male Drivers	400	1200	550	250	550	200	100	100
Female Drivers	200	1000	325	50	50	10	20	20

a Draw a multiple bar graph to analyse these data.

b Write a short report on the differences between the vehicle types that are involved in accidents by men and women.

3 The table shows the number of road casualties in a London borough by month of the year and by age.

Month	Under 15	16–39 years	40–59 years	Over 60
January	35	130	120	50
February	55	180	150	35
March	65	135	135	60
April	45	115	125	45
May	60	150	130	50
June	45	135	115	45
July	60	130	120	40
August	60	140	120	50
September	70	160	140	45
October	60	160	155	60
November	50	180	170	70
December	30	180	130	65

a Draw a diagram to represent these data.

b Why do you think that the number of casualties aged under 15 gets lower through the Autumn while for other age groups it gets higher?

c Write a short report about the monthly variations in the number of road casualties for the different age groups.

Suggest reasons for the monthly variations in the number of road casualties.

You should know how to ...

1 Communicate interpretations and results of a statistical enquiry using selected tables, graphs and diagrams in support.

2 Present a concise, reasoned argument, using symbols, diagrams, graphs and related explanatory text.

Check out

1 The heights of a class of girls are measured to the nearest cm.

160 154 174 151 161 168 166 161 164 166
154 175 160 168 167 165 155 171 167 172
163 169 169 154 153 168 165 168 155

a Draw a stem and leaf diagram to represent these data.

> You may need to expand your stem :
> 17
> 17
> 16 and so on
> and split the units digits 0–4 and 5–9 on the stem.

b Find the mean, median and range of these data.

c Comment on the shape of your diagram and your results in (**b**).

2 The Tables show the number of tests taken by students at two driving schools before they passed.

Number of tests	1	2	3	4	5
Frequency (school x)	28	12	5	3	2

Number of tests	1	2	3	4	5
Frequency (school y)	45	30	21	4	0

Calculate statistics and draw diagrams to comment on the statement:

> Students in school x did better than students in school y.

This unit will show you how to:

▶▶ Use the laws of arithmetic and inverse operations.

▶▶ Understand the order of precedence and the effect of powers.

▶▶ Solve word problems mentally.

▶▶ Make and justify estimates and approximations of calculations.

▶▶ Use efficient methods to add, subtract, multiply and divide fractions.

▶▶ Multiply and divide by decimals, dividing by transforming to division by an integer.

▶▶ Use a calculator efficiently and appropriately to perform complex calculations.

▶▶ Use the function keys for powers and roots, brackets and the memory.

▶▶ Check results using appropriate methods.

▶▶ Use units of measurement to estimate, calculate and solve problems in everyday contexts.

▶▶ Solve increasingly demanding problems and evaluate solutions.

▶▶ Give solutions to problems to an appropriate degree of accuracy.

8.2 m by 7.9 m gives an area of ...647.8 m².

8 × 8 is 64. He should check his decimal point.

Always estimate first when you calculate with decimals.

Before you start

You should know how to ...

1 Add and subtract using negative numbers.

2 Multiply and divide by powers of 10.

3 Use the standard written methods for multiplication and division of integers.

Check in

1 Work out:

a $36.9 + {}^-4.12 - {}^-0.86$

b $100 - {}^-130.2 + 1.56 - {}^+12$

2 Work out:

a 0.3×90 b $14\,000 \div 200$

c $230 \div 20$ d 90×73

3 Estimate and then work out the answer exactly, or to the accuracy indicated.

a 723×42 b 86×136

c $136 \div 13$ (1 d.p.)   d $952 \div 25$ (2 d.p.)

This spread will show you how to:

▶▶ Extend mental methods of addition and subtraction, working with integers, decimals and fractions.

▶▶ Use the laws of arithmetic and inverse operations.

▶▶ Use standard column procedures to add and subtract integers and decimals of any size.

KEYWORDS

Inverse   Decimal

Commutative   Fraction

Integer

The laws governing addition and subtraction are the same for integers, fractions and decimals.

▶ Addition is the **inverse** of subtraction.

$$135 - 58 = 77 \qquad \Rightarrow \qquad 77 + 58 = 135$$
$$135 - {}^-58 = 193 \qquad \Rightarrow \qquad 193 + {}^-58 = 135$$
$$2.84 - 1.9 = 0.94 \qquad \Rightarrow \qquad 0.94 + 1.9 = 2.84$$
$$\tfrac{3}{8} - \tfrac{1}{6} = \tfrac{5}{24} \qquad \Rightarrow \qquad \tfrac{5}{24} + \tfrac{1}{6} = \tfrac{3}{8}$$

Inverse means opposite. This rule means that subtraction is the opposite of addition too.

▶ Addition is **commutative**, but subtraction is not.

Commutative means reversible.

$$362 + 79 = 79 + 362 \qquad \text{but} \qquad 362 - 79 \neq 79 - 362$$
$$362 + {}^-79 = {}^-79 + 362 \qquad \text{but} \qquad 362 - {}^-79 \neq {}^-79 - 362$$
$$5.64 + 1.57 = 1.57 + 5.64 \qquad \text{but} \qquad 5.64 - 1.57 \neq 1.57 - 5.64$$
$$\tfrac{2}{7} + \tfrac{4}{5} = \tfrac{4}{5} + \tfrac{2}{7} \qquad \text{but} \qquad \tfrac{2}{7} - \tfrac{4}{5} \neq \tfrac{4}{5} - \tfrac{2}{7}$$

You can add or subtract a mixture of decimals and fractions by converting them to the same form.

example

Calculate $\tfrac{3}{8} + 1.65$

a by converting to fractions   **b** by converting to decimals.

You should estimate your answer first.

Approximate first: $\tfrac{3}{8} + 1.65 \approx \tfrac{1}{2} + 1.5 = 2$

a Convert to fractions:
$$\tfrac{3}{8} + \tfrac{165}{100} = \tfrac{3}{8} + \tfrac{33}{20}$$
$$= \tfrac{15}{40} + \tfrac{66}{40}$$
$$= \tfrac{81}{40}$$
$$= 2\tfrac{1}{40}$$

b Convert to decimals:
$$\tfrac{3}{8} + 1.65 = 0.375 + 1.65$$
Now use a column method for addition:
$$\begin{array}{r} 0.375 \\ +1.650 \\ \hline 2.025 \end{array}$$

Include this zero to help with the calculation.

Exercise N4.1

1 Work out each of these giving your answer as a decimal.

   a $\frac{2}{5} + 1.69$ **b** $0.8 - \frac{1}{8}$

   c $\frac{4}{5} - 2.6$ **d** $5\frac{1}{2} - 7.03$

   e $1.3 - 4\frac{7}{8}$ **f** $16.2 + \frac{1}{8} + 1\frac{1}{5}$

2 Give each of your answers to question **1a–f** as a fraction in its lowest terms.

3 Look at the shape. Work out
   a an estimate for its perimeter
   b its exact perimeter as a decimal.

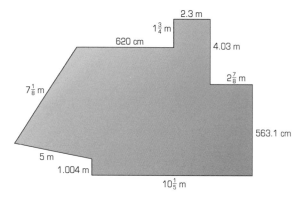

4 Puzzle
In each pyramid the brick that sits directly above two bricks is the sum of these two bricks.
Copy and complete these pyramids.

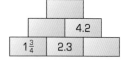

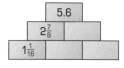

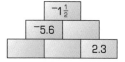

5 The difference between two numbers is 0.12 and the sum of the two numbers is 1.32.
Write the two numbers as decimals and as fractions.

6 Puzzle
Use the numbers in the rectangle to complete the number sentences below.

  a ☐ − ☐ + ☐ = 0.9̇6̇

  b ☐ + ☐ − ☐ = ⁻9.33

  c ☐ − ☐ − ☐ = ⁻0.552

⁻1.3	0.68	0.3
⁻8.4	$\frac{-1}{4}$	$\frac{7}{8}$
$\frac{2}{3}$	⁻0.023	⁻1

7 Puzzle
In these pyramids the brick which sits directly above two bricks is the sum of those two bricks, for example.

```
      20
   11    9
  7   4   5
```

Copy and complete these pyramids.

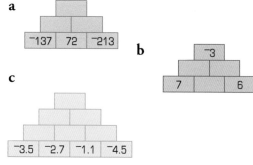

This spread will show you how to:

▶▶ Use efficient methods to multiply and divide fractions, interpreting division as a multiplicative inverse.

▶▶ Use the laws of arithmetic and inverse operations.

▶▶ Extend mental methods of calculation, working with decimals and fractions.

KEYWORDS

Inverse

Commutative

Reciprocal

The laws governing multiplication and division are the same for integers, fractions and decimals.

▶ **Multiplication is the inverse of division.**

This means that division is the inverse of multiplication as well.

$$12 \times 11 = 132 \qquad \Longrightarrow \qquad 132 \div 11 = 12$$
$$12 \times {}^{-}11 = {}^{-}132 \qquad \Longrightarrow \qquad {}^{-}132 \div {}^{-}11 = 12$$
$$12 \times 1.1 = 13.2 \qquad \Longrightarrow \qquad 13.2 \div 1.1 = 12$$
$$12 \times \tfrac{3}{7} = 5\tfrac{1}{7} \qquad \Longrightarrow \qquad 5\tfrac{1}{7} \div \tfrac{3}{7} = 12$$

▶ **Multiplication is commutative, but division is not.**

$$12 \times 11 = 11 \times 12 \qquad \text{but} \qquad 132 \div 11 \neq 11 \div 132$$
$$12 \times {}^{-}11 = {}^{-}11 \times 12 \qquad \text{but} \qquad {}^{-}132 \div {}^{-}11 \neq {}^{-}11 \div {}^{-}132$$
$$12 \times 1.1 = 1.1 \times 12 \qquad \text{but} \qquad 13.2 \div 1.1 \neq 1.1 \div 13.2$$
$$12 \times \tfrac{3}{7} = \tfrac{3}{7} \times 12 \qquad \text{but} \qquad 5\tfrac{1}{7} \div \tfrac{3}{7} \neq \tfrac{3}{7} \div 5\tfrac{1}{7}$$

You can multiply any fraction or decimal by an integer.

example

Calculate:

a $\tfrac{3}{4} \times {}^{-}9$

b 1.3×7

....

a $\tfrac{3}{4} \times {}^{-}9 = \tfrac{3}{4} \times \tfrac{{}^{-}9}{1}$

$\qquad = \dfrac{3 \times {}^{-}9}{4 \times 1}$

$\qquad = \dfrac{{}^{-}27}{4}$

$\qquad = {}^{-}6\tfrac{3}{4}$

b $1.3 \times 7 = 13 \div 10 \times 7$

$\qquad = 13 \times 7 \div 10$

$\qquad = (10 \times 7 + 3 \times 7) \div 10$

$\qquad = (70 + 21) \div 10$

$\qquad = 91 \div 10$

$\qquad = 9.1$

It is sometimes easier to solve a division by turning it into a multiplication.

example

Calculate $0.9 \div 4$.

Remember: 4 is the reciprocal of $\tfrac{1}{4}$.

....

$0.9 \div 4 = 0.9 \times \tfrac{1}{4}$

$\qquad = 0.9 \times 0.25$

$\qquad = 9 \div 10 \times 25 \div 100$

$\qquad = 9 \times 25 \div 1000$

$\qquad = 225 \div 1000$

$\qquad = 0.225$

Exercise N4.2

1 Calculate these:
a $^-16 \times 0.7$
b $^-35 \div 0.5$
c $\frac{5}{8} \times \,^-14$
d $^-6 \div 0.03$
e $\frac{2}{5} \times 18$
f $^-1.5 \div 0.3$
g 25×1.8
h 4.8×0.3

2 Complete these multiplication pyramids. The number in each cell is the product of the two below it:

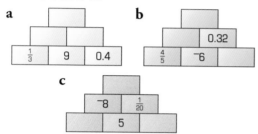

a

b

c

3 a Work out the value of each of the expressions **i** to **iv** if

$a = 2 \quad b = 0.6 \quad c = \,^-0.8 \quad d = \,^-9$

Write your answers as fractions where appropriate.

i $\frac{a}{c}$ **ii** $3b + 2c$ **iii** $3b - 2c$ **iv** d^2

b Convert each of your fractions in part **a** to decimals.

4 The result

$^-0.6 \times 0.37 = \,^-0.222$

allows you to write the solution to

$^-0.222 \div \,^-0.6 = 0.37$

a Write down any **one** other problem and its solution that you can derive from knowing that
$^-0.6 \times 0.37 = \,^-0.222$

b Write two problems and their solutions that you can derive from

$0.003 \div \,^-0.2 = \,^-0.015$

5 Explain in your own words what the term 'commutative' means and write down two examples that show that multiplication is commutative but division is not.

6 **Puzzle**
If $m = 0.5$, $n = \frac{1}{9}$ and $p = \frac{2}{3}$, write expressions using any combination of m, n and p that produce the following answers.
You may only use the letters **once** in any one expression, but you may not have to use them all.

a $^-\frac{1}{18}$
b $1\frac{1}{3}$
c $\frac{2}{27}$
d $^-\frac{2}{9}$

7 **Puzzle**
a Using the digits 1 to 10 once only complete the boxes:

$$\frac{2}{\square} \times \frac{\square}{10} \times \frac{\square}{\square} \times \frac{7}{\square} \times \frac{\square}{\square} = \frac{14}{648} = \frac{?}{?}$$

b Write the final answer as a decimal to 3 decimal places.
c Is there more than one correct solution to this problem? Explain your answer.

8 **Investigation**
Investigate this statement:

> Multiplying makes things bigger and dividing makes things smaller.

a Using only positive numbers, do some calculations to test this statement. You may use a calculator to help you.
b Write a paragraph to explain whether you agree or disagree with this statement.

Order of operations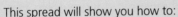

This spread will show you how to:
▶▶ Understand the order of precedence and effect of powers.
▶▶ Use the laws of arithmetic and inverse operations.
▶▶ Make and justify estimates and approximations of calculations.

KEYWORDS
Inverse
Power

When you tackle complex calculations you need to use the correct order of operations.

example

Calculate: $\dfrac{(6.8-2.3)^2-5\times3}{7\times5\div(2.5-0.5)^3+5}$

Estimate first:
$(7-2)^2-15=25-15=10$
$35\div8+5\approx36\div9+5=4+5=9$
$10\div9\approx10\div10=1$

First evaluate the numerator and denominator separately,
using a written method and a calculator where appropriate.

Numerator
▶ **Brackets:** $4.5^2-5\times3$
▶ **Indices:** $20.25-5\times3$
  (use the x^2 key on a calculator)
▶ **Division and Multiplication:**
  $20.25-15$
▶ **Addition and Subtraction:**
  5.25

$\dfrac{(6.8-2.3)^2-5\times3}{7\times5\div(2.5-0.5)^3+5}$

Denominator
▶ **Brackets:** $7\times5\div2^3+5$
▶ **Indices:** $7\times5\div8+5$
▶ **Division and Multiplication:**
  $35\div8+5=4.375+5$
▶ **Addition and Subtraction:**
  9.375

Now divide the numerator by the denominator (using a calculator):

$5.25\div9.375=0.56$

You could perform the calculation in the example all in one go on a calculator.

▶ Calculate the denominator (use the brackets and x^y keys): ⬛ 9.375
▶ Store your answer in the memory (often Min or STO): ⬛ 9.375 Min
▶ Calculate the numerator (use the brackets and x^y keys): ⬛ 5.25
▶ Divide the answer by the recalled memory (often MR or RCL): ⬛ 0.56

Knowing inverse operations can help you to solve problems.

example

If $x^3=140$, find the value of x.

The cube root key
often looks like $\sqrt[3]{}$.

Read the equation: $x^3=140\Longrightarrow$ A number cubed equals 140.

Reverse the operations: The answer is $\sqrt[3]{140}$.

Use a calculator: $\sqrt[3]{140}=5.19$ to 2 decimal places.

Exercise N4.3

1 Work out:

  a $3 \times 4 + 6 \times 2$ **b** $(4 + 2)^2 - 3$

  c $6 \times 2 \div (5 - 3)^2$ **d** $3.5^2 - 4 \div 2$

2 Add one pair of brackets to each of the following to make the equations correct.

  a $6 + 7^2 - 9 - 4 = 50$

  b $7 \times 6 \div {}^-4 - 10 = {}^-3$

  c $8 \times 7 + 8 - 7 = 64$

3 Insert the operations that produce the answer shown in each calculation below.

  a $(8 \ ? \ 7) \ ? \ 6 \ ? \ 5 = 18$

  b $1 \ ? \ 2 \ ? \ 3 \ ? \ 4 = {}^-1$

  c $(10 \ ? \ 9 \ ? \ 8) \ ? \ 7 = {}^-49$

  d $(5 \ ? \ 10 \ ? \ 15) \ ? \ 2 = 310$

4 Work out each of these when $m = 6.5$, giving your answer correct to 2 decimal places.

  a $\dfrac{4m^2 - 6(m - 5.7)}{2m}$

  b $\sqrt{(m^2 - m)} - 3(4 - \sqrt{m})$

  c $\dfrac{({}^-m)^3 - 5(m - 5.4)}{7 - m}$

5 The expression $6(7 - 8) = 6({}^-1) = {}^-6$ can be thought of as

  $6(7 - 8) = 6 \times 7 - 6 \times 8 = {}^-6$

Complete the expressions below:

  a $10(7 - 3) = 10 \times ? - 10 \times ? = 40$

  b $8(? + ?) = 8 \times 7 + ? \times 4 = 88$

  c $7(? - ?) = ? \times 10 - ? \times ? = 28$

  d $6(a + b) = 6a + ?$

  e $5(f + {}^-5) =$

6 a Write this expression in full (as a sentence).

  $\dfrac{(6 + {}^-7)^2 - 6 \times {}^-9}{7^2 - 8}$

  b Estimate the answer to this expression.

  c Work out the exact answer to the expression, giving your answer to 2 d.p.

7 Calculator investigation

The key sequence for calculating $\sqrt[3]{1728}$ is

However, there is another possible key sequence using the y^x key. Can you discover it? Write it out using the notation shown above.

8 Puzzle

All the people who live in Elzzup Avenue love to play mathematical tricks on their postman.

They regularly change house numbers and then give the postman puzzles he must solve to work out their new house numbers.

Help the postman by working these out for him – remember all door numbers are integers:

  a My number lies between 70 and 80, and is made up by using the following

    ${}^-3, 9, {}^-5, (\quad), 2$

  b My number lies between 1 and 10 and uses the number 5 four times, and the operations + and ÷ once each.

> **Hint:** one of the 5s is used as a power.

9 Puzzle

Use the digits 1 to 5, each of the operations ×, ÷, +, − once only, and two pairs of brackets to produce the answer $\frac{1}{15}$.

10 a Explain in words the difference between the expressions:

    $({}^-h)^2$ and ${}^-h^2$

  b Show using values for h that these two expressions produce different results.

  c Are there any values for which $({}^-h)^2$ and ${}^-h^2$ are equal? Explain your answer.

Multiplying decimals

This spread will show you how to:
▶▶ Multiply by decimals.
▶▶ Make and justify estimates and approximations of calculations.
▶▶ Solve word problems mentally.

KEYWORDS
Justify   Approximate
Estimate   Equivalent

When a multiplication is too hard to do in your head you can often use a written method.

example

Calculate 17.3×3.9.

First estimate: $20 \times 4 = 80$
Write an equivalent calculation: $173 \div 10 \times 39 \div 10$
                                                          $= 173 \times 39 \div 100$

You could write it as fractions:
$\frac{173}{10} \times \frac{39}{10} = \frac{173 \times 39}{100}$

Now use the standard method:

$$
\begin{array}{r}
1\,7\,3 \\
\times \quad 3\,9 \\
\hline
5\,1\,9\,0 \\
1\,5\,5\,7 \\
\hline
6\,7\,4\,7 \\
\end{array}
$$

Complete the calculation: $17.3 \times 3.9 = 173 \times 39 \div 100$
                                                  $= 6747 \div 100$
                                                  $= 67.47$

Reasonably close to estimate of 80.

You can multiply fractions by converting them to decimals.

example

Calculate the area of a rectangular hallway that measures $6\frac{3}{4}$ m $\times 1\frac{4}{5}$ m

a by converting to decimals   **b** by calculating as fractions.

a Convert to decimals: $6\frac{3}{4} \times 1\frac{4}{5} = 6.75 \times 1.8$
    Estimate: $7 \times 2 = 14$
    Transform the calculation: $675 \div 100 \times 18 \div 10$
                                              $= 675 \times 18 \div 1000$
    Use the standard method: $675 \times 18 = 12\,150$
    Complete the calculation: $12\,150 \div 1000 = 12.15$
    Convert back to a fraction: $0.15 = \frac{15}{100} = \frac{3}{20}$
                                              $12.15 = 12\frac{3}{20}$
    The answer is close to the
    estimate of 14 m^2.

b Convert to improper
    fractions:
    $6\frac{3}{4} = \frac{27}{4}$ $1\frac{4}{5} = \frac{9}{5}$
    Multiply the fractions:

    $\frac{27}{4} \times \frac{9}{5} = \dfrac{27 \times 9}{4 \times 5}$

    $= \dfrac{27 \times 10 - 27}{20}$

    $= \frac{243}{20}$
    Convert back to a mixed
    number:
    $12 \times 20 = 240 \Longrightarrow \frac{243}{20} = 12\frac{3}{20}$

The hallway has an area of $12\frac{3}{20}$ square metres.

▶ You should leave your answer in the same form as the original question.

Exercise N4.4

1 Use a written method to work out the exact answer to each of the following. You must write an approximate answer before you begin each calculation.

a 13.2×6.3 b 766×0.34

c 3.45×34 d 0.34×561

e 5.21×92 f 72×154

g 452×0.56 h 3.5×6.91

i 30.2×9.2 j 84.6×0.014

k 0.45×0.0341 l 0.87×851

2 Work out the areas of these rectangles.

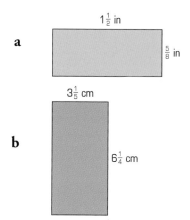

a $1\frac{1}{2}$ in, $\frac{5}{8}$ in

b $3\frac{1}{5}$ cm, $6\frac{1}{4}$ cm

3 Investigation

Two plants, X and Y, are 15 cm tall and 20 cm tall respective. The rate of growth for the two plants is:

Plant X $\frac{1}{20}$ of its height each year
Plant Y $\frac{1}{22}$ of its height each year

How many years will it take until Plant X is taller than Plant Y?

4 Investigation

$(1\frac{1}{2})^2 = 1\frac{1}{2} \times 1\frac{1}{2} = \frac{3}{2} \times \frac{3}{2} = \frac{9}{4} = 2\frac{1}{4}$
$(1\frac{1}{2})^3 = 1\frac{1}{2} \times 1\frac{1}{2} \times 1\frac{1}{2} = \frac{3}{2} \times \frac{3}{2} \times \frac{3}{2} = \frac{27}{8} = 3\frac{3}{8}$

Find the lowest value of n such that $(1\frac{1}{2})^n$ is:

a greater than 10

b greater than 20

c equal to 1.

5 The table shows the salaries of five workers. The figure in brackets shows the fraction by which each employee's wage increases each year.

Complete the table:

Employee	A($\frac{2}{17}$)	B($\frac{2}{15}$)	C($\frac{1}{10}$)	D($\frac{1}{25}$)	E($\frac{2}{47}$)
Current salary	£21 000	£32 000	£12 000	£17 000	£40 000
After 1 year					
After 2 years					

6 **Game** (for two or three players)
Copy this board.

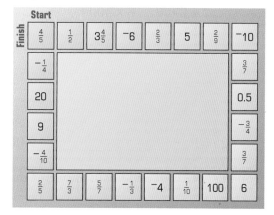

Place counters on the Start square.
Roll a dice to establish a 'start number'.
Each player takes it in turns to roll the dice.
Players move the number of squares rolled and multiply their 'current total' by what it says in the square. For example if Player 1 throws 3 as his start number and his next two throws are 4 and 1 his current total would be $3 \times {}^-6 \times \frac{2}{3} = {}^-12$.

The game ends when one player reaches or passes the Finish square.
The player with the highest total is the winner.

This spread will show you how to:
▶▶ Divide by decimals, transforming to division by an integer.
▶▶ Make and justify estimates and approximations of calculations.
▶▶ Check a result by considering whether it is of the right order of magnitude.

KEYWORDS
Integer
Estimate
Approximation

You can simplify a division involving decimals by transforming the divisor to an integer.

example

Calculate: $256.8 \div 0.06$ using a written method.

a Estimate: $256.8 \div 0.06 \approx 250 \div 0.05$
$= 250 \times 20 = 5000$

Transform the divisor: $256.8 \div 0.06 = 25\,680 \div 6$

$$6\overline{)25680}$$
$\quad\quad 24000 \quad 6 \times 4000$
$\quad\quad\; 1680$
$\quad\quad\; 1200 \quad 6 \times 200$
$\quad\quad\quad 480$
$\quad\quad\quad 480 \quad 6 \times 80$
$\quad\quad\quad\quad\; 0$
$\Rightarrow \quad\quad\quad 6 \times 4280 = 25\,680$
$25\,680 \div 6 = 4280$ and $256.8 \div 0.06 = 4280$

You can check your results by working each problem backwards:
$4280 \times 0.06 = 256.8$

You may need to round your answer if there is a remainder.

example

Calculate $0.054 \div 1.1$, giving your answer to 3 decimal places.

Estimate: $\quad\quad\quad\quad\quad\quad\quad 0.05 \div 1 = 0.05$
Transform the divisor: $\quad\quad 0.054 \div 1.1 = 0.54 \div 11 = 54 \div 100 \div 11$
$\quad\quad\quad\quad\quad\quad\quad\quad\quad\quad = (54 \div 11) \div 100$

$$11\overline{)54}$$
$\quad\; 44 \quad\quad\quad\quad 11 \times 4$
$\quad\; 10$
$\quad\quad 5.5 \quad\quad\quad 11 \times 0.5$
$\quad\quad 4.5$
$\quad\quad 4.4 \quad\quad\quad 11 \times 0.4$
$\quad\quad 0.1$
$\quad\quad 0.0 \quad\quad\quad 11 \times 0$
$\quad\quad\quad\quad 54 \div 11 = 4.90 \text{ (2 d.p.)}$
$\Rightarrow 0.054 \div 1.1 = 4.90 \div 100 = 0.049 \text{ (3 d.p.)}$

Exercise N4.5

1 The numbers in the table follow this rule:

$a \times b = c$

a Copy and complete the table.
b Check your answers by mentally working
out an approximate answer.

a	b	c
2.41	2.3	
6		21.9
	0.045	0.2025
0.004	0.45	
	0.57	1.5732
0.0078		6.552

2 Calculate these quantities, giving your answer to 2 decimal places where appropriate:
a 70.3 m ÷ 3.4 **b** 0.456 mm ÷ 71
c 5.03 cm ÷ 0.42 **d** 0.21 kg ÷ 0.56
e 4536 m ÷ 0.8 **f** 5.003 g ÷ 0.43

3 The table shows how a problem that involves
dividing by a fraction can be written as a
multiplication problem.

Copy and complete the table.

Division problem	Equivalent multiplication problem
$3\frac{1}{2} \div \frac{4}{5}$	$3\frac{1}{2} \times \frac{5}{4}$
$4\frac{1}{8} \div \frac{6}{7}$	
$\frac{5}{8} \div 3\frac{1}{5}$	
$6 \div \frac{-1}{20}$	
$5\frac{7}{10} \div {}^{-}4\frac{3}{19}$	

4 One of the world's highest buildings is in Colorado, USA. It is 1053 ft high. Using
3.25 ft = 1 m work out its height in metres.

5 Work out the missing numbers.
Following the left and right paths should both lead to 0.2.

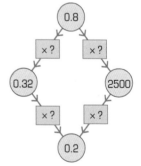

6 The diagram shows a trapezium with parallel sides labelled a and b.
Find the length of side b when:
Area = 56.7 m^2
    $a = 3.4$ m
    $h = 7$ m

Use the formula: Area = $\dfrac{(a + b)h}{2}$ and show all your working out.

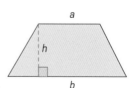

This spread will show you how to:

▶▶ Use units of measurement to calculate, estimate and solve problems in everyday contexts.

▶▶ Enter numbers into a calculator and interpret the display in context.

KEYWORDS
Estimate
Calculate
Metric
Hectare

You need to know these metric relationships:

Length	**Weight**	**Capacity**
1 km = 1000 m	1 tonne = 1000 kg	1 m^3 = 1000 litres
1 m = 100 cm	1 kg = 1000 g	1 litre = 100 cl (or 1000 cm^3)
1 cm = 10 mm	1 g = 1000 mg	1 cl = 10 ml (so $1 \text{ ml} = 1 \text{ cm}^3$)

You also need to know how to convert between units of area or volume.

example

Convert

a 1 m^2 to cm^2

b 5.4 km^3 to m^3.

a $1 \text{ m}^2 = 1 \text{ m} \times 1 \text{ m}$
$= 100 \text{ cm} \times 100 \text{ cm}$
$= 10\ 000 \text{ cm}^2$

b $1 \text{ km}^3 = 1 \text{ km} \times 1 \text{ km} \times 1 \text{ km}$
$= 1000 \text{ m} \times 1000 \text{ m} \times 1000 \text{ m}$
$= 1\ 000\ 000\ 000 \text{ m}^3$
$5.4 \text{ km}^3 = 5\ 400\ 000\ 000 \text{ m}^3$

You can use the relationship between metric units to solve problems.

example

a A rectangular field measures 850 m by 670 m. Calculate its area in hectares.

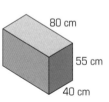
670 m
850 m

a $850 \text{ m} \times 670 \text{ m} = 569\ 500 \text{ m}^2$
1 hectare = $10\ 000 \text{ m}^2$
$\Rightarrow 569\ 500 \text{ m}^2 \div 10\ 000 = 56.95 \text{ ha}$

b A water tank is in the shape of a cuboid and measures 80 cm by 55 cm by 40 cm. Calculate its capacity in litres.

80 cm
55 cm
40 cm

b $80 \text{ cm} \times 55 \text{ cm} \times 40 \text{ cm} = 176\ 000 \text{ cm}^3$
$1 \text{ l} = 1000 \text{ cm}^3$
$\Rightarrow 176\ 000 \text{ cm}^3 \div 1000 = 176 \text{ l}$

Remember:
1 hectare = $10\ 000 \text{ m}^2$

Exercise N4.6

1 Convert each of these measurements into the units given in brackets.

    a 450 cm (m)   **b** 63 234 g (kg)   **c** 0.03 m (mm)

    d 1 000 000 cl (litres) **e** 6.89 tonnes (kg) **f** 0.276 m (cm)

2 Calculate the volume of this cuboid

    a in cubic metres   **b** in cubic centimetres.

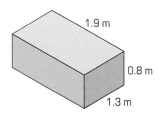

1.9 m

0.8 m

1.3 m

3 The table shows some 'rough' metric and imperial unit relationships:

Metric unit	2.5 cm	1 kg	1 km	4.5 litre	1 m
Imperial unit	1 inch	2.2 lb	$\frac{5}{8}$ mile	1 gallon	39 inches

Use the information in the table to convert each of these units to the units shown in brackets.

    a 500 cm (inches) **b** 30.8 lb (kg)   **c** 189 litres (gallons)

    d 43 km (miles)   **e** 4758 inches (metres) **f** 10 miles (m)

4 Wendy estimated the lengths of six pieces of string.
The table shows the actual and estimated lengths.
The accuracy ratio for the first piece of string is calculated for you.

    a Copy and complete the table.

Actual length	Estimate	Accuracy ratio (2 d.p.)
4.3 cm	4.0 cm	$\frac{4.3}{4.0} = 1.08$
6.9 cm	6.5 cm	
19 cm	17.7 cm	
10 cm	11.9 cm	
12 cm	13.2 cm	
5.4 cm	6.1 cm	

    b Which estimate was most accurate and why?

You should know how to ...

1 Make and justify estimates and approximations of calculations.

2 Use efficient methods to add, subtract, multiply and divide fractions.

3 Give solutions to problems to an appropriate degree of accuracy.

Check out

1 Working in pairs, discuss what would be the best numbers to use to estimate the answers to each of the following calculations.
  a The area of a floor 3.14 m by 2.6 m
  b 23% of a football crowd of 27 326
  c The area of a trapezium with vertical height 2.6 m and parallel sides 4.9 m and 8.71 m.

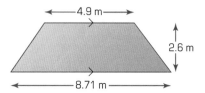

2 Work out
  a $\frac{3}{4} \times {}^-7$
  b $\frac{2}{3} \div \frac{1}{4}$
  c $2\frac{1}{4} + 3\frac{1}{8} - \frac{1}{3}$
  d $-5\frac{1}{2} \times 6$
  e $1\frac{3}{8} \div 2\frac{1}{2}$
  f $3\frac{1}{9} \times \frac{2}{3} \div 1\frac{1}{5}$

3 Work out the distance travelled by a security guard who walks seven times around the perimeter of the building shown.

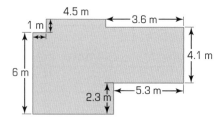

5 Equations and graphs

This unit will show you how to:

- ▶▶ Write an expression to describe the *n*th term of an arithmetic sequence.
- ▶▶ Simplify or transform algebraic expressions by taking out single-term common factors.
- ▶▶ Use systematic trial and improvement methods to find approximate solutions to equations.
- ▶▶ Solve problems involving direct proportion.
- ▶▶ Plot graphs of linear functions.

- ▶▶ Find the gradient of lines given by equations of the form $y = mx + c$.
- ▶▶ Construct functions arising from real-life problems and plot their graphs.
- ▶▶ Interpret graphs arising from real situations.
- ▶▶ Solve increasingly demanding problems and evaluate solutions.
- ▶▶ Give solutions to problems to an appropriate degree of accuracy.

How many pounds shold we change into euros?

Looking at that graph, for £50 we'll get 74 euros.

You can use a graph to convert between quantities, such as currency.

Before you start

You should know how to ...

1 Find the general term of a linear sequence.

2 Expand a single bracket.

Check in

1 For each sequence, complete the next two terms and find a formula for the *n*th term.
   a 5, 8, 11, 14, 17, _, _, ...
   b 3, 7, 11, 15, 19, _, _, ...
   c 3, 13, 23, 33, _, _, ...
   d 20, 18, 16, 14, 12, _, _, ...

2 In each case, expand the brackets. Simplify your answer where possible.
   a $3(x + 4)$ b $5(x + 6) + 3(x - 2)$
   c $x(x - 6)$ d $x(x + 7) + 2x(x - y)$

Investigating a task

This spread will show you how to:
▶▶ Solve substantial problems by breaking them into simpler tasks.
▶▶ Represent problems in algebraic form.
▶▶ Suggest extensions to problems, conjecture and generalise.

KEYWORDS
Evidence   Formula
Generalise   Predict

Here is a pattern of L-shapes. Write a formula for the perimeter of the *n*th shape.

▶ Gather **evidence** by breaking the task into small steps.

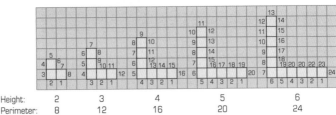

Collect enough evidence to find a **pattern**.

| Height: | 2 | 3 | 4 | 5 | 6 |
| Perimeter: | 8 | 12 | 16 | 20 | 24 |

▶ Organise your results in a table and **describe** what you see.

Height	2	3	4	5	6
Perimeter	8	12	16	20	24

I notice that the perimeter is 4 extra every time the height increases by 1. I notice the perimeter is 4 times the height.

▶ Generalise your results.

Perimeter = 4 × height

If possible, create a **formula** to work for any size.

$P = 4h$ where P = perimeter, h = height

You can use your formula to **predict** the result for a larger pattern number.

When the height is 7, I predict that the perimeter will be 28.

My prediction is correct.

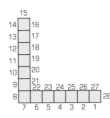

▶ Try to **explain** your results.

Hint: When you **describe** something you say what you see. When you **explain** something you say why it is.

Why does the perimeter go up in 4s?
As the height increases, you add two squares. Each of these adds 3 more to the perimeter but you lose two ends as they get a square stuck on.

Exercise A5.1

Investigate these tasks using the step-by-step approach suggested.
Try to generalise and explain your results.

1 In a square grid of varying sizes, the key counter ● must move from the top left square to the empty space in the bottom right.
All counters can be moved horizontally or vertically only, and only into an empty space.
Investigate the minimum total number of counter moves to do this.

 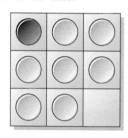

2 Investigate the total number of diagonals that can be drawn from one vertex of a polygon.

3 **a** Investigate the total number of diagonals that can be drawn in a polygon.

   b Use your answer to give the number of diagonals in a 'Mystic Rose'.
   This is a 36-sided polygon with all diagonals drawn in. (You might like to construct one yourself.)

4 Investigate the number of leads needed to connect different numbers of computers, if all computers must be attached to each other.

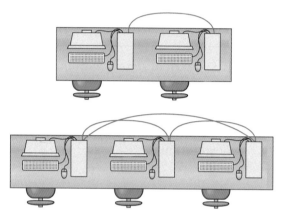

5 **a** Investigate the number of different arrangements of a family lining up for a photograph.

   b Can you find a button on your calculator that generates these results? If so, how many different arrangements of a family of 20 would there be?

6 **a** Investigate the number of different ways you can pay for a phone call in a phone box if the call costs a multiple of 10 pence and you have 10 pence coins and 20 pence coins available.

   b What would happen if the slot also took 5 pence coins?

Generalising and justifying findings

This spread will show you how to:

▶▶ Solve substantial problems by breaking them into simpler tasks.

▶▶ Present a concise, reasoned argument.

▶▶ Suggest extensions to problems, conjecture and generalise.

KEYWORDS

Explain   Conclusion

Justify   Generate

If you look at how a pattern builds systematically, it can often help you to construct and justify your formula.

Here is a pattern of straws, with increasing heights.

a Draw the fourth and fifth patterns, and hence draw a table of results.

b By considering how the diagrams are built, find a general formula.

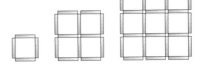

a

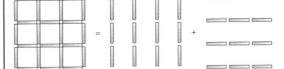

Height, h	1	2	3	4	5
Number of straws, s	4	12	24	40	60

b Look at the diagram with $h = 3$:

In the third diagram:
$$s = (4 \times 3) + (4 \times 3)$$

In general:
$$s = (h + 1) \times h + (h + 1) \times h$$
$$\Rightarrow \quad s = 2h(h + 1)$$

Check with $h = 5$:

$$s = 2 \times 5 \times 6 = 60$$

Note: You could alternatively use the method of **differences** to find a formula.

However, the formula you get ($s = 2h^2 + 2h$) would be difficult to justify.

You can always **extend** an investigation.

Sanjiv has been investigating the number of corner, middle and edge pieces in a square jigsaw.

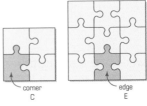

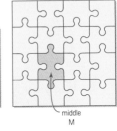

corner
C

edge
E

middle
M

Sanjiv could extend the problem by ...

▶ moving on to rectangular puzzles

▶ moving on to 3-D puzzles.

Exercise A5.2

Investigate each problem in this exercise.
Focus on generalising your results and justifying your findings by thinking about the structure of the problem.

1 T-shapes

Investigate the relationship between:
▶ height and perimeter
▶ height and number of squares.

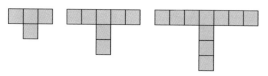

2 Crossings

Investigate the largest number of crossings that occur when different numbers of straight sticks are placed on a surface.

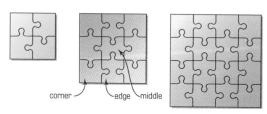

3 Jigsaws

corner   edge middle

▶ Investigate how the number of corner, edge and middle pieces in a square jigsaw is related to its size.
▶ **Prove** that your three results add together give the total number of jigsaw pieces.
▶ Extend to rectangular puzzles.

4 Staircases

▶ Investigate the number of blocks in up-down staircases of differing heights:

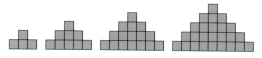

▶ Extend to symmetrical stairways:

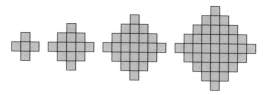

▶ Extend the problem in a way of your choice ...
Three dimensional staircases is a possibility!

5 Painted cubes

 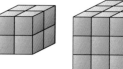

The large cube has its outside painted silver.

▶ Cubes are made up of small $1 \times 1 \times 1$ cubes. If the large cube is now broken down, investigate the number of small cubes with:
▶ 0 faces painted
▶ 1 face painted
▶ 2 faces painted ...
▶ **Prove** that all of your formulae add to give the total number of cubes.
▶ Extend your problem to cuboids.

This spread will show you how to:

▶▶ Simplify or transform algebraic expressions by taking out single-term common factors.

▶▶ Derive a formula.

KEYWORDS

Factorise	Identity
Equation	HCF

Factorising is the opposite of expanding brackets.

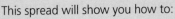

factorising

$4x + 10y \quad 2(2x + 5y)$

expanding

Factorising is introduced on page 66.

You factorise an expression by:

▶ finding the highest common factor of the terms in the expression

▶ rewriting the expression with the HCF outside a bracket.

$2a^2 + 3a$ has HCF a

$2a^2 + 3a = a(2a + 3)$

example

Factorise:

a $5a + 20b$

b $x^2 + 2xy + xy$

c $15ab + 20a^2 + 5a$

a Common factor is 5
$5a + 20b = 5(a + 4b)$

b Common factor is x
$x^2 + 2xy + xy$
$= x(x + 2y + y)$

c Common factor is $5a$
$15ab + 20a^2 + 5a$
$= 5a(3b + 4a + 1)$

When you factorise an expression it remains mathematically **identical** to the original expression.

An **equation** is only true for particular values of x.
$5x + 10 = 25 \Rightarrow x = 3$

An **identity** is true for all values of x.
$5x + 10 \equiv 5(x + 2) \Rightarrow x = 1, 2, 3, 4, ...$

= means 'is equal to'
≡ means 'is identical to'

Factorising can help you to explain a formula.
Here is a sequence of coloured squares:

You can construct a table of values.

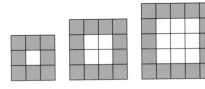

Length, l	3	4	5	6
Number of coloured squares, S	8	12	16	20

From the sequence 8, 12, 16, 20, ... you can find the formula $S = 4l - 4$

Factorise: $\quad 4l - 4 = 4(l - 1)$
$\Rightarrow \quad S = 4(l - 1)$

Now you can explain either formula:

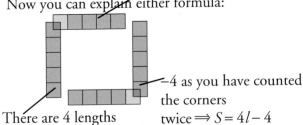

There are 4 lengths

−4 as you have counted the corners twice $\Rightarrow S = 4l - 4$

4 strips, each 1 less than the length $\Rightarrow S = 4(l - 1)$

Exercise A5.3

1 Factorise by removing all common factors. Check your solutions by expanding.

  a $10a + 50b$ **b** $12xy + 24x$ **c** $9c - 3d$ **d** $7w + 14w^2 - 21$

  e $xy + yz$ **f** $3cd - 12c$ **g** $4a + 16a^2$ **h** $11pq + 33q^2 - 22q^3$

  i $5x^6 + 20x^7$ **j** $38m^2 - 190mn$ **k** $4\pi r + 8\pi r^2 + 2\pi$

2 Copy and complete these identities.

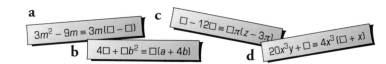

a $3m^2 - 9m \equiv 3m(\Box - \Box)$

b $4\Box + \Box b^2 \equiv \Box(a + 4b)$

c $\Box - 12\Box \equiv \Box\pi(z - 3\pi)$

d $20x^3y + \Box \equiv 4x^3(\Box + x)$

3 The surface area of a cylinder is the total of the areas of all of its faces. The formula is $S = 2\pi r^2 + 2\pi rh$.

  a Explain why the formula has a $2\pi r^2$ in. Repeat for $2\pi rh$.
    (Hint: think about cutting open and laying flat the inner tube from a toilet roll!)

  b Factorise this formula.

4 Obtain your own, **factorised** formula for the required measurement in each case.

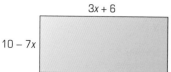

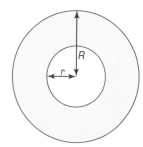

  a The perimeter of this rectangle.

  b The perimeter of this semicircle.

  c The area of this ring.

5 In each case, devise a formula and a factorised formula to connect the given variables. Justify each formula you write.

a

Number of squares and height of rectangle (n).

b

Number of black squares and number of white squares.

c

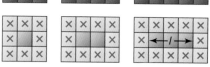

Length (l) of inner rectangle and number of crosses.

d

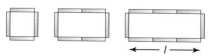

Length of rectangle (l) and number of straws.

Trial and improvement

This spread will show you how to:
▶▶ Use systematic trial and improvement methods to find approximate
    solutions to equations.

KEYWORDS
Trial and improvement
Inequality

Some equations are best solved using a **trial and improvement** method.

example

Solve $x^3 + x = 222$ by trial and improvement.

Try $x = 4$: $\quad 4^3 + 4 = 64 + 4 = 68 \quad\Rightarrow$ too small
Try $x = 5$: $\quad 5^3 + 5 = 125 + 5 = 130 \Rightarrow$ too small
Try $x = 6$: $\quad 6^3 + 6 = 216 + 6 = 222 \Rightarrow$ just right   The solution is $x = 6$.

You should keep your trials **systematic**, particularly where decimals are involved.

example

Solve $x^2 - x = 3.0624$

It can help to draw a table.

x	x^2	$x^2 - x$	
2	4	$4 - 2 = 2$	too small
3	9	$9 - 3 = 6$	too big
		$2 < x < 3$	
2.2	4.84	2.64	too small
2.3	5.29	2.99	too small
2.4	5.76	3.66	too big
		$2.3 < x < 2.4$	
2.32	5.3824	3.0624	just right

x lies between 2 and 3

x lies between 2.3 and 2.4

The solution is $x = 2.32$.

Often you only need to give an approximate solution.

example

The diagram shows a cuboid with a square cross-section.
Its length is 1 cm more than its width, x.
The volume of the cuboid is 200 cm³. Find x to 1 d.p.

Width $= x$
Length $= x + 1$
Height $= x$
Volume $=$ length $\times$ width $\times$ height
$\quad = (x + 1) \times x \times x$
$\Rightarrow x^2(x + 1) = 200$
The solution is between 5 and 5.5.
$\Rightarrow x = 5.5$ to 1 d.p.

x	x^2	$x + 1$	$x^2(x + 1)$	
5	25	6	150	too small
6	36	7	252	too big
		$5 < x < 6$		
5.5	30.25	6.5	196.625	too small
5.6	31.36	6.6	206.976	too big
		$5.5 < x < 5.6$		
5.55	30.8025	6.55	201.756	too big
		$5.5 < x < 5.55$		

Exercise A5.4

1 Solve these equations to 1 d.p. using trial and improvement.
   a $x^2 + x = 132$ **b** $x^3 + 2x = 186.816$
   c $2x^2 + 7 = 20.52$ **d** $2^x = 4096$
   e $\sqrt{x} = 2.5$

2 Write an equation to solve each problem. Using trial and improvement, find the required quantity.

   a Area = 38.44 cm². What is the length?

   b Area = 63.75 m². Length is 1 m more than width. What is the length?

   c Volume = 769.488 m³. Length is 1 m more than the width. The width is 1 m more than the height. What is the height?

   d Volume = 178.9555 mm³. What is the base length?

3 These equations have inexact solutions. Find each solution to the required number of decimal places, using trial and improvement.
   a $m(m + 1) = 100$ (1 d.p.)
   b $p(p - 4) = 63$ (2 d.p.)
   c $y^3 - 2y = 70$ (1 d.p.)
   d $x^5 = 5000$ (2 d.p.)
   e $\frac{56}{q} + q = 19$
   (2 solutions ... both to 1 d.p.).

4 The shaded area is 17 mm². Construct an equation and use trial and improvement to find the exact length of the large square.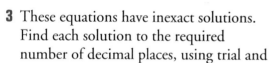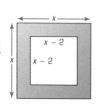

5 Solve the equation $4^x = 50$, giving your answer correct to 2 d.p.

6 The cube of a number is 200 more than the number itself.
   a Show that this statement can be written as $x(x^2 - 1) = 200$.
   b Find x correct to 1 d.p.

7 $\square^3 = 30 \times \square^2$ ... use trial and improvement to find the number whose cube is thirty times as much as its square.

8 This cuboid has a volume of 150 cm³. It has a square cross-section and its length is 2 cm more than its width.
   a Show that $x^3 - 2x^2 = 150$.
   b Find x to 1 d.p.

9 The surface area of a cylinder is given by the formula $A = 2\pi r(r + h)$.  Find the radius of a 10 cm high cylinder with surface area 550 cm², to 1 d.p.

10 a Solve $x^x = 200$ to 1 d.p.
   b Solve $\sqrt[x]{64\text{ million}} = 20$ exactly.

11 The graph shown is $y = x^2 + x$. Use trial and improvement to complete the coordinates of P = $(\square, 93.84)$.

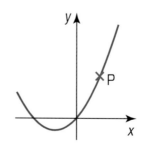

183

Graphs of proportions

This spread will show you how to:

▶▶ Solve problems involving direct proportion using graphical representation.

▶▶ Construct functions arising from real-life problems.

▶▶ Interpret graphs arising from real situations.

KEYWORDS

Proportion   Equation
Gradient   Conversion

A recipe for two people requires four eggs.

If there are ...   three people, you will need ...   six eggs
                        four people   eight eggs
                        five people   ten eggs

The number of eggs is **directly proportional** to the number of people.
You can plot the information on a graph.

The gradient is $\frac{2}{1} = 2$

The *y*-intercept is 0.

The equation of a straight line is $y = mx + c$
$m = 2$ and $c = 0$
$\Rightarrow$ The equation is $y = 2x$

▶ Two quantities that are in direct proportion will produce a linear graph that goes through the origin.

example

The table shows the conversion between UK pounds sterling and US dollars.

Pounds £	3	6	9	12
Dollars $	5	10	15	20

Use a graphical method to estimate how many dollars you would get for £7.

Draw axes and plot the points (3, 5), (6, 10), (9, 15) and (12, 20).
Draw a straight line between them.

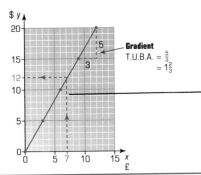

Gradient
T.U.B.A. = $\frac{5}{3}$
= $1\frac{2}{3}$

Alternatively you could:
▶ Work out the equation of the graph
▶ Substitute $x = 7$

Read off the value for £7:
7 along the *x*-axis is roughly equivalent to 11.7 on the *y*-axis.

£7 is roughly equivalent to $11.70.

Exercise A5.5

1 Construct a graph to represent each of these direct proportion relationships. Find the equation of your graph.

a
> 1 minute mobile phone call costs 8 pence

x = number of minutes, y = cost in pence

b
> 8 km is equal to 5 miles

x = number of km, y = number of miles

c
> I can walk 1 mile in 20 minutes

y = number of miles, x = number of hours

2 Link each graph equation with a proportion statement.

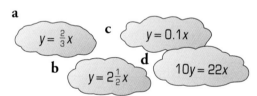

a $y = \frac{2}{3}x$

c $y = 0.1x$

b $y = 2\frac{1}{2}x$

d $10y = 22x$

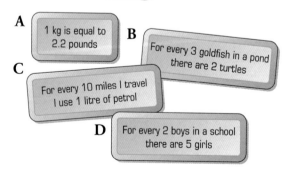

A 1 kg is equal to 2.2 pounds

B For every 3 goldfish in a pond there are 2 turtles

C For every 10 miles I travel I use 1 litre of petrol

D For every 2 boys in a school there are 5 girls

3 a A proportion graph has equation $y = \frac{3}{5}x$. Write a statement that could be modelled using this graph.
b Repeat for $y = 3\frac{1}{3}x$.

4 This graph allows you to convert your weight in stones into your weight in kg.

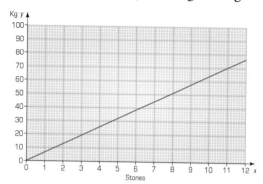

a Use the graph to find the weight, in kg, of an 11-stone female.
b Find the gradient of the line and, hence, its equation.
c Use your equation to find the weight, in kg, of a 15-stone male.
d Use your equation to find the weight, in stone, of a 200-kg elephant.
e Show, using the graph and your equation, that 6 stones is less than 40 kg.
f Which is heavier, 13 stones or 80 kg?

5 Two quantities are in inverse proportion if, as one increases by a certain amount, the other decreases by a certain amount. For example the number of men needed to dig a hole is inversely proportional to the number of days taken to dig the hole.
a Copy and complete this table:

Number of men, x	1	2	3	4	5
Number of days to dig, y		6			

b Suggest an equation to connect x and y.
c Plot a graph of this equation.

Proportion and algebra

This spread will show you how to:

▶▶ Solve problems involving direct proportion using algebraic methods.

KEYWORDS

Proportion   Ratio
Reciprocal   Similar

▶ Two quantities are in direct proportion if they both increase or decrease at the same rate.

The symbol ∝ means 'is proportional to':
Number of bars of chocolate ∝ amount of money spent

Fewer bars of chocolate – less to pay   More bars of chocolate – more to pay

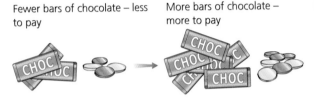

▶ Quantities are directly proportional if the corresponding ratios stay the same.

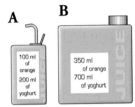

A: Orange/yoghurt = $\frac{100}{200} = \frac{1}{2}$
B: Orange/yoghurt = $\frac{350}{700} = \frac{1}{2}$
Ratios are equal, so:
orange ∝ yoghurt

A: Pay/hours = $\frac{£16.20}{3}$ = £5.40
B: Pay/hours = $\frac{£27}{5}$ = £5.40
Ratios are equal, so:
pay ∝ hours worked

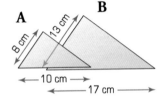

A: Base/slant = $\frac{10}{8} = 1\frac{1}{4}$
B: Base/slant = $\frac{17}{13} = 1\frac{4}{13}$
Ratios are not equal, so
the triangles are not in proportion

You can use corresponding ratios to set up an equation.

example

a A recipe for five people requires 11 eggs.

How many eggs are needed for 15 people?

b £6 is roughly equivalent to $10 in US currency.
How many dollars could you get for £17?

....

a Number of people ∝ number of eggs
So $\frac{11}{5} = \frac{x}{15}$
$\frac{11 \times 15}{5} = x$
$33 = x$
So 33 eggs are needed!

b Number of pounds ∝ number of dollars
$\frac{10}{6} = \frac{y}{17}$
$10 \times \frac{17}{6} = y$
$28.33 = y$
So £17 is worth $28.33.

These rearrangements are useful to remember:

reciprocal   **cross-multiply**

$$\frac{10}{2} = \frac{15}{3}$$

$$\frac{2}{10} = \frac{3}{15}$$

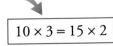

$$10 \times 3 = 15 \times 2$$

Exercise A5.6

1 Decide if these quantities are in direct proportion.
  a The speed you travel and the distance you cover.
  b The number of people in a room and the amount of space each person has.
  c The amount you talk on your mobile and the price of your calls.
  d The amount of cereal you eat and the amount of protein you receive.
  e The number of people digging and the time taken to dig a 2m³ trench.
  f Your age and the number of presents you receive on your birthday.

2 The stated quantities are in direct proportion. Set up an algebra equation and solve it to find the missing value in each case.
  a

  Amount of nuts and weight of bar.
  b

  Green paint is made by mixing 11 parts of blue with 4 parts of yellow paint.
  How many litres of blue paint should be mixed with 900 litres of yellow?
  c

  5 | 8 | ? | 28.8

  Length and width.

  d How much flour is needed to serve 5 people?

  Recipe
  SERVES 6
  340 g flour

3 Ben has a small tube of tasty 'Dummies' sweets. Matt has a large one. They both love blue sweets so they counted how many they had:

	Total	Blue
Ben	37	7
Matt	108	23

  a Is the number of blue sweets in proportion to the total number of sweets?
  b Using an equation to help you, decide how many blue sweets Ben should have so that there is direct proportion between the number of blues and the total number.

4 Ayeesha performed a scientific experiment. She measured the height of a plant in the first few days of its life:

Age (days)	1	2	3	4	5	6	7
Height (cm)	2.8	5.6	8.4				

  a Is age in direct proportion to height?
  b Copy and complete the table.
  c Write a formula connecting age and height.
  d How tall should the plant be at the end of a fortnight?
  e After 3 weeks, Ayeesha found the plant to be 50 cm high. Do age and height remain in proportion after this time? Explain your answer.

A5.7 Real-life graphs

This spread will show you how to:

▶▶ Find the gradient of lines given by equations of the form $y = mx + c$.

▶▶ Construct functions arising from real-life problems and plot their graphs.

▶▶ Interpret graphs arising from real situations.

KEYWORDS

Gradient

Intercept

Linear

You can use a linear graph to describe many real-life situations.

The gradient and y-intercept can often give you further information.

The graph shows a mobile phone company's monthly billing system.

Its equation is $y = \frac{15}{2}x + 10$ where $y = $ cost (£), and $x = $ time on phone (hours)

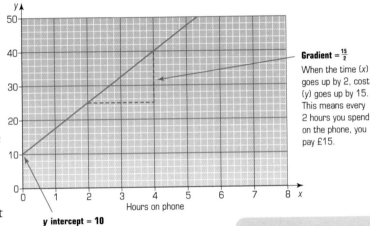

Gradient $= \frac{15}{2}$

When the time (x) goes up by 2, cost (y) goes up by 15. This means every 2 hours you spend on the phone, you pay £15.

y intercept = 10

When the time (x) is zero, the cost (y) is £10. This is the amount you have to pay even before you use the phone.

Scatter graphs are explained on page 154.

Often with real data, the x and y values do not form an exact straight line. This **scatter graph** shows the ages and heights of nine children.

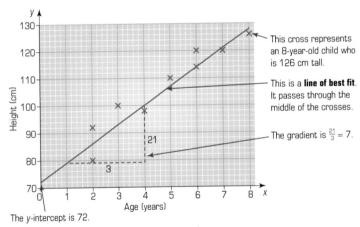

This cross represents an 8-year-old child who is 126 cm tall.

This is a **line of best fit**. It passes through the middle of the crosses.

The gradient is $\frac{21}{3} = 7$.

The y-intercept is 72.

$m = 7$, $c = 72 \Rightarrow$ the equation of the line of best fit is $y = 7x + 72$

You can **interpret** m and c:

$m = 7 \Rightarrow$ every time you grow one year older, you grow by 7 cm.

$c = 72 \Rightarrow$ if you are 0 years old, your height is 72 cm.

This analysis is not totally accurate, because children do not grow at a steady rate. 55 cm is a better estimate for the length of a newborn baby.

Exercise A5.7

1 Match these statements with the line graph equations that would represent them.

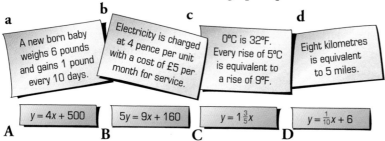

a A new born baby weighs 6 pounds and gains 1 pound every 10 days.

b Electricity is charged at 4 pence per unit with a cost of £5 per month for service.

c 0°C is 32°F. Every rise of 5°C is equivalent to a rise of 9°F.

d Eight kilometres is equivalent to 5 miles.

A $y = 4x + 500$

B $5y = 9x + 160$

C $y = 1\frac{3}{5}x$

D $y = \frac{1}{10}x + 6$

2 For each graph, find its equation and explain what the equation tells you.

a

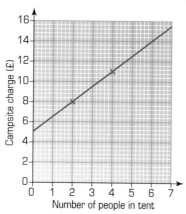

Campsite charge (£) vs Number of people in tent

b

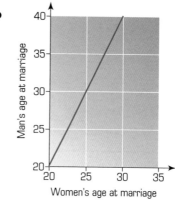

Man's age at marriage vs Women's age at marriage

3 a Draw scatter graphs for each set of data and find the equation of the line of best fit.

i

Maths	14	37	35	23	24	29	46	21	44	48
Physics	7	29	34	17	27	28	37	9	40	39

... 10 students in a maths test and physics test.

ii

Temperature °C of day	24	32	20	27	25	29	19	23	28	28
Number of ice-creams sold in one hour	8	20	2	15	11	19	1	5	15	18

... ice-creams sold on 10 days in summer.

b In each case, explain what the line shows you.
Discuss possible limitations of each line.

4 Mr Edwards came up with this equation to represent a person's weight in stones(x) and their pulse rate each minute(y).

$y = 8x + 20$

Interpret the equation and discuss its limitations.

Further line graphs

This spread will show you how to:

▶▶ Plot the graphs of linear functions given by implicit equations.

If y is not the subject of an equation, the equation is in **implicit form**.

$3x + 2y = 7$ and $5y - 6 = 3x$ are in implicit form.

You can plot the graph of an implicit equation either by:

▶ Rearranging to make y the subject:
$2x + 5y = 30 \Rightarrow y = \frac{-2}{5}x + 6$
▶ Substituting simple values into the implicit form:
$2x + 5y = 30$
If $x = 0$, then $y = 6$.
If $y = 0$, then $x = 15$.

Implicit equations can help you to solve problems.

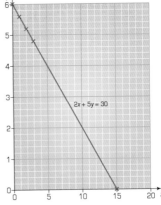

example

Two times one number plus three times another number equals 12.
The sum of the same two numbers is 5.
By forming two equations and plotting a graph, find the two numbers.

Two times one number plus
three times another number equals 12 $\Rightarrow 2x + 3y = 12$

x	0	6
y	4	0

The sum of the same two numbers is 5 $\Rightarrow x + y = 5$

x	0	5
y	5	0

Plot the graphs of both equations on the same axes:

The two numbers are 2 and 3.

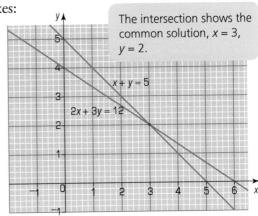

The intersection shows the common solution, $x = 3$, $y = 2$.

▶ Two equations that hold true at the same time are called simultaneous equations.

Exercise A5.8

1 Copy and complete the table of values for each equation. Hence, on a single set of axes labelled $^-8$ to $^+8$, plot all of the graphs.

a $x + y = 6$

x	0	☐
y	☐	0

b $3x + 4y = 12$

x	0	☐
y	☐	0

c $2x + 5y = 15$

x	0	☐
y	☐	0

2 Match the explicit equations in Sheet A with the implicit equations in Sheet B.

$y = -\frac{3}{8}x + 3$

$y = \frac{1}{3}x + 6$

$y = 2\frac{1}{2} - 4x$

$y = 7 - 2x$

Sheet A

$2x + y = 7$

$3x + 8y = 24$

$8x + 2y = 5$

$3y - x = 18$

Sheet B

3 a Write an explicit equation that would pair with $5y + 2x = 10$.

b Write an implicit equation that would pair with $y = \frac{2}{3}x + 7$.

4 a Plot the graphs of $x + 2y = 8$ and $y = x - 2$ on a single pair of axes.

b Use your graphs to solve these equations simultaneously.

$$\left.\begin{array}{l} x + 2y = 8 \\ y = x - 2 \end{array}\right\}$$

5 Repeat question 4 for these pairs of equations.

a $x + y = 9$
$y = 2x - 3$

b $x + y = 9$
$5y - 4x = 18$

c $3x + 4y = 24$
$3x + 2y = 18$

6 Why would these pairs of simultaneous equations have no solutions? (Hint: think about their graphs, drawing them if necessary.)

a $y = 3x - 3$
$y = 3x + 3$

b $9x + 3y = 12$
$y = 4 - 3x$

c $x + 3y = 11$
$x + 3y = 20$.

7 In each problem, **i** write a pair of equations to represent the information **ii** plot the equations on a graph and **iii** find the solution to the equations using your graph.

a Two numbers have a sum of 8 and a difference of 2.

b The sum of two numbers is 6. The sum of one of the numbers and 3 times the other is 14.

c A bar of chocolate and a can of coke cost 85p. Three bars and two cokes costs £2.05.

8 Invent a problem that could be represented by these simultaneous equations.
Solve the problem using a graph.

$x + 3y = 10$
$2x + y = 5$

You should know how to …

1 Write an expression to describe the *n*th term of an arithmetic sequence.

2 Given values for *m* and *c*, find the gradient of lines given by equations of the form $y = mx + c$.

3 Construct functions arising from real-life problems and plot their corresponding graphs.

4 Give solutions to problems to an appropriate degree of accuracy.

Check out

1 a Find a formula connecting the number of straws (*n*) and the number of squares (*s*).

b i Find a formula connecting the number of cubes (*n*) and the number of faces that can be seen (*f*).

ii Why does this formula work?

2 a

Pay in £

(graph showing a line; y-axis "Pay in £" marked at 10 and 20, x-axis "number of models produced" marked at 4)

i The graph shows how many model boats Danny makes and how much he gets paid for them. Find an equation for this graph.

ii What does the equation tell you?

b What does the equation $y = x + 58$ tell you, if *x* represents age and *y* represents your heart beat in 1 minute?

3 'A herdsman can trade 5 camels for 13 sacks of food'.

a Draw a conversion graph for camels and sacks of food, showing possible exchanges for up to 30 camels. Use your graph to find the number of camels needed for 200 sacks of food.

b Use an algebraic method to find the number of camels needed for 75 sacks of food.

4 The area of this rectangle is 36 cm². Find *x*, to 1 d.p.

$(x + 4)$

$2x$

1 Solving problems

This unit will show you how to:

▶▶ Solve increasingly demanding problems and evaluate solutions.

▶▶ Present a concise, reasoned argument, using symbols, diagrams, graphs and related explanatory text.

▶▶ Represent problems and synthesise information in algebraic or graphical form.

▶▶ Move from one form to another to gain a different perspective on the problem.

▶▶ Solve substantial problems by breaking them into simpler tasks.

▶▶ Suggest extensions to problems, conjecture and generalise.

▶▶ Identify exceptional cases or counter-examples, explaining why.

▶▶ Compare two ratios.

▶▶ Interpret and use ratio in a range of contexts.

▶▶ Use proportional reasoning to solve a problem.

▶▶ Explore connections in mathematics across a range of contexts.

▶▶ Give solutions to problems to an appropriate degree of accuracy.

You can use the unitary method to find the best buy.

Before you start

You should know how to ...

1 Generate and describe non-linear sequences.

2 Draw a graph from a table of results.

3 Write and simplify an integer ratio.

4 Increase or decrease an amount by a given percentage.

Check in

1 i Write down the next two terms in these sequences.

ii Describe how you would find the nth term.

a 1 4 9 16 **b** 2 8 18 32
c 2 5 10 17

2 Draw a graph to show this sequence.

Term (T)	1	2	3	4
Sequence (S)	1	4	9	16

3 a Simplify these ratios **i** 4:12 **ii** 15:24
b Write these ratios in the form 1:n
  i 3:18 **ii** 5:16

4 a Increase £30 by 20%
b Decrease £40 by 15%

Understanding the problem

This spread will show you how to:
▶▶ Solve increasingly demanding problems and evaluate solutions.

KEYWORDS
Investigate   Problem
Solve   Results

At Belham Library there are five steps leading to the entrance. Kate wants to know how many different ways there are to walk up the steps.

One way would be to walk one step at a time.

A second way would be a giant step over all five at once.

Kate thinks about the problem some more.

I could climb four steps and then one step, but I could also climb one and then four.

▶ To find the information to solve a problem you need to start with the simplest case and then increase in difficulty by one step at a time.

Kate investigates the problem by starting with one step.

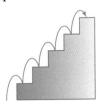

1 step	2 steps	3 steps	4 steps
1 way	2 ways	4 ways	8 ways
(1)	(1, 1) (2)	(1, 1, 1) (3)	(1, 1, 1, 1) (4)
		(1, 2) (2, 1)	(1, 3) (3, 1) (2, 2)
			(1, 1, 2) (1, 2, 1) (2, 1, 1)

Key: (1, 3) means 1 step and then 3 steps.

Kate notices that:
Each time the number of steps **increases** by **1**, the number of different ways **doubles**.

Kate predicts that there should be 16 different ways to climb five steps.

▶ To solve problems and find solutions you need to work in a logical manner.
▶ When you list results in order you can use them to predict future results.

Exercise P1.1

City lights investigation 1

The buildings of Glow City are square blocks arranged in square arrays.

Street lamps are placed at the corners of the blocks to light up the city, but can only light up the distance of half a block.

There are three types of lamp:

Corner lamps (*C*)	Side lamps (*S*)	Multi lamps (*M*)
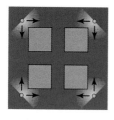	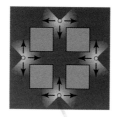	
These shine in two directions.	These shine in three directions.	These shine in four directions.

1 How many of each type of lamp would you need to light up this square array of nine blocks?

2 Repeat question 1 for different sized square arrays up to and including 25 blocks.
Start with the simplest possible arrangement, and draw diagrams to illustrate your answers.

3 Write about any patterns that you notice for:
   a corner lamps
   b side lamps
   c multi lamps.

Organising your results

This spread will show you how to:
▶▶ Present a concise reasoned argument.
▶▶ Represent problems and synthesise information in algebraic and
graphical form.

KEYWORDS
Explain   Generalize
Predict   Symbol

Kate wants to know the number of ways to climb a staircase with 20 steps.
She draws a table of the results she has found so far:

Number of steps	1	2	3	4	5
Number of ways	1	2	4	8	16

Kate uses colour in her table to
show that this is a **prediction**.

Kate tests her prediction by listing the number of ways to climb five steps.
(1, 1, 1, 1, 1) (1, 1, 1, 2) (1, 1, 2, 1) (1, 2, 1, 1) (2, 1, 1, 1) (1, 1, 3)
(1, 3, 1) (3, 1, 1) (1, 4) (4, 1) (1, 2, 2) (2, 1, 2) (2, 2, 1) (2, 3) (3, 2) (5)

There are 16
ways in total.
My prediction is
correct.

Kate draws a graph of her results.

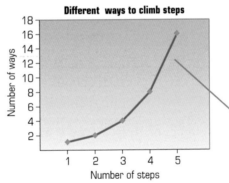

Different ways to climb steps

To find a general result,
Kate needs to use algebra.
She thinks that multiplying
by 2 should be part of the
general rule.

The number of ways
does not steadily
increase, but grows
quickly.

Kate adds an extra row to her table.

Number of steps (n)	1	2	3	4	5
Number of ways (W)	1	2	4	8	16
	$1 = 2^0$	$2 = 2^1$	$2 \times 2 = 2^2$	$2 \times 2 \times 2 = 2^3$	$2 \times 2 \times 2 \times 2 = 2^4$

Kate notices that:

The power of 2 is 1 less than the number of steps (n).
So the number of ways, $W = 2^{n-1}$.
For $n = 20$, $2^{19} = 524\ 288$.
There are 524 288 ways to climb 20 steps.

▶ Tabulate and graph results and use these to predict future results.
▶ Test any predictions where possible.
▶ Explain your results and, if possible, use symbols to represent the nth term.

Exercise P1.2

City lights investigation 2

1 Look at your results from Exercise P1.1 on page 195.
Draw a graph to show the number of corner lamps needed
for different sized square blocks. Use the axes shown.

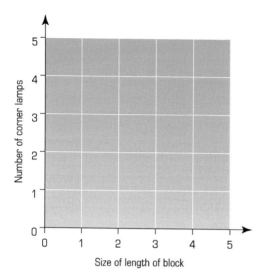

2 Repeat question 1 for side lamps and multi lamps using your
results from Exercise P1.1.

3 Write one or two sentences for each graph in questions 1 and
2, describing how the number of lamps needed changes as
the number of blocks increases.

4 Predict how many of each type of lamp you would need for:

a 36 blocks
b 49 blocks.

Test your predictions in each case by drawing the square
arrangement.

5 Find a general result for each type of lamp needed for an
$n \times n$ arrangement of blocks.
Explain how you found your general results, and try to
justify each rule by looking back at the square arrangement.

> **Hint:** Try to use
> algebra for questions
> 5 and 6.

6 Investigate the **total** number of lamps required for different
square arrays of blocks.
Try to find a general formula for the total number of lamps
needed to light up an $n \times n$ array of blocks.

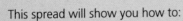

This spread will show you how to:

▶▶ Solve substantial problems by breaking them into simpler tasks.

▶▶ Suggest extensions to problems, conjecture and generalise.

KEYWORDS

Counter example

Conjecture   Generalise

The entrance to Belham Art Gallery is symmetrically arranged with four steps on either side.
Kate wants to know the number of ways to climb up and back down the steps.

Kate introduces the condition that you have to land on the step at the top.
She investigates the problem systematically.

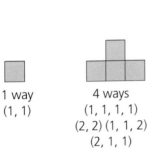

1 step high   2 steps high

3 steps high

4 steps high

1 way
(1, 1)

4 ways
(1, 1, 1, 1)
(2, 2) (1, 1, 2)
(2, 1, 1)

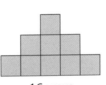

16 ways
(1, 1, 1, 1, 1, 1) (1, 1, 1, 1, 2) (1, 1, 1, 2, 1)
(1, 1, 1, 3) (1, 2, 1, 1, 1) (1, 2, 1, 2)
(1, 2, 2, 1) (1, 2, 3) (2, 1, 1, 1, 1)
(2, 1, 1, 2) (2, 1, 2, 1) (2, 1, 3)
(3, 1, 1, 1) (3, 2, 1) (3, 1, 2) (3, 3)

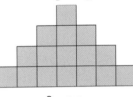

? ways

Kate draws a table of her results.

Height of steps	1	2	3	4
Number of ways	1	4	16	?

She looks at the pattern of numbers.

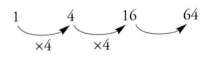

Kate has made a **conjecture** that four steps make 64 ways.
You need more than three results to make **predictions**.

▶ A conjecture is a conclusion based upon incomplete information.

Kate's friend Cathy is also investigating a number problem.
She was told that all numbers could be written as sums of consecutive numbers.
Cathy found: $3 = 1 + 2$
    $5 = 2 + 3$
    $6 = 1 + 2 + 3$
    $7 = 3 + 4$
    $9 = 4 + 5$
    $10 = 1 + 2 + 3 + 4$

However, Cathy could not write 1, 2, 4 or 8 as the sum of consecutive numbers.

▶ **Counter examples** show that a rule does not always work.

Exercise P1.3

City lights investigation 3

Extend your city lighting investigation from Exercises P1.1 and P1.2.

You could have …

… a city whose buildings are square blocks arranged in rectangular arrays.

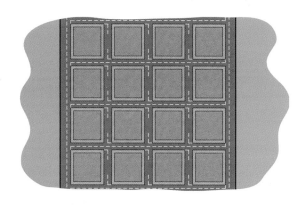

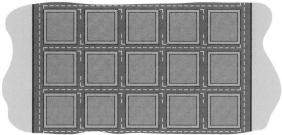

… building blocks organised in the shape of cubes.

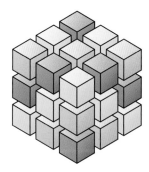

… a city where the buildings are equilateral triangles or regular hexagons when viewed from above.

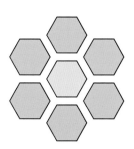

This spread will show you how to:
- ▶ Simplify a ratio expressed in decimals.
- ▶ Interpret and use ratio in a range of contexts.
- ▶ Compare two ratios.

KEYWORDS
Ratio
Proportion
Unitary ratio

Focus Print Ltd. is a company that develops photographs.
Daniel is deciding which print size to choose.

Compact
9 cm × 12.5 cm

30% Bigger
10 cm × 15 cm

100% Bigger
12.5 cm × 17.5 cm

Daniel is not convinced that the print sizes are in the same
proportion.

Objects that are in proportion
have the same shape.

▶ Quantities are in proportion if the ratio between the parts
stays the same.

Daniel finds the ratio of width to height for each size.

Compact	30% Bigger	100% Bigger
$9 : 12.5$	$10 : 15$	$12.5 : 17.5$
$= 18 : 25$	$= 2 : 3$	$= 25 : 35 = 5 : 7$

▶ You can express a ratio in its simplest form when the numbers used are the smallest whole
numbers possible.

Daniel wants to compare the ratios, so he changes them to the **unitary form, 1 : n.**

Compact	30% Bigger	100% Bigger
$18 : 25 = 1 : 1.389$	$2 : 3 = 1 : 1.5$	$5 : 7 = 1 : 1.4$

$\div 18$ $\div 2$ $\div 5$

The ratios are different so the print sizes are not in exact proportion.

▶ You use the unitary method, expressing a ratio in the form 1 : n or n : 1, to compare ratios.

Daniel wants to check the descriptions '30% Bigger' and '100% Bigger'. He works out the area
of each print size:

Compact	30% Bigger	100% Bigger
$9 \text{ cm} \times 12.5 \text{ cm} = 112.5 \text{ cm}^2$	$10 \text{ cm} \times 15 \text{ cm} = 150 \text{ cm}^2$	$12.5 \text{ cm} \times 17.5 \text{ cm} = 218.75 \text{ cm}^2$

The area ratio Compact : 30% Bigger is $112.5 : 150 = 1 : 1.333$
$\Rightarrow$ The '30% Bigger' is 33% larger than the Compact.

The area ratio Compact : 100% Bigger is $112.5 : 218.75 = 1 : 1.944$
$\Rightarrow$ The '100% Bigger' is 94% larger than the Compact.

Daniel deduces that the print sizes are named because of their approximate relative areas.

Exercise P1.4

Investigation

Consider the digits: 0   1   2   3   4   5   6   7   8   9

For example:

Step 1 Choose any three of these digits.

Choose 2, 8, 5

Step 2 Add them up. Call the answer A.

$A = 2 + 8 + 5 = 15$

Step 3 Make all the possible two-digit numbers from your chosen three digits in step 1. Add them up. Call the answer B.

The possible two-digit numbers are 28, 25, 82, 85, 52, 58

$B = 28 + 25 + 82 + 85 + 52 + 58 = 330$

Step 4 Find the ratio A : B in its simplest form.

$A : B = 15 : 330$

$= 1 : 22$

1 Choose your own set of three numbers and find the ratio A : B using steps 1 to 4.

2 Choose a different set of three numbers and find the ratio A : B.

3 What do you notice about the example and your answers to questions 1 and 2?
Try to explain why this might always happen.

Hint: It may help if you use algebra.

4 Choose four of the digits from the list.
Work through Steps 1 to 4 using these numbers and find the ratio A : B.
(Remember to work systematically to find all possible two-digit numbers in Step 3).

5 Choose a different set of four numbers and find the ratio A : B.

6 Choose a third set of four numbers and find the ratio A : B.

7 What do you notice about your answers to questions 4, 5 and 6?
Try to use algebra to explain your answer.

8 Choose a set of five numbers from the list and use these to find the ratio A : B.

9 Compare and comment on your answers to questions 1, 4 and 8.

Proportional reasoning

This spread will show you how to:

▶▶ Use proportional reasoning to solve a problem.

▶▶ Explore connections in mathematics across a range of contexts.

KEYWORDS

Ratio

Proportion

Fizzbuzz Drinks Corporation manufacture their own special brand of lemonade.

They plan to run a promotion on their lemonade to boost sales.

They want to know if they should:

– Increase the contents by 25%, or

– Reduce the price by 25%.

Ruth works for Fizzbuzz.

She solves the problem using ratio and proportion.

Ruth examines both possibilities.

Increase the contents by 25%:
1000 ml (1 litre) × 1.25 = 1250 ml
1250 ml would cost 100p (£1)
So 1p buys 12.5 ml

Reduce the price by 25%:
100p × 0.75 = 75p
1000 ml would cost 75p
So 1p buys 13.33 ml

This is an example of the **unitary method**.

An alternative method would be to work out the cost for the same quantity.

1250 ml would cost 100p (£1)
250 ml would cost 20p

1000 ml would cost 75p
250 ml would cost 18.75p

This does not take account of other factors such as the cost of producing a larger bottle.

Both methods lead Ruth to conclude that:

▶ The customer gets better value for money when the price is reduced.

▶ The company might do better if they were to increase the contents.

When you use proportion to make comparisons you:

▶ Make one of the quantities the same

▶ Compare the other quantity.

Exercise P1.5

1 A manufacturer wants to run a promotion on a bottle of cola.
They need to decide whether to increase the contents or
reduce the price.
The usual size bottle is 1 litre and costs £1.

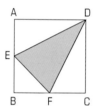

  a Compare the effect of increasing the
contents by 10% or reducing the price
by 10%.

  b Repeat the comparison using
    i 20%
    ii 40%
    iii 50%.

  c Comment on your answers to **a** and **b**.

  d If the contents were increased by 25%, what price reduction on the usual size bottle
would give the same value for money?

2 A square ABCD has a triangle DEF inside.

The ratio of lengths AE : EB = 1 : 1
The ratio of lengths BF : FC = 1 : 1

Find the ratio
shaded area : unshaded area for this shape.

3 Primary colours are red (R), blue (B) and yellow (Y).
Different shades of brown can be made mixing any two of green, orange and violet.

| You can make green (G) by mixing blue and yellow in the ratio B : Y = 2 : 5 | You can make orange (O) by mixing red and yellow in the ratio R : Y = 2 : 3 | You can make violet (V) by mixing red and blue in the ratio R : B = 3 : 5 |

  a Yellowy-brown is made mixing green and orange in the ratio 2 : 3.
What is the ratio of red to blue to yellow in yellowy-brown?

  b Reddish-brown is made mixing violet and orange in the ratio 3 : 2.
What is the ratio of red to blue to yellow in reddish-brown?

203

This spread will show you how to:

▶▶ Compare ratios.

▶▶ Interpret and use ratio in a range of contexts.

KEYWORDS

Compare   Interpret

Ratio

Joshua gets through a lot of paper!

He starts to wonder how paper sizes got their names.

Joshua investigates with the paper he can find in his classroom.

A sheet of A3 paper folded in half is the size of A4 paper.

Fold A4 paper in half and the paper size is A5.

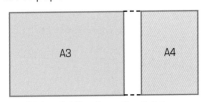

width of A3 = length of A4

width of A4 = length of A5

Joshua measures the length and width of a sheet of A3, A4, A5 and A6 paper. He then calculates the ratio of width (W) to length (L).

Paper sizes A0 to A6 are known as **metric paper sizes**.

Paper size	A3	A4	A5	A6
Width (mm)	297	210	148	105
Length (mm)	420	297	210	148
Ratio $W : L$	1 : 1.41414	1 : 1.41429	1 : 1.41892	1 : 1.40952

Joshua notices that the ratios are all roughly equal to $1 : \sqrt{2}$ (1.41421...), and he deduces that:

▶ The width of one paper size is the length of paper the next size smaller

▶ Metric paper sizes have width : length ratio = $1 : \sqrt{2}$.

Joshua predicts the dimensions of A2, A1 and A0 paper:

A2 paper has width 420 mm (this is the length of A3).
A2 length should be $420 \times \sqrt{2} = 594$ mm.
A1 width = 594 mm, length = $594 \times \sqrt{2} = 840$ mm.
A0 width = 840 mm, length = $840 \times \sqrt{2} = 1188$ mm.

Joshua checks his prediction by measuring.

▶ **You can compare ratios and interpret the results to solve problems.**

Exercise P1.6

Investigation

Morse code uses patterns of dots and dashes to represent letters of the alphabet.

A ._	I ..	Q __._	Y _.__
B _...	J .___	R ._.	Z __..
C _._.	K _._	S ...	
D _..	L ._..	T _	
E .	M __	U .._	
F .._.	N _.	V ..._	
G __.	O ___	W .__	
H	P .__.	X _.._	

When you transmit a letter in Morse code:

▶ A dash takes three times longer than a dot to transmit (so if a dot is 1 unit, a dash is 3 units).

▶ The gap between dots and dashes is 1 unit.

The time (in units) to transmit the letter A is: $\bar{1} + 1 + \bar{3}$ $= 5$

The time (in units) to transmit the letter D is: $\bar{3} + 1 + \bar{1} + 1 + \bar{1}$ $= 7$

The transmitting ratio of A : D is 5 : 7.

1 Find the transmitting ratio of:
   a E : T   **b** A : N   **c** S : O
   d E : Q   **e** K : X

2 Choose a passage of writing in any novel (about ten lines of writing).
   a Count the number of times the letter E appears and the number of times the letter T appears.
   b Work out the ratio of the number of times E appears to the number of times T appears, E : T. (You may want to express this as a unitary ratio).
   c Compare your ratio with your answer to question 1**a** and comment on what you notice.

3 In a standard popular game set there are 12 letter Es and 6 letter Ts.
   a Write down the ratio E : T.
   b Compare with your answer to question 2 and comment.

4 **a** Combine your total number of Es and Ts from question 2 with the totals from one or more people.
   b Work out the new ratio E : T.
   c Comment on your answer.

5 Choose another pair of letters to compare and work out their Morse transmitting ratio.
   Choose a passage of writing, count the number of times the letters appear and work out their ratio. Compare your two ratios.

Summary

You should know how to ...

1 Present a concise, reasoned argument, using symbols, diagrams, graphs and related explanatory text.

2 Use proportional reasoning to solve a problem, choosing the correct numbers to take as 100%, or as a whole.

Check out

1 Find how many squares there are on a chessboard (an 8 × 8 square grid).

2 Windowbrite and Klearglass are equally effective products to use to clean windows.

> Windowbrite costs £2.40 for 500 ml.
> Klearglass costs £1.90 for 400 ml.

Which product represents the best value for money?

Dimensions and scales

This unit will show you how to:

- Visualise and use 2-D representations of 3-D objects.
- Analyse 3-D shapes through 2-D projections, including plans and elevations.
- Use and interpret maps and scale drawings.
- Use straight edge and compasses to construct a triangle, given right angle, hypotenuse and side (RHS).
- Find, by reasoning, the locus of a point that moves according to a simple rule.

- Calculate the surface area and volume of right prisms.
- Use bearings to specify direction and solve problems.
- Given the coordinates of points A and B, find the midpoint of the line segment AB.
- Solve increasingly demanding problems and evaluate solutions.
- Solve substantial problems by breaking them into simpler tasks.

Looking at the map scale, it's 2 km away. Come on!

Yes, but it's on a bearing of 045° – that's this way!

You can use a map and a compass to find distance and direction.

Before you start

You should know how to ...

1 Identify planes of symmetry in 3-D shapes.

2 Calculate the volume of a simple prism.

3 Convert between metric units.

4 Read and plot coordinates in all four quadrants.

Check in

1 How many planes of symmetry does this cuboid have?

2 **a** Find the volume of this shape.   **b** What is the area of A?

4 cm

3 cm

7 cm

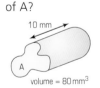

10 mm

A

volume = 80 mm³

3 Copy and complete:
   a 4 cm = ___ mm   **b** 42 mm = __ cm
   c 52 cm = ___ m   **d** 1000 g = __ kg
   e 3.5 ℓ = ___ ml   **f** 2000 kg = ___ g

4 Plot on a grid:
   A(4, 2)   B(⁻3, 2)   C(⁻2, 1)
   D(5, ⁻1)   E(0, 5)   F(⁻3, 0)

3-D shapes

This spread will show you how to:
▶▶ Analyse 3-D shapes through 2-D projections and cross-sections.

KEYWORDS
Edge   Face
Vertex   Plane of symmetry
Section   Octahedron

You can describe a 3-D shape using its properties.

example

The diagram shows a solid made from a square-based pyramid on top of a cube.

a   Identify the edges that are parallel to AB.
b   Identify the edges that are perpendicular to AB.
c   EBGID is a plane of symmetry of the solid.
    State another plane of symmetry.
    Describe it in words and sketch it.

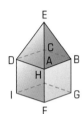

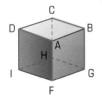

a   CD, FG and HI are parallel to AB.

b   CB, AD, AF and BG are perpendicular to AB.

c   EAFHC is another plane of symmetry.
    It is a pentagon.

You can analyse a shape through its cross-sections.

example

The diagram shows an octahedron, made from two square-based pyramids.

a   How many edges, faces and vertices does the octahedron have?
b   Which two edges are perpendicular to AB?
c   If you cut a section through the midpoints of EA, EB, EC and ED what shape do you get?

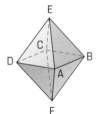

a   The octahedron has 12 edges, 8 faces and 6 vertices.
b   CB and DA are perpendicular to AB.
c   The resulting section is a square.

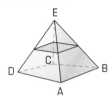

Exercise S4.1

1 Here are two triangular prisms joined to make a new solid.

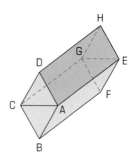

   a Use words like *parallel, perpendicular, faces, edges* and *vertices* to describe the new solid.

   b Sketch another solid using the two triangular prisms. Draw it and write a description of it below your diagram.

   c Repeat part **b** to make another solid.

2 Use the shapes shown to sketch as many different solids as you can. The faces shaded blue are identical.

   a

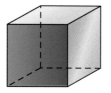 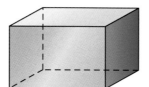 

   b

3 This cube has been sliced to give a rectangular cross-section. Is it possible to slice a cube so that the cross-section is:

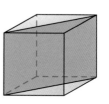

   a a square
   b a triangle
   c a pentagon
   d a hexagon?

If so, describe how it can be done.
Which of these cross-sections are planes of symmetry?

4 Can you make a solid with:

   a only two faces
   b only three faces
   c four faces
   d five faces
   e six edges
   f five vertices
   g six vertices
   h three vertices?

In each case, explain your answer and sketch the solid where appropriate.

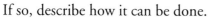

Plans and elevations

This spread will show you how to:

▶▶ Analyse 3-D shapes through plans and elevations.

KEYWORDS

Plan   Net

Elevation   Solid

View

You can represent a 3-D shape using plans and elevations:

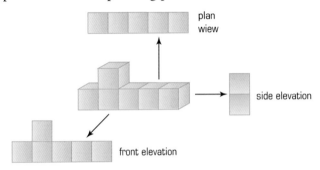

plan wiew

side elevation

front elevation

If plans and elevations are labelled with measurements, you can sketch the net of the solid.

example

The diagrams show the plan view, and the front and side elevations, of a solid.

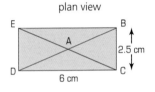

plan view

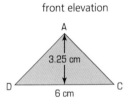

front elevation

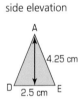

side elevation

a   Draw the plan view accurately.
b   Using the information in the diagrams, sketch the net of the solid. Indicate any relevant measurements on your sketch.
c   Name the solid.

a   Draw the rectangle accurately using a ruler and protractor:

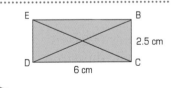

b   The net looks like this:

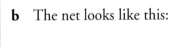

c   The solid is a rectangular pyramid.

Note:
These diagrams have been reduced to fit.

Exercise S4.2

1 By making appropriate measurements draw the nets of the solids shown in these plans and elevations. Sketch each solid first.

a   Plan   Front elevation   Side elevation

b   Plan   Front elevation   Side elevation

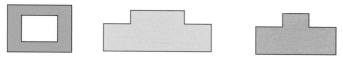

c   Plan   Front elevation   Side elevation

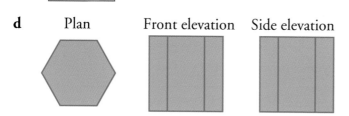

d   Plan   Front elevation   Side elevation

2 Construct plans and elevations of these solids.

3 Here is the net of a solid.

Draw its plan and elevations.
Sketch the solid.

4 For each of these shapes, decide whether it could be the plan of a solid. Justify your answer.

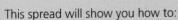

S4.3 Volume and surface area

This spread will show you how to:

▶▶ Calculate the surface area and volume of a right prism.

▶▶ Solve problems involving surface area and volume in context.

KEYWORDS

Volume

Surface area

You can use your knowledge of the volume of a prism to solve real-life problems.

example

The diagram shows a ramp for disabled access to a sports centre.

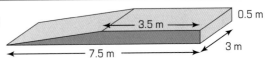

a Calculate the area of the shaded face.   b Calculate the volume of the ramp.

a The red face is a trapezium.

$A = \frac{1}{2}(a + b)h$

$= \frac{1}{2}(7.5 + 3.5) \times 0.5$

$= 2.75$ So the area of the shaded face is 2.75 m².

b The ramp is a prism.

V = area of cross-section × length

$= 2.75 \times 3$

$= 8.25$ So the volume of the ramp is 8.25 m³.

If you are given sufficient information, you can work out the surface area of a prism.

example

A tent is in the shape of a triangular prism.
The front and back of the tent are both isosceles triangles.

a Calculate the volume of the tent.

b Sketch the net of the triangular prism.

c Hence calculate the amount of material that is used in making the tent (ignore any overlaps).

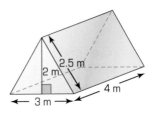

a Area of triangular front $= \frac{1}{2} \times 3$ m $\times 2$ m $= 3$ m²

Volume $= 3$ m² $\times 4$ m $= 12$ m³

b

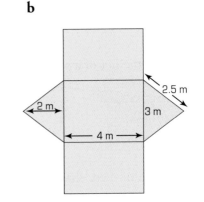

c Area of rectangular sides $= 2 \times (4$ m $\times 2.5$m$) = 20$ m²

Area of rectangular base $= 4$ m $\times 3$ m $= 12$ m²

Area of triangular front and back $= 2 \times 3$ m² $= 6$ m²

Total surface area $= 20$ m² $+ 12$ m² $+ 6$ m² $= 38$ m²

Exercise S4.3

1 Find the volume of this box of cornflakes. The cornflakes have a volume of 120 cm^3. What percentage of the box do they fill?

2 This toy house is in the shape of a cuboid with a triangular prism on top. What is the volume of the house?

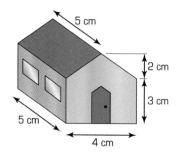

3

a The walls of this room are to be painted. What area is to be painted? (The door will be painted separately, so don't count it!)
b What area of carpet is required?
c If carpet costs £19.99 a square metre, how much will it cost to carpet the room?
d What is the volume of the room?

4 The diagram shows a rather strange-shaped jug.

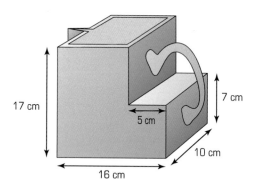

a Find the volume of the jug (excluding the handle and the spout).
b The jug is to be filled with water. What capacity of water will it hold? (1 cm^3 = 1 ml.)
c The outside (except the handle and spout) is to be painted blue. What is the area that is to be painted? (Include the base of the jug.)

5 a Find the volume of water (in millilitres) that this vase will hold.

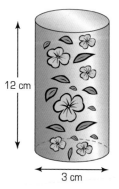

b The curved surface area and the base are to be painted pink. What area is to painted?

Scale drawings

This spread will show you how to:

▶▶ Use and interpret scale drawings and maps.

KEYWORDS

Scale   Ratio

Map   Unit

Architects draw plans to a particular **scale**.

In this plan of an office, every 1 cm is equal to 4 m in the actual office.

You can give a scale as a ratio, without units.

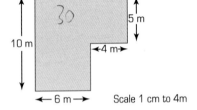

Scale 1 cm to 4m

---

example

A plan of a field is drawn to a scale of 1 cm to 10 m.

a   Write the scale as a ratio.
b   The field is three-quarters of a kilometre in length.
     What length should this be represented by on the plan?

....

a   1 m = 100 cm, so 10 m = 1000 cm.
     The scale is 1 cm to 1000 cm, or 1 cm: 1000 cm.
     As a ratio without units, the scale is 1 : 1000.
b $\frac{3}{4}$ km = $\frac{3}{4}$ × 1000 m = 750 m across the field.
     The scale is 1 : 1000 ⟹ all distances will be 1000 times smaller on the plan.
     750 m ÷ 1000 = 0.75 m = 75 cm
     The field will be 75 cm across on the plan.

> You can write two quantities together in a ratio when they are both given in the same units.

You use a scale when you interpret a map.

example

The map shown is drawn to a scale of 1 : 25 000.

Measure the distance between Grotto Island and Church Farm on the map, and hence calculate the real distance.

Using a ruler, the distance between Grotto Island and Church Farm is 3.2 cm.

The scale is 1 : 25 000, so the real
distance is 3.2 × 25 000 = 80 000 cm
                        = (80 000 ÷ 100) m
                        = 800 m, or 0.8 km.

▶ On a map with a scale of 1 : k

   ▶ Real distance = map length × k

   ▶ Map length = real distance ÷ k

Exercise S4.4

1 Here is a plan of Sally's bedroom.

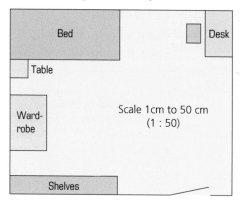

Scale 1cm to 50 cm (1 : 50)

a What are the dimensions of her real bed?
b What are the dimensions of her real wardrobe?
c What are the dimensions of her real table?
d What are the dimensions of her real desk?
e What are the dimensions of her real shelves?
Sally wants to place a table 2 m by 1 m next to the desk. Will it fit?

2 A boat travels 100 km due South and 80 km due East as shown by the sketch.

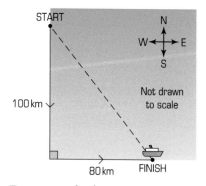

Draw a scale diagram to work out how far the boat is from its starting point. (Scale 1 cm : 10 km)

3 Here is a map of three islands.

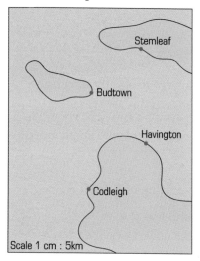

Scale 1 cm : 5km

Find the distance in kilometres from:
a Stemleaf to Havington
b Havington to Budtown
c Budtown to Stemleaf.
On a copy of the map plan a sea route from Stemleaf to Codleigh via Havington. Estimate how far your journey would be.

4 The map shows a part of a town.

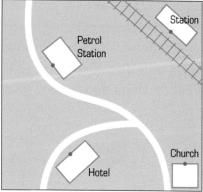

Scale 1 cm : 50 m

a How far is it 'as the crow flies' from:
  i the station to the church
  ii the hotel to the petrol station
  iii the petrol station to the church?
b Estimate the distance along the road from:
  i the petrol station to the church
  ii the petrol station to the hotel.

This spread will show you how to:

▶▶ Use bearings to specify directions and solve problems.

KEYWORDS

Bearing   Clockwise
Scale drawing

You use **bearings** to specify directions.

▶ **A bearing is a clockwise angle measured from North.**

You should know the points of the compass: North, South, East and West.

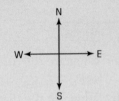

To find the bearing of B from A:

1 Draw a North line at A.
2 Measure the angle clockwise from A.
3 Always write three figures, so 062° not 62°.

The bearing of B from A is 062°.

The bearing of B from A is **not** the same as the bearing of A from B.

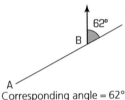

Draw a North line at B.   Mark in the corresponding angle.   Extend the angle clockwise to line AB.

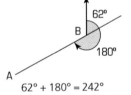

Corresponding angle = 62°

62° + 180° = 242°
The bearing of A from B is 242°.

You can use bearings to solve problems involving scale drawings.

example

A ship travels for 25 km on a bearing of 042°, then 35 km on a bearing of 127°.

a Use a scale drawing of 1 cm to 10 km to show the ship's path.
b Find the ship's distance and bearing from its starting point.

a

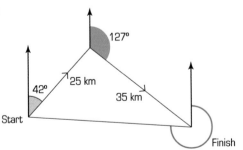

It is a good idea to draw a rough sketch first:

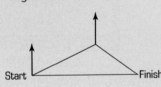

b The distance on the scale drawing, using a ruler, is 4.5 cm.

The real distance is (4.5 × 10) km = 45 km to nearest km
The bearing, using a protractor, is 275°.

Exercise S4.5

1 The bearing of P from Q is 045°.

What is the bearing of Q from P?

2 The bearing of X from Y is 107°.

What is the bearing of Y from X?

3 A ship travels on a bearing of 120° for 100 km and then on a bearing of 230° for a further 200 km.
Represent this with a scale drawing.
What is the ship's distance and bearing from the starting point?

4 A plane flies on a bearing of 060° for 200 km, changes course to fly 300 km on a bearing of 200° and changes course again to fly 250 km on a bearing of 135°.
What is its bearing and distance from its original position?

5 A dog walks across a field from C on a bearing of 045° at a steady speed of 1 m/s.

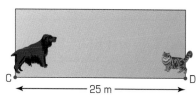

At the same time a cat starts at D at a steady speed of 1 m/s on a bearing of 315°. Do they meet?
Explain your answer.

6 P and Q are two ships 20 km apart. R is a submarine which is on a bearing of 075° from P and 290° from Q.

Using a scale of 1 cm : 2 km draw a scale diagram of P and Q and hence locate R.

7 A ship travels from S on a bearing of 042° for 25 km, then on a bearing of 140° for 25 km.

Draw a scale diagram to show the ship's course. (Use a scale of 1 : 200 000.)

8 A boat is seen on a bearing of 160° from lighthouse B. At the same time, it is seen on a bearing of 300° from lighthouse A.

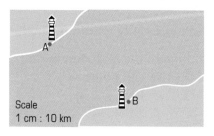

Copy the diagram and mark the position, B, of the boat.

This spread will show you how to:

▶▶ Read and plot points in all four quadrants.

▶▶ Given the coordinates of points A and B, find the midpoint of the line segment AB.

KEYWORDS
Line segment
Midpoint

When you join two points with a straight line, you create a **line segment**.

Point A has coordinates $(1, 3)$ and B has coordinates $(5, 9)$.

The line segment AB has midpoint $M(x_m, y_m)$.

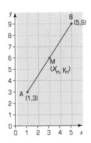

To find the coordinates of the midpoint, you can form a right-angled triangle ABC.

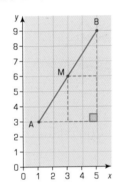

Triangles AMP and MQB are congruent because:

▶ AM = MB (M is the midpoint)

▶ $\angle$MAP = $\angle$BMQ (corresponding angles)

▶ $\angle$MPA = $\angle$BQM (both 90°)

So $BQ = MP = \frac{6}{2} = 3$, and $AP = MQ = \frac{4}{2} = 2$.

The midpoint M is $(1 + 2, 3 + 3)$, or $(3, 6)$.

There is an easier way to find the midpoint of a line segment ...

You can think of the midpoint as the **mean** of the two end points.

$$x_m = \frac{x_1 + x_2}{2} \qquad y_m = \frac{y_1 + y_2}{2}$$

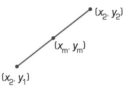

The formula works with the example because:

$\frac{1+5}{2} = 3$

$\frac{3+9}{2} = 6$

So the midpoint is (3, 6).

example

Find the midpoint of the line segment joining the points $A(^-1, 3)$ and $B(2, ^-5)$.

Use the formula:

$$x_m = \frac{^-1 + 2}{2} = \frac{1}{2} \qquad y_m = \frac{3 + ^-5}{2} = \frac{^-2}{2} = {}^-1$$

So the midpoint has coordinates $(\frac{1}{2}, {}^-1)$.

Exercise S4.6

1 Plot these pairs of points on a grid and calculate the midpoints of
the lines joining them.

   a A(6, 3)   B(4, 7)
   b C(4, 2)   D(2, 5)
   c E(1, 2)   F(5, 4)
   d G($^-$1, 2)   H($^-$3, 2)
   e I(0, 4)   J(0, 5)
   f K(2, $^-$1)   L(2, $^-$5)
   g M(3, $^-$2)   N(5, $^-$2)
   h O($^-$1, $^-$3) P($^-$4, $^-$5)
   i Q(6, 2)   R($^-$3, $^-$7)
   j S($^-$2, $^-$1) T(4, 2)

2 Look at your results for question 1.
If two points have coordinates A(x, y) and B(a, b) what
are the coordinates M of the midpoint of AB?

3 If A is point (2, 3) and the midpoint, M of AB is (3, 4),
what is the point B?

4 If A is (5, 6) and M is (9, 10) what is B?

5 If A is ($^-$1, 4) and M is (2, 3) what is B?

6 **a** If A(2, 4) and B(3, 5), could M(1, 6) be the midpoint?
Explain your answer.
   b If A($^-$1, 5) and B(1, $^-$2), could M(1, 3) be the midpoint?
Explain.

7 The midpoint of a line segment AB is (x_m, y_m).
The point A has coordinates (x_1, y_1).

Derive two formulae that would give the
coordinates of B(x_2, y_2).

$x_2 =$ _____
$y_2 =$ _____

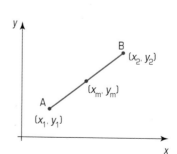

Finding simple loci

This spread will show you how to:

▶▶ Find the locus of a point that moves according to a simple rule.

KEYWORDS
Path
Locus
Loci

▶ The **locus** of a moving object is its path.

You can often construct loci accurately.

The plural of locus is loci.

example

The diagram shows a rectangular window.
An ant starts at A and moves so that it is always
the same distance away from the edges
AB and AD.

a Describe the path that the ant takes.
b Construct the ant's path accurately.

a The locus is the angle bisector of angle A.
b Put the point at A and draw   Draw equal arcs from   AR bisects ∠ A.
    equal arcs on AD and AB.   P and Q.

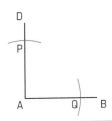 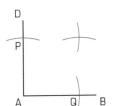 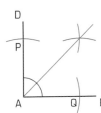

example

Shakira plays for the school football team.
She wants to run between two stationary defenders,
who are 6 m apart, so that she is always the same
distance from each of them.

a Describe Shakira's planned path.
b Construct the locus accurately, using a scale of 1 cm to 1 m.

a Shakira's path is the perpendicular bisector of the line joining the two defenders.
b Put the point at A and   Put the point at B and   XY is the perpendicular
    draw two arcs.   draw two arcs.   bisector of AB.

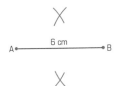  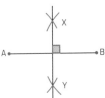

Exercise S4.7

1 Draw two points A and B, 15 cm apart.
Draw 20 points that are *equidistant* (the same
distance) from A and B.
Join these points to form the locus of points
equidistant from A and B.

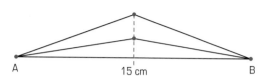

2 Describe your route to school using instructions such as left, right, and
straight on.

3 Describe the route from your form room to the school gym or sports hall.

4 Draw a diagram to show:
  a the path traced out by a conker on a string
  b the path of the tip of a windscreen wiper
  c the path of the ball thrown into the air
  d the path of your nose as you walk along a straight road
  e the path of a stone on a car wheel as the car moves.

5 Draw an angle BAC of 70° with arms AB and AC 8 cm long.
Use a ruler to draw 20 points that are equidistant from AB and AC.
Join up the points to form a straight line. This line is the angle bisector
of BÂC.

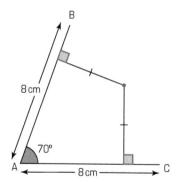

6 Construct the angle bisector of angle WXY, which will show the
locus of points equidistant from XY and XW.

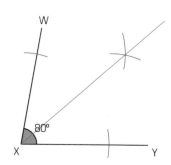

This spread will show you how to:
▶▶ Find the locus of a point that moves according to a simple rule.

KEYWORDS

Locus　　　　　Circle
Loci　　　　　Sphere
Bisector

Loci often fall into simple categories.
Here are three types of loci that you should learn.

P moves so that it is always a fixed distance from Q.

P forms a **circle**.

P moves so that it is always equidistant from Q and R.

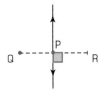

P forms a **perpendicular bisector**.

P moves so that it is always equidistant from QR and QS.

P forms an **angle bisector**.

example

A point A moves so that it is always 5 cm away from a fixed point B.
Describe the locus of A.
....

The locus is a circle, centre B, radius 5 cm.

Some paths are more complicated.

example

Sian rolls a coin on a flat table top.
Describe the locus of a point on the edge of the coin.
....

Imagine the point P as it moves along the table surface.

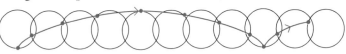

P moves in a repeated curve.

You can also visualise loci in three dimensions.

example

A young bird flies so that it is never more than 15 m away from
its nest at the top of a very tall tree.
Describe the locus of the bird.

15 m
Nest

....　..................

The bird's locus consists of all points
within a sphere radius 15 m.

Exercise S4.8

1 Construct the locus of all points 6 cm from a fixed point A.

2 A radio mast can transmit within a 40 km radius. Draw a scale drawing to show the region that can receive the signal.
Use a scale of 1 : 1 000 000.

3 Construct the loci of the paths of the points which are equidistant from these pairs of lines.

a

b

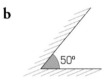

c

(Copy the diagrams first.)

4 Cut out a 2 cm square ABCD and place it on a straight line. Mark the corner B of the square as shown.
Rotate the square about corner D. Mark the position of B as you rotate the square.

When CD is on the line, continue rotating, now about corner C to keep the square moving along the line and finish the locus of B.

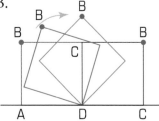

5 ABCD is a plan of a garden on a scale 1 cm : 10 m. Construct the locus of points:

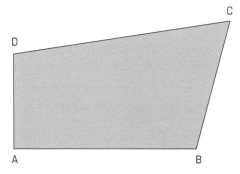

a equidistant from AB and AD
b 30 m from B.
c Trees must be planted nearer to AB than AD, and less than 30 m from B. Show where they could be planted on your diagram.

6 The diagram shows an accurate scale drawing of a field, on a scale of 1 cm to 2 m.

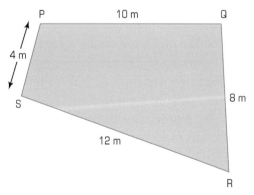

Copy the diagram (you could use tracing paper).
A man walks so that he is always equidistant from P and Q.
A dog is tethered to R on a rope 3 m long. Can the dog reach the man?

223

Constructing triangles

This spread will show you how to:

▶▶ Use a straight edge and compasses to construct a triangle, given right angle, hypotenuse and side.

KEYWORDS

Right-angled triangle
Hypotenuse

You can use a ruler and compasses to construct a triangle given a right angle, side, and hypotenuse (RHS).

This technique is introduced on page 27.

---

example

Construct triangle PQR where PQ = 5 cm, ∠P = 90° and QR = 7 cm.

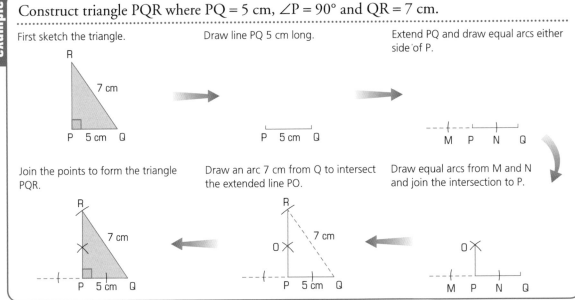

First sketch the triangle.

Draw line PQ 5 cm long.

Extend PQ and draw equal arcs either side of P.

Join the points to form the triangle PQR.

Draw an arc 7 cm from Q to intersect the extended line PO.

Draw equal arcs from M and N and join the intersection to P.

Many real-life problems can be solved by constructing right-angled triangles to scale.

---

example

a Construct a triangle to scale to represent this tower. Use a scale of 1 cm to 4 m.

b Using a protractor measure the angle that the light from the sun makes with the ground.

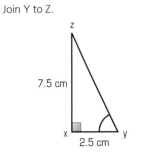

30 m

10 m

a First calculate the dimensions of the scale drawing:
30 ÷ 4 = 7.5, and 10 ÷ 4 = 2.5
so the tower will be 7.5 cm tall with a shadow of 2.5 cm on the drawing.

Draw a horizontal line XY 2.5 cm long.

Construct a perpendicular XZ at X, 7.5 cm long

Join Y to Z.

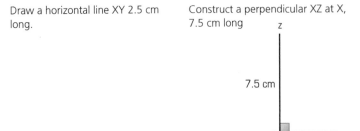

b The angle ZYX is 72° to the nearest degree.

Exercise S4.9

1 Construct △EFG where EF = 6 cm, ∠E = 30° and ∠F = 60°.

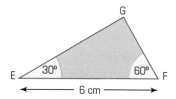

2 Construct △ABC where AB = BC = 10 cm and ∠B = 45°.

3 Construct △XYZ where XY = 5.9 cm, YZ = 6.2 cm and ∠XZ = 6.5 cm.

4 A 10 m ladder rests against a wall with its foot 3 m away from the wall.

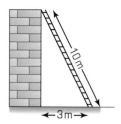

Construct a scale diagram and use the diagram to find:
a how far the ladder reaches up the wall
b the angle between the ladder and the ground.

5 The net of a tetrahedron is made from equilateral triangles of side 4 cm.
Draw an accurate construction of the net.

6 Boat A can see plane C at an angle of 42°. Boat B can see plane C at
angle of 49°, and AB = 85 m.
Find the height h of C above the horizontal.

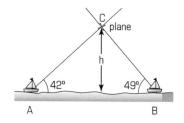

7 Is it possible to construct △ABC such that
a ∠A = 60°, ∠B = 60°, ∠C = 60°
b ∠A = 40°, ∠B = 60°, AB = 5 cm
c BC = 6 cm, AC = 10 cm, ∠B = 90°
d BC = 7 cm, AC = 4.95 cm, ∠B = 45°?
Give reasons for your answers, and construct the triangle where possible.

Summary

You should know how to ...

1 Use and interpret maps and scale drawings.

2 Find the locus of a point that moves according to a simple rule.

3 Solve substantial problems by breaking them into simpler tasks, using a range of efficient techniques, methods and resources.

Check out

1 A boat travels 55 km due North, then 225 km due East.

Using a scale 1 cm : 10 km, construct a scale drawing to help you find the distance of the boat from its original position.

2 A flea moves so that it is always equidistant from A and B.

Construct its path.

A•

•B

3 An 8.5 m ladder rests against a wall, with its top end reaching 6 m up the wall.

a Sketch the ladder, wall and ground.

b Construct a scale diagram to show how far the base of the ladder is away from the wall.

c Measure the angle between the ladder and the ground.

d What do you think would happen if the ladder reached only 3 m up the wall?

This unit will show you how to:

- ▶▶ Suggest a problem to explore using statistical methods, frame questions and raise conjectures.
- ▶▶ Design a survey or experiment to capture the necessary data from one or more sources.
- ▶▶ Determine the sample size and degree of accuracy needed.
- ▶▶ Design, trial and, if necessary, refine data collection sheets.
- ▶▶ Construct tables for large discrete and continuous sets of raw data, choosing suitable class intervals.

- ▶▶ Interpret graphs and diagrams and draw inferences to support or cast doubt on initial conjectures.
- ▶▶ Communicate interpretations and results of a statistical enquiry.
- ▶▶ Solve increasingly demanding problems and evaluate solutions.
- ▶▶ Present a concise, reasoned argument, using symbols, diagrams, graphs and related explanatory text.

How long do you think this line is, to the nearest centimetre?

You should always start a survey with clear questions or statements.

Before you start

You should know how to ...

1 Find the range, mean, median and mode for a set of data.

2 Use an assumed mean.

3 Draw frequency diagrams for continuous data.

Check in

1 Find the range, mean, median and mode of this data set.

| 6 | 4 | 5 | 2 | 9 | 4 |

2 Using an assumed mean find the mean of these data sets.

a 2006 2004 2005 2002 2009 2004
b 1.6 1.4 1.5 1.9 1.4 1.2

3 Draw a frequency diagram to represent this data.

Time (seconds)	0–15	15–30	30–45	45–60
Frequency	4	7	8	5

This spread will show you how to:
▶▶ Discuss how data relate to a problem.
▶▶ Identify possible sources of data, including primary and secondary sources.
▶▶ Design a survey or experiment to capture the data from one or more sources.

KEYWORDS
Experiment
Hypothesis
Primary data
Secondary data

Charlie is spinning coins on a table.
She wonders how long it would be possible to keep a coin spinning.

Charlie thinks about the type of data she could collect.

She considers how she could collect the data.

I could ask people to spin a coin – that would be primary data.

Should I use the same coin each time? What about the table surface?

She starts to focus on a set of aims for her experiment.

Charlie thinks further about how to collect the data.

10p coins are bigger than 5p coins, so they should spin longer.

Would the coin's age make a difference? How will I time the spin?

Charlie writes each possible aim in the form of a **hypothesis**.

Remember: A hypothesis is a statement that you are trying to test.

Hypothesis	Reason
1 A 10p coin will spin for longer than a 5p coin.	10p coins are bigger.
2 An older coin will spin for longer than a new coin.	Older coins have a smoother edge.
3 If you spin a coin five times, the longest spin will be the fifth one.	Practice makes perfect!

▶ When you write an aim or hypothesis you should try to give a reason.
▶ Data you collect yourself is primary data.
▶ Data you look up in books or on the internet is secondary data.

Exercise D3.1

For each of the situations described in questions 1 to 5:

a Write down a hypothesis that you can test, giving reasons for your choice.
b Identify what data you will need to test your hypothesis.

State if it is primary or secondary data.
(You may be able to collect data from more than one source.)

1 Dave was investigating spinning coins at his school.
He had two ideas that he wanted to investigate.
  i Does your age make any difference to how long you can spin a coin?
  ii Does it make a difference to how long you can spin a coin if you are left-handed or right-handed?

2 Kylie listens to many different types of music.
She thinks that the length of a song depends upon what type of music it is.

3 Sally had become very forgetful.
She wondered if men and women got forgetful as they got older.

4 Helen's mum was always saying, 'I'll do that in a minute' and not doing it for ages.
Helen wondered whether people actually knew how long a minute was.

5 Evan read in a book that hand span and wrist measurement were related.

He wondered if any other body measurements were related.

This spread will show you how to:
▶▶ Design a survey or experiment to capture the data from one or more sources.
▶▶ Determine the sample size and degree of accuracy needed.
▶▶ Design, trial and, if necessary, refine data collection sheets.

KEYWORDS
Observation   Sample size
Questionnaire   Experiment
Data logging

Charlie decides to investigate two hypotheses:

▶ You can spin a 2p coin longer than a 10p coin.
▶ Girls will be more consistent spinning 2p and 10p coins than boys.

Charlie asks class 8R to carry out the coin spinning experiment.
There are 27 pupils in the class, 12 girls and 15 boys.
This is a small **sample size**.

When Charlie collects the data she will need to note:

1 the spin times of the 2p and 10p coin from each person
2 if it is a boy or a girl.

Generally the larger the sample size, the more accurate the results.

Her first **data collection sheet** has three columns.

Gender	2p time	10p time

To answer her second hypothesis Charlie sorts her data into two sheets, one for girls and one for boys.

Girls

2p time	10p time

Boys

2p time	10p time

Charlie collects her data in a **controlled experiment**.

Some other ways to collect primary data are:

▶ **Observation**
You watch what happens and record the results.

▶ **Data Logging**
Data is collected automatically by a device and can be saved by a computer.

▶ **Questionnaire**
You ask individuals a set of questions.
The data can be facts or opinions.

Exercise D3.2

1 For each of the hypotheses you chose for each question in exercise D3.1 on page 229:

    a describe how you would carry out a survey or experiment to collect this data

    b design a data collection sheet to collect this data.

2 You are going to carry out a coin spinning experiment.

You can work in small groups on this question.

    a Write out one or more hypotheses that you would like to test.

       Give reasons for choosing these hypotheses.

    b Write down how you are going to carry out the experiment.

       i Include the sample size that you will need.

       ii Say how you are going to time each spin, and how accurate your times need to be.

       iii Write about what you are going to do to ensure that the experiment is fair.

    c Design the data collection sheet that you will use to collect the data.

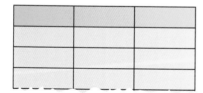

       You need to ensure that it is easy to use and that it will enable you to answer your hypotheses.

       You may want to refine the data collection sheet to sort the data.

    d Carry out your experiment and record your results in your data collection sheet.

       You should aim to collect at least 30 pieces of data.

This spread will show you how to:
▶▶ Calculate statistics.
▶▶ Communicate the results of a statistical enquiry.
▶▶ Justify the choice of what is presented.

KEYWORDS
Median Mode
Mean Range
Frequency diagram

These are the results of Charlie's coin spinning experiment.

Charlie performs some **analysis** on her results.

Gender	2p	10p
Boy	13	11
Boy	16	14
Girl	12	13
Girl	15	11
Boy	16	11
Boy	17	17
Boy	18	12
Girl	10	12
Boy	16	14
Girl	15	10
Boy	15	21
Girl	16	9
Boy	17	15
Girl	10	12
Girl	15	10
Girl	14	10
Boy	15	10
Girl	5	13
Boy	18	14
Girl	10	13
Girl	13	11
Boy	17	12
Boy	12	15
Girl	18	10
Boy	14	13
Boy	16	17
Boy	12	13

▶ Charlie finds the range and the mean of the times for each coin:
2p Range $18 - 5 = 13$; Mean $= 10 + \left(\frac{115}{27}\right) = 14.3$
10p Range $21 - 9 = 12$; Mean $= 10 + \left(\frac{73}{27}\right) = 12.7$

Charlie used an assumed mean of 10.

The spread of times is similar for both coins, but on average people can spin a 2p coin for longer than a 10p coin.

▶ Charlie displays the results in a graph.
The data is continuous so she decides to use **frequency diagrams**. Charlie groups the data first so that there will not be too many bars to see a pattern.

Time (s)	5–7	8–10	11–13	14–16	17–19	20–22
2p	1	2	6	12	6	0
10p	0	6	13	5	2	1

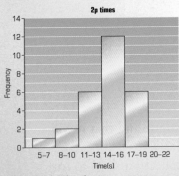

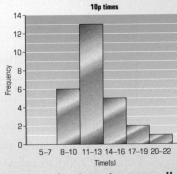

Although the longest time recorded is for a 10p coin, 2p coins generally spin for longer than 10p coins.

▶ You need to find the range and an average (mean, median or mode) to compare data.
▶ You should display data using graphs that will help answer your hypothesis.

Exercise D3.3

1   Use the results of Charlie's experiment, shown in the table on page 232.
   a Calculate the median and mode for   **i** 2p coins   **ii** 10p coins.

   b Comment on these results and suggest which average (mean, median or mode) is the most appropriate to use for these data. Give reasons for your choice.

   c Draw a scatter graph to display the results. Comment on what it shows.

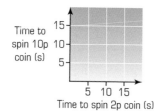

   d Group the data differently from Charlie's groupings, and draw frequency diagrams for your grouped data.

   e Compare your graphs with the graphs on page 232, and comment on any differences and similarities in how the data is represented.

2   Use the results of your own coin spinning experiment that you carried out in Exercise D3.2 on page 231.
   a Calculate:
      i the range
      ii the mean
      iii the median
      iv the mode of your data.
      Comment on what these results show and which average is the best to use.

   b Draw graphs to display your results that will help answer your hypothesis. Comment on your graphs.

Interpreting and discussing data

This spread will show you how to:
▶▶ Interpret tables, graphs and diagrams for continuous data.
▶▶ Compare two distributions using the range and one or more of the mode, median and mean.

KEYWORDS

Interpret

Infer

Scatter graph

Charlie organises results in order of the 2p spinning times.

Girls' times (seconds)

2p	5	10	10	12	12	13	14	15	15	15	16	18
10p	13	12	13	12	13	11	10	10	10	11	9	10

The 5 seconds value for the 2p coin may have been incorrect recorded, as it does not seem to fit with the rest of the data

Boys' times (seconds)

2p	12	12	13	14	15	15	16	16	16	16	17	17	17	18	18
10p	13	15	11	13	10	21	11	14	14	17	12	15	17	12	14

By inspection, Charlie notes the range and modal times in seconds.

	Girls		Boys	
	2p	10p	2p	10p
Range (s)	13	4	6	11
Mode (s)	15	10	16	14

If the 5 seconds value is ignored, the range for girls' 2p times is 8 seconds.

The statistics suggest that:

▶ Boys could keep a coin spinning longer than girls.

Modes (Girls)	15	10	(Boys)	16	14

The mode times for both coins are greater for boys than girls.

▶ Boys show more consistency between coins.

Range (Girls)	13	4	(Boys)	6	11

The range of spin times for both coins are closer for the boys.

Charlie draws scatter graphs for the results of the girls and boys.

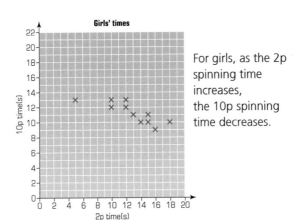

Girls' times

For girls, as the 2p spinning time increases, the 10p spinning time decreases.

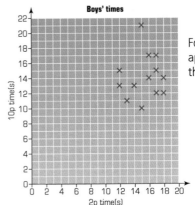

Boys' times

For boys, there is no apparent trend in the spinning times.

Exercise D3.4

1 The diagram shows a bar chart of the number of deaths per day, and a line graph of the sulphur levels in London during the great smog in December 1952. Compare and comment on the two graphs.

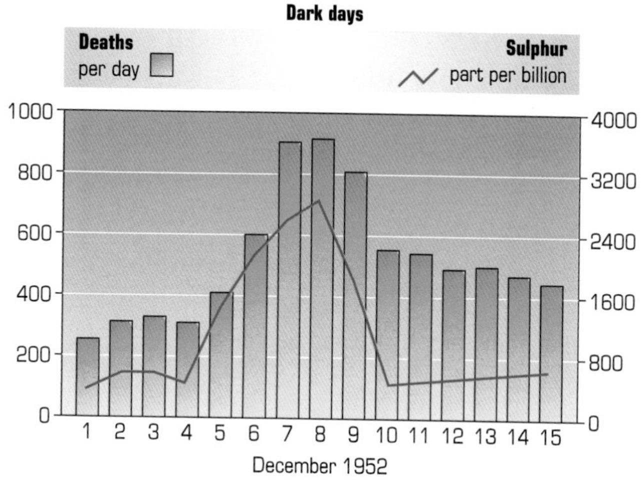

2 The table gives the number of pedestrian injuries (to the nearest 5) among children in Great Britain in 2000.

Age of casualty	0	1	2	3	4	5	6	7	8	9	10	11	12	13	14	15
Number of casualties	25	105	360	565	715	770	925	1035	1185	1335	1430	1765	1920	1565	1365	1125

a Draw a frequency polygon to represent these data and comment on your graph.
b Compare and comment on the figures for primary and secondary school children.
c Calculate the mean, median and mode for this data.
d Which of the three averages would you choose to represent the data? Give a reason for your answer.

3 The table gives the total number of student days absent for each year group in two schools.

	Year					
School	7	8	9	10	11	Total
Student numbers						
Cowpers	24	31	11	42	56	600
Darwings	57	65	29	84	135	1100

a Draw graphs to represent these data.
b Calculate statistics to compare these data.
c Use your graphs and statistics and compare the numbers of student absences in these two schools.

Summary

You should know how to ...

1 Design a survey or experiment to capture the necessary data from one or more sources.

2 Determine the sample size and degree of accuracy needed.

3 Design, trial and, if necessary, refine data collection sheets.

Check out

1 Design a survey and write out a hypothesis to investigate if there is a relationship between wrist circumference and hand span.
(You can expand on your answer to question 5 on page 229.)

2 For your survey in question 1 decide how much data you need to collect and how accurate your measurements need to be.

3 Design a data collection sheet to collect the data for your survey.

Experiments

I still haven't got the one I need for the full set – and it's my seventh packet!

You can use a simulation to help work out probability.

Before you start

You should know how to ...

1 List all outcomes from two events.

2 Calculate the mean of a set of discrete data.

3 Estimate probabilities from a simple experiment.

4 Solve a linear equation.

Check in

1 Two coins are thrown. List all the possible ways they could land.

2 Calculate the mean of these numbers:

$$41 \quad 32 \quad 29 \quad 37 \quad 21$$

3 In a survey of 30 people, 8 were left-handed and 22 were right-handed.
Estimate the probability that the next person you ask will be right-handed.

4 Solve these equations.

  a $3x = 630$ b $\frac{1}{25} = \frac{4}{x}$ c $\frac{2}{7} = \frac{7}{x}$

Experiment and theory

This spread will show you how to:
- ▶▶ Design an experiment to capture the necessary data.
- ▶▶ Compare experimental evidence and theoretical probabilities.
- ▶▶ Appreciate the difference between mathematical explanation and experimental evidence.

KEYWORDS

Experimental evidence

Theoretical probability

Two-dice bingo is a game for two or more players.

- ▶ Each player has a card with ten numbers, chosen from 2 to 12 (some numbers may be repeated).
- ▶ Two dice are thrown and the scores are added. If you have their sum on your card you cross it off. Only one number may be crossed off per throw.
- ▶ The first person to cross off all ten numbers wins.

Rukshana and Lauren change the numbers on their cards to give them a better chance of winning.
They wonder what numbers they should choose.

First they draw a possibility space diagram.

+	1	2	3	4	5	6
1	2	3	4	5	6	7
2	3	4	5	6	7	8
3	4	5	6	7	8	9
4	5	6	7	8	9	10
5	6	7	8	9	10	11
6	7	8	9	10	11	12

This shows the number of ways to score each number.

Then they draw a bar chart for the frequencies.

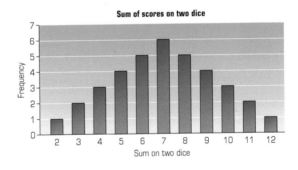

Sum of scores on two dice

The value with the highest frequency is 7.

Rukshana and Lauren make up their cards ...
Rukshana makes up a card with all 7s.

Lauren makes up a card with mainly 7s, but also a few numbers either side.

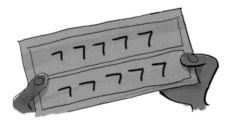

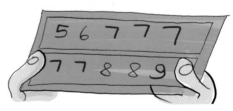

Rukshana knows that the theoretical probability of a 7 is higher than any other number.

From experimental evidence, Lauren suspects that you are very unlikely to get all 7s.

Lauren wins (this time)!

▶ Experimental evidence is not always the same as theoretical probability.

Exercise D4.1

In the game of dominoes there are 28 pieces.
Each piece is divided into two halves.
Each half is marked with between 0 and 6 dots.

1 The sum of the dots on a domino is from 0 to 12 inclusive.

  a Draw a sample space diagram to show the different ways you can
  get each sum of dots on a domino.

	1st half						
	0	1	2	3	4	5	6
2nd half 0							
1							

  b Draw a frequency table to show the total frequency of each score.

Total score	0	1	2
Frequency			

  c Devise, with reasons, a strategy to win a game similar to two-dice bingo,
  but where the sum of dots on a domino is used in place of two dice.

  d In pairs, use your strategy to play several games of domino bingo.

  e Comment on your strategy and that of your partner.

2 Courtney has a bag of 28 dominoes.
He chooses a domino at random, makes a note of the total sum,
and replaces it in the bag.
He repeats this 100 times.
His results are shown in the table.

Sum	0	1	2	3	4	5	6	7	8	9	10	11	12
Frequency	2	3	7	7	11	13	14	12	10	6	5	6	4

  a Use the frequency table in question **1b** to calculate the theoretical
  probability of each score.

  b Compare the theoretical and experimental probabilities.
  Comment on your answer.

3 Poppy invents an enlarged domino set in which each half is marked
with between 0 and 7 dots.

  a How many pieces will there be?

  b Draw a sample space diagram to show the different total scores.

  c Draw a bar chart to show the frequency of each score.

There is a free car inside every packet of a certain breakfast cereal. Karl wants to collect the whole set of toy cars.

There are six different coloured cars: blue, green, red, yellow, orange and white.

Karl may be lucky and get a different colour in each of the first six boxes of cereal that he opens.
He may have to open 20, 30 or even 100 boxes of cereal before he has collected the set.

To find out how many boxes may be needed Karl decides to run a **simulation**.

He matches each colour to a number on a dice.
Karl then rolls the dice until he has one of each number.

The first time that Karl ran the simulation he got:

5	5	4	3	5	4	2	5	1	1	6

It took 11 rolls of the dice to get one of each number, so 11 boxes of cereal would be needed.
The second time that Karl ran the simulation he got:

6	2	3	2	4	1	4	5

This time it only took 8 rolls of the dice.

The average of these two trials is $\frac{11 + 8}{2} = 9.5$, so on average Karl would need 9.5 boxes of cereal (10 boxes in practice!).

▶ The more times you repeat a simulation the more confident you can be in the results.

Exercise D4.2

1 A restaurant offers three starters on its set menu: prawn cocktail, melon and soup.

> **Menu**
>
> Starters
> ___
> Prawn cocktail
> Melon
> Soup of the day

a Describe how you could use a dice to simulate the choice of starter that people might choose.
What assumptions do you need to make?

b Suppose that 20 people choose the set menu one evening.
Use a dice to carry out a simulation and find out how many of each starter the chef may need.

c Compare your answers with others in your class.

Over a long period of time the chef notices that, on average out of every six customers, 3 choose prawn cocktail, 2 choose melon and 1 chooses soup.

d Describe how you could use a dice to simulate the choice of starter that people might choose.

e Carry out this simulation for a group of 20 people.

2 Find the function on a scientific calculator that generates random digits.
Each time you press this key a different number between 0 and 1 is shown.

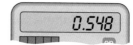

You are going to run a simulation using only the **first** digit after the decimal point that your calculator generates.

The restaurant offers four desserts.

> **Desserts**
> ___
> Chocolate fudge cake
> Ice-cream sundae
> Creme caramel
> Fresh fruit salad

Over a long period of time the chef notices that:

> 40% of customers choose chocolate fudge cake.
> 30% of customers choose ice-cream sundae.
> 20% of customers choose creme caramel.
> 10% of customers choose fresh fruit salad.

a Assign the digits 0 to 9 to the choices for dessert in the proportions given.

b Use your calculator to simulate the choices made by 50 customers at the restaurant.

c Compare your results with other people in your class.

Statistical experiments

This spread will show you how to:
- ▶▶ Suggest a problem to explore using statistical methods, frame questions and raise conjectures.
- ▶▶ Design an experiment to capture the data necessary from one or more sources.
- ▶▶ Determine the sample size needed.

KEYWORDS

Sample   Population

Proportion   Experiment

Alex had a bag of rice.
She wanted to know how many grains of rice there were in the bag.

Alex tipped out an initial sample of 100 grains and she coloured all of them.

Proportion of coloured grains = $\frac{100}{n}$, where n is the number of rice grains in the bag.
Alex put all 100 grains of rice back and shook the bag.

Alex then took out 50 grains of rice.
She found that in this sample four were coloured.

Proportion of coloured grains = $\frac{4}{50}$

If the two proportions are the same then

$$\frac{4}{50} = \frac{100}{n}$$
$$n = \frac{100 \times 50}{4}$$
$$n = 1250$$

So an estimate of the number of grains of rice in the bag is 1250.

This is an example of the **capture-recapture** method of sampling.

▶ You can use the capture-recapture method to estimate the size of a self-contained population.

▶ You need to thoroughly mix the initial sample with the whole population for the estimate to be reliable.

Exercise D4.3

1 Lewis wanted to estimate the number of deer living in an area of woodland.
A sample of 30 of the deer were caught, tagged and set free.
The next day a second sample of 12 deer were caught.
Five of this sample were tagged.
Estimate the number of deer in this area of woodland.

2 At a bird sanctuary, 60 ducks were caught, tagged and returned to the sanctuary.
In a second sample of 100 ducks, 24 were tagged.
Find an estimate of the number of ducks in the bird sanctuary.

3 Jenna wanted to estimate how many fish were living in her pond.
She caught an initial sample of 12 fish, tagged them and returned them to
the pond.

After a short while the fish had all intermingled and Jenna caught a second
sample of eight fish. In this sample three were tagged.
a Find an estimate of how many fish are living in the pond.

Later that day Jenna took a sample of ten fish. In this sample four were tagged.
b Use this sample to find an estimate of the number of fish in the pond.
c How could Jenna obtain a better estimate of the number of fish in her pond?

Experiment

4 This is an experiment to do in small groups.
a Take a number of like objects , such as uncooked pasta
or marbles, and place them in a large bag.

> Three-coloured pasta
> (tricolore) is widely available
> in supermarkets.

b Remove some of the objects and mark them in some way
to make them different from the rest.
c Put the objects back in the bag and shake up the bag.
d Each person in the group takes turns to remove a sample of the objects
(you decide for yourself how big you want the sample to be), and then
finds an estimate for the total number in the bag.
e Compare your estimates and decide on the best estimate for your group.
f Tip out all the objects and count them to find how close your estimate
was to the actual number in the bag.
g Compare the estimate of your group with the estimates of other groups
in the class.

You should know how to ...

1 Design an experiment to capture the necessary data from one or more sources.

Check out

1 a You are running the treasure hunt stall at your school fete.

You want to make a profit to donate to the charity your school is supporting.

Design an experiment to find out how much you might make if the treasure costs £4 and you charge 50p for each guess. (You win the treasure if you guess correctly).

b On a particular stretch of road there are three sets of traffic lights.

For each set of lights:

p(green) = 0.6, p(amber) = 0.1, p(red) = 0.3

Hanif knows that if all three sets of lights are green, he can cycle home in five minutes.
In a typical week, Hanif cycles along the stretch of road 10 times.
Use the random number key on your calculator to perform a simulation of the traffic lights.
Hence estimate the number of times in a week that Hanif can expect to cycle home in five minutes.

algebra

Algebra is the branch of mathematics where symbols or letters are used to represent numbers.

algebraic expression
A2.5

An algebraic expression is a term, or several terms connected by plus and minus signs.

alternate
S1.1, S1.2

A pair of alternate angles is formed when a straight line crosses a pair of parallel lines. Alternate angles are equal.

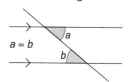

angle: acute, obtuse, right, reflex

An angle is formed when two straight lines cross or meet each other at a point.
The size of an angle is measured by the amount one line has been turned in relation to the other.

An acute angle is less than 90°.

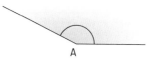

An obtuse angle is more than 90° but less than 180°.

A right angle is a quarter of a turn, or 90°.

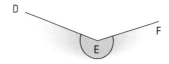

A reflex angle is more than 180° but less than 360°.

angles on a straight line
S1.1, S1.2

Angles on a straight line add up to 180°.

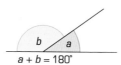

approximate
N3.5, A4.4

To approximate an answer is to work out a rough answer using easier figures.

area
S2.1

The area of a surface is a measure of its size.
Square millimetre, square centimetre, square metre, square kilometre are all units of area.

arc
S1.4

An arc is part of a curve.

bar chart
D2.6, D4.2

The heights of the bars on a bar chart represent the frequencies of the data.

base (number)
A2.1

The base is the number which is raised to a power. For example in 2^3, 2 is the base.

bearing, three-figure bearing
S4.5

A bearing is a clockwise angle measured from the North line giving the direction of a point from a reference point.
A bearing should always have three digits.

The bearing of B
from A is 120°.

bias
D1.6

An experiment or selection is biased if not all outcomes are equally likely.

BIDMAS
A2.1, A4.2, N4.3

BIDMAS is a mnemonic to remind you of the correct order of operations: **b**rackets, **i**ndices, **d**ivision or **m**ultiplication, **a**ddition or **s**ubtraction.

bisect, bisector
S4.7

To bisect is to cut in half.
A bisector is a line that cuts something in half.

cancel
N4.5

You cancel a fraction by dividing the numerator and denominator by a common factor.

capacity
S2.2

Capacity is a measure of how much liquid a hollow 3-D shape can hold.

centre
S4.8

The centre of a circle is the point from which all points on the circumference are equidistant.

centre of rotation
S3.1

The centre of rotation is the fixed point about which a rotation takes place.

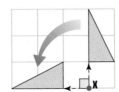

chord
S1.4

A chord is a straight line joining two points on a curve, or a circle.

circumference
S1.4, S2.3, S2.4

The circumference is the distance around the edge of a circle.

coefficient
A2.3, A3.2, A3.3,

The coefficient is the number part of an algebraic term. For example in $3n^5$ the coefficient of n^5 is 3.

collect like terms
A2.3

To collect like terms is to put together terms with the same letter parts. For example $5x + 3x = 8x$ and $4y^2 - y^2 = 3y^2$.

common factor
NA1.3, A2.3

A common factor is a factor of two or more numbers or terms. For example $2p$ is a common factor of $2p^2$ and $6p$.

commutative
N4.1, N4.2

An operation is commutative if the order of combining two terms does not matter.

compasses
S1.5

A pair of compasses is a geometrical instrument used to draw circles or arcs.

compensation
N3.3

The method of compensation is used to make calculations easier. For example to add 99, add 100 and then compensate by subtracting 1.

conclude, conclusion
A5.2

To conclude is to formulate a result or conclusion based on evidence.

congruent
S3.1, S3.2, S3.3

Congruent shapes are exactly the same shape and size.

constant
A3.3

A constant is an algebraic term that remains unchanged. For example, in the expression $5x + 3$ the constant is 3.

construction lines
S1.5

Construction lines are the arcs drawn when making an accurate diagram.

continuous
D3.3

Continuous data can take any value between given limits, for example height.

coordinates
S4.6

The coordinates of a point give its position in terms of its distance from the origin along the x- and y- axes.

correlation
D2.4

Correlation is a measure of the relationship between two variables.

corresponding
S1.1, S1.2

A pair of corresponding angles is formed when a straight line crosses a pair of parallel lines. Corresponding angles are equal.

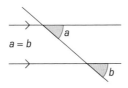

Glossary

counter-example
P1.3

A counter-example is an example that shows that a rule does not work.

cross-multiply
A4.1

Cross-multiplying is a method for removing fractions from equations.

cross-section
S2.5

The cross-section of a solid is the shape of its transverse section.

cube root
NA1.4

The cube root of x is the number that when cubed gives you x. For example $\sqrt[3]{64} = 4$, because $4 \times 4 \times 4 = 64$.

cubic
S2.5

A cubic equation contains a term in x^3 as its highest power.

data
D2.1, D3.1

Data are pieces of information.

data collection sheet
D3.2, D3.4

A data collection sheet is a form designed for the systematic collection of data.

data logging
D3.2

Data logging is the automatic collection of data.

decagon
S1.3

A decagon has ten sides.

decimal
N2.1, N2.6, N3.6, N4.1

A decimal number is a number written using base ten notation.

decimal place
N3.2

Each column after the decimal point is called a decimal place.

degree (°)

Angles are measured in degrees. There are 360° in a full turn.

degree of accuracy
N3.2

The degree of accuracy of an answer depends on the accuracy of the figures used in the calculation.

denominator
N2.2, A4.2

The denominator is the bottom number in a fraction. It shows how many parts there are in the whole.

diagonal
A3.1

A diagonal line is one which is neither horizontal nor vertical.

diameter
S1.4, S2.3, S2.4

The diameter is a chord that passes through the centre of a circle.

difference pattern
NA1.5, NA1.6

You can find a general rule for a sequence by looking at the pattern of differences between consecutive terms.

digit
N3.1

A digit is any of the numbers 0, 1, 2, 3, 4, 5, 6, 7, 8, 9.

dimension
P1.6

A dimension is a length, width or height of a shape or solid.

direct proportion
A5.5, A5.6

Two quantities are in direct proportion if one quantity increases at the same rate as the other.

distance-time graph
A3.6

A distance-time graph is a graph of distance travelled against time taken.
Time is plotted on the horizontal axis.

distribution
D3.4

A distribution is a set of observations of a variable.

divisible, divisibility
NA1.3

A whole number is divisible by another if there is no remainder after division.

divisor

The divisor is the number that does the dividing.
For example, in $14 \div 2 = 7$ the divisor is 2.

edge (of solid)
S4.1

An edge is a line along which two faces of a solid meet.

edge

elevation
S4.2

An elevation is an accurate drawing of the side or front of a solid.

enlargement
33.5, S3.6

An enlargement is a transformation that multiplies all the sides of a shape by the same scale factor.

equation
A2.6

An equation is a statement showing that two expressions have the same value.

equation (of a graph)
A3.3

An equation is a statement showing the relationship between the variables on the axes.

equidistant
S4.7, S4.8

Equidistant means the same distance apart.

equivalent, equivalence
N3.5, N3.6

Two quantities, such as fractions which are equal, but are expressed differently, are equivalent.

estimate
S2.1, N3.2, N3.5, N3.6,
N4.4, N4.5, N4.6

An estimate is an approximate answer.

evaluate
P1.1, A4.5

Evaluate means find the value of an expression.

event
D1.1, D1.2

In probability an event is a trial or experiment.

expand
A2.4

To expand an expression you remove all the brackets.

Glossary

experiment
D4.2, D4.3

An experiment is a test or investigation to gather evidence for or against a theory.

experimental probability
D1.4, D1.5, D1.6

You can find the experimental probability of an event by conducting trials.

expression
A2.1, A2.4

An expression is a collection of terms linked with operations but with no equals sign.

exterior angle
S1.2, S1.3

An exterior angle is made by extending one side of a shape.

face
S4.1

A face is a flat surface of a solid.

face

factor
NA1.2, A2.4, N3.4

A factor is a number that divides exactly into another number. For example, 3 and 7 are factors of 21.

factorise
A2.4, A5.3

You factorise an expression by writing it with a common factor outside brackets.

formula, formulae
NA1.6, A2.4, S2.1, A4.5,
A4.6, A5.1

A formula is a statement that links variables.

frequency
D4.2

The frequency is the number of times an event occurs.

frequency diagram
D3.3

A frequency diagram uses bars to display data.
The height of the bars corresponds to the frequencies.

function, linear function
A5.5, A5.7

A function is a rule.
The graph of a linear function is a straight line.

generalise
A5.1, A5.2, P1.2, P1.3

Generalise means find a statement or rule that applies to all cases.

general term
NA1.6

The general term in a sequence allows you to evaluate unknown terms.

gradient
A3.1, A3.2, A3.3, A3.4,
A3.6, A5.5, A5.7

Gradient is a measure of the steepness of a line.

graph
A3.1

A graph is a diagram that shows a relationship between variables.

greater than or equal to (⩾)
A4.4

The symbol ⩾ means that the term on the left-hand side is greater than or equal to the term on the right-hand side.

hectare
S2.1, N4.6

A hectare is a unit of area equal to 10 000 (100 × 100) square metres.

hexagon
S1.3

A hexagon has six sides.

highest common factor (HCF)
NA1.3, A2.5, A5.3

The highest common factor is the largest factor that is common to two or more numbers.
For example the HCF of 12 and 8 is 4.

horizontal
A3.1, S4.9

A horizontal line is parallel to the ground.

hypotenuse
S1.6, S4.9

The hypotenuse is the side opposite the right angle in a right-angled triangle.

hypothesis
D3.1

A hypothesis is a statement used as a starting point for a statistical investigation.

identically equal to (≡)
A5.3

One expression is identically equal to another if they are mathematically equivalent.

identity
A5.3

An identity is an equation which is true for all possible values.
For example $3x + 6 \equiv 3(x + 2)$ for all values of x.

image
S3.6

An image is an object after it has been transformed.

implicit
A5.8

An equation in x and y is in implicit form if y is not the subject of the equation.

improper fraction
A4.2

In an improper fraction the numerator is bigger than the denominator.

index, indices
A2.1, A2.2

The index tells you how many of a quantity must be multiplied together. For example x^3 means $x \times x \times x$.

index laws
NA1.4, A2.3

To multiply powers of the same base add the indices, for example $2^5 \times 2^3 = 2^8$.
To divide powers of the same base subtract the indices.
For example $5^6 \div 5^3 = 5^2$.

index notation
NA1.4, A2.2

A number written as a power of a base number is expressed in index notation, for example $\frac{1}{1000} = 10^{-3}$.

inequality
NA1.1, A4.4, A5.4

An inequality is a relationship between two numbers or terms that are comparable but not equal.
For example, $7 > 4$.

infer
D2.3

Infer means to conclude from evidence.

inscribe, inscribed
S1.4

An inscribed polygon has every vertex lying on the perimeter of a shape, such as a circle.

Glossary

integer
NA1.1, N2.3, N3.5, N3.6,
A4.4, N4.1, N4.5

An integer is a positive or negative whole number (including zero).
The integers are: ..., ⁻3, ⁻2, ⁻1, 0, 1, 2, 3, ...

intercept
A3.1, A3.3, A5.7

The intercept is the point at which a graph crosses the axis.

interior angle
S1.2, S1.3

An interior angle is inside a shape, between two
adjacent sides.

interpret
D2.3

You interpret data whenever you make sense of it.

intersection
S1.6

The intersection of two lines is the point where they cross.

inverse function
A3.1

An inverse function acts in reverse to a
specified function.

justify
NA1.5, A2.5, N3.5, N3.6,
N4.3, N4.4, A5.2

You justify a solution of a formula by explaining why it is correct.

less than or equal to ($\leqslant$)
A4.4

The symbol $\leqslant$ means that the term on the left-hand side is less than
or equal to the term on the right-hand side.

like terms
A4.2

Like terms are terms with the same letter parts, for example $3x^2$ and
$-5x^2$ are like terms.

line graph
D2.6

On a line graph points are joined with straight lines.

line of best fit
A5.7

A line of best fit passes through the points on a scatter graph,
leaving roughly as many above the line as below it.

line segment
S4.6

A line segment is the part of a line between two points.

linear equation, linear graph
A4.1, A4.3, A5.7

A linear equation contains no squared or higher terms.
The graph of a linear equation is a straight line.

linear expression
A2.3

A linear expression contains no square or higher terms, for example
$3x + 5$ is a linear expression.

linear sequence
NA1.5

The terms of a linear sequence increase by the same amount each
time.

locus, loci
S4.7, S4.8

A locus is a set of points (a line, a curve or a region) that satisfies certain conditions.

lowest common multiple (LCM)
NA1.3, N2.2

The lowest common multiple is the smallest multiple that is common to two or more numbers, for example the LCM of 4 and 6 is 12.

mapping
A3.1

A mapping is a rule that can be applied to a set of numbers to give another set of numbers.

mass
S2.2

The mass of an object is a measure of the quantity of matter in it.

mean
D2.3, D2.5, D3.3

The mean is the average value found by adding the data and dividing by the number of data items.

median
D2.3, D2.5, D3.3

The median is the average which is the middle value when the data is arranged in order of size.

metric system
N4.6, P1.6

In the metric system, units of measurement are related by multiples of ten.

mid-point
S4.6

The mid-point of a line segment is the point that is halfway along.

mirror line
S3.1

A mirror line is a line or axis of symmetry.

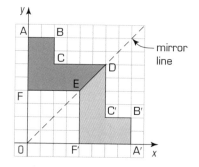

modal class
D2.3

The modal class is the most commonly occurring class when the data is grouped.
It is the class with the highest frequency.

mode
D2.3, D3.3

The mode is an average.
It is the value that occurs most often.

multiple
NA1.3

A multiple of an integer is the product of that integer and any other. For example 12, 18 and 30 are multiples of 6.

multiple bar chart
D2.6

A multiple bar chart is a bar chart with two or more sets of bars.
It is used to compare two or more data sets.

mutually exclusive
D1.2

Two events are mutually exclusive if they cannot occur at the same time.

negative
NA1.1, A2.2

A negative number is a number less than zero.

net
S2.6, S4.2

A net is a 2-D shape that can be folded to make a 3-D solid.

Glossary

nth term
NA1.6

The *n*th term is the general term of a sequence.

numerator
A4.2

The numerator is the top number in a fraction.
It tells you how many parts of the whole you have.

object, image
S3.1

The object is the original shape before a transformation.
An image is the shape after a transformation.

operation
N4.3

An operation is a rule for processing numbers.
The basic operations are addition, subtraction, multiplication and division.

order of operations
N4.3

The conventional order of operations is:
brackets first, then indices,
then division and multiplication,
then addition and subtraction.

order of rotational symmetry
S3.4

The order of rotation symmetry is the number of times that a shape will fit on to itself during a full turn.

origin

The origin is the point where the *x*- and *y*-axes cross, that is (0, 0).

outcome
D1.1, D1.2, D1.5

In probability an outcome is the result of a trial.

parallel
S1.1, A3.1,
A3.2, A3.4

Parallel lines are always the same distance apart.

partitioning
N3.3, N3.4

Partitioning means splitting a number into smaller parts.

perimeter
A4.3, S3.6

The perimeter is the distance round the edge of a shape.

perpendicular
S1.6, A3.4

A line or plane is perpendicular to another line or plane if they meet at a right angle.

perpendicular bisector
S4.7

The perpendicular bisector of a line is the line that divides it into two equal parts and is at right angles to it.

AM = MB

pi (π) S2.3	The ratio $\dfrac{circumference}{diameter}$ is the same for all circles. This ratio is denoted by the Greek letter π.
pie chart D2.2	A pie chart is a circular diagram used to display data. The angle in each sector is proportional to the frequency.
place value N3.1	The place value is the value of a digit in a decimal number. For example in 3.65 the digit 6 has a value of $\frac{6}{10}$.
plan, plan view S4.2	The plan or plan view of a solid is an accurate drawing of the view from directly above.
plane S4.1	A plane is a flat surface.
plane of symmetry S3.4, S4.1	A plane of symmetry divides a solid into two halves.
polygon S1.3	A polygon is a shape with three or more straight sides.
population D4.2, D4.3	The population is the complete set of individuals from which a sample is drawn.
position-to-term rule NA1.5	A position-to-term rule tells you how to calculate the value of a term if you know its position in the sequence.
positive NA1.1, A2.2	A positive number is greater than zero.
power NA1.4, NA1.6, A2.5, N3.1, N4.3	The power of a number or a term tells you how many of the number must be multiplied together. For example 10 to the power 4 is 10 000.
primary data, primary source D2.1, D3.1	Primary data is data you have collected yourself.
prime NA1.3	A prime number is a number that has exactly two different factors.
prime factor NA1.3	A prime factor is a factor that is a prime number.
prime factor decomposition NA1.3	Prime factor decomposition means splitting a number into its prime factors.
prism S2.5	A prism is a solid with a uniform cross-section.

product NA1.2, N3.4	The product is the result of a multiplication. For example, the product of 3 and 4 is 12.
proportion A5.5, A5.6, N2.1, N2.6, N3.8, P1.4, P1.5, D4.3	A proportion compares the size of a part to the size of the whole.

Glossary

proportional to (∝)
N3.9

When two quantities are in direct proportion one quantity is proportional to the other.

prove, proof
S1.1

You prove a statement is true by arguing from known facts.

quadratic
A3.5

A quadratic expression contains a square term.

quadratic sequence
NA1.6

In a quadratic sequence the second difference is constant.

quadrilateral
S1.3

A quadrilateral is a polygon with four sides.

rectangle   parallelogram   kite

All angles are right angles.   Two pairs of parallel   Two pairs of adjacent sides
Opposite sides equal.   sides.   equal. No interior angle
                                                           greater than 180°.

rhombus   square   trapezium

All sides the same length.   All sides and angles equal.   One pair of parallel sides.
Opposite angles equal.

quotient
NA1.2

A quotient is the result of a division.
For example, the quotient of $12 \div 5$ is $2\frac{2}{5}$, or 2.4.

radius
S1.4, S2.3, S2.4

The radius is the distance from the centre to the circumference of a circle.

random process
D1.1

The outcome of a random process cannot be predicted.

range
D2.3, D2.5, D3.3

The range is the difference between the largest and smallest values in a set of data.

ratio
N3.7, N3.8, N3.9, S3.6, A5.6,
P1.4, P1.5, P1.6, S4.4

A ratio compares the size of one part with the size of another part.

raw data
D2.5

Raw data is data before it has been processed.

reciprocal
A2.2, A3.4, N4.2, A5.6

The reciprocal of a quantity k is $1 \div k$.
For example the reciprocal of 5 is $\frac{1}{5}$ or 0.2; the reciprocal of x^2 is $\frac{1}{x^2}$.

recurring
N2.1

A recurring decimal has a repeating pattern of digits after the decimal point, for example 0.33333 ...

reflect, reflection
S3.1

A reflection is a transformation in which corresponding points in the object and the image are the same distance from the mirror line.

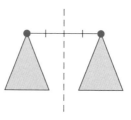

reflection symmetry
S3.4

A shape has reflection symmetry if it has a line of symmetry.

regular
S1.3

A regular polygon has equal sides and equal angles.

rotate, rotation
S3.1

A rotation is a transformation in which every point in the object turns through the same angle relative to a fixed point.

rotation symmetry
S3.4

A shape has rotation symmetry if when turned it fits onto itself more than once during a full turn.

right prism
S2.5

Apart from its two end faces, the faces of a right prism are all rectangles.

rounding
N3.2, N3.3, N3.5

You round a number by expressing it to a given degree of accuracy.

sample
D1.5, D4.1

A sample is a set of individuals or items drawn from a population.

sample space, sample space diagram
D1.1, D1.2

In probability the set of all possible outcomes in an experiment is called the sample space.
A sample space diagram is a diagram recording all the outcomes.

scale
S4.4

A scale gives the ratio between the size of an object and its diagram.

scale drawing
S4.5

A scale drawing is an accurate drawing of a shape to a given scale.

scale factor
N3.7, N3.9, S3.5, S3.6

A scale factor is a multiplier.

scatter graph
D2.4, D3.4

Pairs of variables, for example age and height, can be plotted on a scatter graph.

Glossary

secondary data, secondary source
D2.1, D3.1

Secondary data is data that someone else has collected. Common secondary sources include books, magazines and the Internet.

sector
S1.4, S2.4

A sector is part of a circle bounded by an arc and two radii.

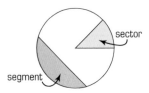

segment
S1.4

A segment is part of a circle bounded by an arc and a chord.

sequence
NA1.5, NA1.6

A sequence is a set of numbers, objects or terms that follow a rule.

similar, similarity
S2.3, A5.6

Similar shapes have the same shape but are different sizes.

simulation
D4.2

A simulation is an experiment designed to model a real-life situation.

simultaneous equations
A5.8

Simultaneous equations are two or more equations whose unknowns have the same values.

slope
A3.1

The slope of a line is measured by the angle it makes with the *x*-axis.

solid
S4.1, S4.2, S4.3

A solid is a shape formed in three-dimensional space.

cube

six square faces

cuboid

six rectangular faces

prism

the end faces are constant

pyramid

the faces meet
at a common vertex

tetrahedron

all the faces are
equilateral triangles

square-based pyramid

the base is a square

solution, solve
NA1.1, A2.6, A4.4, P1.1

The solution of an equation is the value that makes it true.

speed A3.6	Speed is a measure of the rate at which distance is covered. It is often measured in miles per hour or metres per second.
sphere S4.8	A sphere is a 3-D shape in which every point on its surface is equidistant from the centre.

square root NA1.4	A square root is a number that when multiplied by itself is equal to a given number. For example $\sqrt{25} = 5$, because $5 \times 5 = 25$.
steepness A3.1	The steepness of a line depends on the angle the line makes with the x-axis.
stem-and-leaf diagram D2.2, D2.3	A stem-and-leaf diagram is used to display raw data in numerical order.
straight-line graph A3.1, A3.2, A3.3, A3.4, A5.8	A straight-line graph is the graph of a linear equation.

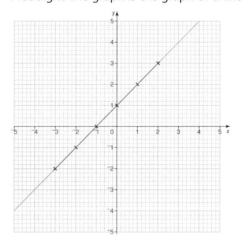

subject A3.3, A4.5, A4.6, A5.8	The subject of an equation or formula is the term on its own in front of the equals sign. For example, the subject of $v = u + at$ is v.
substitute A4.5, A5.4	To substitute is to replace a variable with a numerical value.
sum N3.4	The sum is the total of an addition.
supplementary S1.1	You can form a pair of supplementary angles on a straight line. Supplementary angles add up to 180°.

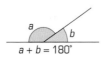

$a + b = 180°$

Glossary

surface area
S2.6, S4.3

The surface area of a solid is the total area of its faces.

symmetry, symmetrical
S4.1

A shape is symmetrical if it is unchanged after a rotation or reflection.

T(n)
NA1.6

T(n) stands for the general term in a sequence.

term
A2.3

A term is a number or object in a sequence.
It is also part of an expression.

terminating

A terminating decimal has a limited number of digits after the decimal point.

tessellation
S3.2

A tessellation is a tiling pattern with no gaps.

theoretical probability
D1.1, D1.3, D1.6, D4.1

The theoretical probability of an event
$$= \frac{\text{number of favourable outcomes}}{\text{total possible number of outcomes}}$$

tonne
S2.2

The tonne is a unit of mass, equal to 1000 kg.

transform
A2.5

You transform an expression by taking out single-term common factors.

transformation
S3

A transformation moves a shape from one place to another.

translate, translation
S3.1

A translation is a transformation in which every point in an object moves the same distance and direction.
It is a sliding movement.

tree diagram
D1.2, D1.3

A tree diagram shows the possible outcomes of a probability experiment on branches.

trend
D2.4, D3.4

A trend is a general tendency.

trial
D1.1, D1.5, D4.1

In probability a trial is an experiment.

trial and improvement
NA1.4, A5.4

Square roots, cube roots and solutions to equations can be estimated by the method of trial and improvement.
An estimated solution is tried in the expression and refined by a better estimate until the required degree of accuracy is achieved.

triangle
S1.6, S4.9

A triangle is a polygon with three sides.

equilateral	isosceles	scalene	right-angled

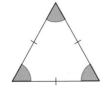

three equal sides	two equal sides	no equal sides	⌐ angle is 90°

triangular number
NA1.6

A triangular number is the number of dots in a triangular pattern:
The numbers form the sequence
1, 3, 6, 10, 15, 21, 28 ...

triangular prism
S2.6

A triangular prism is a prism with a triangular cross-section.

unit fraction
N2.3

A unit fraction has a numerator of 1.
For example, $\frac{1}{3}$ and $\frac{1}{7}$ are unit fractions.

unitary method
N2.5, N3.9

In the unitary method you calculate the value of one item or 1% first.

variable
A4.4, D2.4

A variable is a quantity that can have a range of values.

vector
S3.1

A vector describes a translation by giving the x- and y-components of the translation.

vertex, vertices
S4.1

A vertex of a shape is a point at which two or more edges meet.

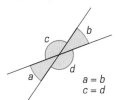

vertex

vertical
A3.1

A vertical line is at right angles to the horizontal.

vertically opposite angles
S1.1, S1.2

When two straight lines cross they form two pairs of equal angles called vertically opposite angles.

$a = b$
$c = d$

view
S4.2

A view of a solid is an accurate drawing of the appearance of the solid above, in front or from the side.

volume
S2.2, S4.3

Volume is a measure of the space occupied by a 3-D shape.
Cubic millimetres, cubic centimetres and cubic metres are all units of volume.

Glossary

x-axis, y-axis

A3.1

On a coordinate grid, the x-axis is the horizontal axis and the y-axis is the vertical axis.

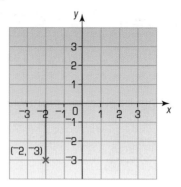

x-coordinate, y-coordinate

A3.1

The x-coordinate is the distance along the x-axis.
The y-coordinate is the distance along the y-axis.
For example, (⁻2, ⁻3) is ⁻2 along the x-axis and ⁻3 along the y-axis.

zero

N3.1

Zero is nought or nothing.
A zero place holder is used to show the place value of other digits in a number.
For example, in 1056 the 0 allows the 1 to stand for 1 thousand. If it wasn't there the number would be 156 and the 1 would stand for 1 hundred.

NA1 Check in

1 a 111   **b** 49   **c** 20

2 a 8   **b** $^-8$ **c** 36

   d 3   **e** 61   **f** 13

NA1 Check out

1 a $300 \times 1500 = 450\,000$

   b $20 \times 9 \times 5 = 900$ m

2 2.5 m by 2.5 m (square)

3 a i 10, 13, 16, 19, 22

     ii 3, 6, 11, 18, 27

     iii 5, 3, 1, $^-1$, $^-3$

     iv 3, 9, 19, 33, 51

   b i Linear   **ii** Quadratic   **iii** Linear

     iv Quadratic

   c $T(n) = \frac{n^3}{2}$ and 500, $T(n) = 10 - n^2$ and $^-90$, $T(n) = 2^n$ and 1024, $T(n) = (\frac{n}{2} + 3)^2$ and 64, $T(n) = (n + 1)(n + 4)$ and 154

4 a i $T(n) = 5n - 2$ **ii** $T(n) = n^2 - 1$

     iii $T(n) = 33 - 3n$ **iv** $T(n) = 3n^2$

     v $T(n) = \frac{(6n + 2)}{(n^2 + 2)}$

   b i 9, 16, 25, 36, 49

     ii $T(n) = (n + 5)^2$

S1 Check in

1 $a = 60°$, $b = 50°$, $c = 80°$

2 A Quadrilateral   **B** Isosceles trapezium

   C Regular pentagon

S1 Check out

1 $a = 42°$, $b = 138°$, $c = 42°$

   a is the corresponding angle to 42°.

   b is on a straight line with 42°

     $180° - 42 = 138°$.

   c is vertically opposite to a.

1 a $\frac{1}{10}$ **b** $\frac{1}{5}$

2 a $\frac{2}{3}$ **b** 0.76   **c** $\frac{3}{20}$

3

Pet	Tally	Frequency
Dog	ⲊⲊ ‖	7
Cat	ⲊⲊ	5
Rabbit	‖	2

1 a $\frac{7}{8}$ **b** 2   **c** $\frac{5}{8}$

2 a $\frac{1}{16}, \frac{1}{8}, \frac{3}{16}, \frac{1}{4}, \frac{3}{16}, \frac{1}{8}, \frac{1}{16}$

  b $\frac{3}{50}, \frac{7}{50}, \frac{4}{25}, \frac{6}{25}, \frac{9}{50}, \frac{3}{20}, \frac{2}{25}$

  c When you convert the fractions to decimals they are similar.
   The dice seem fair.

1 a $36 = 2^2 \times 3^2$, $48 = 2^4 \times 3$

  b i 12   **ii** 144

2 a 0.45, 45%   **b** 14.5%, $\frac{29}{200}$ **c** 0.26, $\frac{13}{50}$

3 a i 93 mg   **ii** £160

  b i 9.2   **ii** £42

1 a $\frac{-19}{55}$ **b** $1\frac{79}{136}$ **c** $1\frac{37}{60}$

  d $21\frac{7}{33}$ **e** $\frac{4}{21}$ **f** $\frac{16}{63}$

  g $7\frac{37}{45}$ **h** $1\frac{47}{100}$

2 a i 14 500   **ii** 5365

  b 75 km

3 a i $66\frac{2}{3}\%$ **ii** $10\frac{1}{3}\%$

  b £4480

4 pupils $\approx 5 \times 140 = 700$, number of school
   days $\approx 40 \times 5 = 200$

   So amount of water
   $\approx 4 \times 700 \times 200 = 560\,000$ litres

1 $3 \times 4 + 3$, $3 + 2^2 \times 3$, $3^3 - 4 \times 3$

2 $\frac{5}{10}$ and $\frac{11}{22}$, $\frac{4}{14}$ and $\frac{10}{35}$, $\frac{6}{9}$ and $\frac{14}{21}$, $\frac{3}{13}$ and $\frac{12}{52}$

3 a i   1, 2, 3, 4, 6, 12

    ii   1, 2, 3, 5, 6, 10, 15, 30

    iii   1, 2, 3, 4, 6, 8, 12, 16, 24, 48

   b i   6

    ii   12

    iii   6

    iv   6

1 a i   32   ii $^-27$ iii $\frac{1}{16}$

    iv   1   v $\frac{1}{25}$ vi   10 (or $^-10$)

   b i x^{14} ii y^8 iii z^6

    iv x^{-5} v $4x^6$

   c   False, it equals a^{-1}.

2 a $7x^2 + 7x$ b $7ab$ c $30xyz$

   d $3p$ e $20x^7$ f $9a - 10b$

   g $7x$ h $x + 14$ i $24x^3$

3 a $9(x + 2)$ b $5(5y - 3)$

   c $3b(1 + 3a)$ d $5x(2y + x - 3)$

4 a i $x = 1\frac{6}{7}$ ii $x = 3\frac{1}{7}$

   b $x = 5$

1 a   10 mm   b   0.56 m

2 a   21 m^2 b   31.5 m^2 c   2.88 m

   d   22.5 m^2

3   4.488 m^3

4 a   42.4   b   27.9   c   4.26

   d   116.0

1 a   26.4 cm   b   55.4 cm^2

2   42.72 m^2

3   28.2 m^3

1 $abc = ^-30$, $b^3 = ^-8$, $a - 2c = ^-7$, $\frac{(10 - b^2)}{a} = 2$, $c - 3b = 11$, $2a + 3b + 4c = 20$, $c^a = 125$

2 **b** The points form an arrow, which is a heptagon (7 sides).

3 **a** $y = 10 - x$

b $y = 2x + 4$

c $y = 3x + 3\frac{1}{2}$

d $y = \frac{1}{2}x + 7$

e $y = 4 - 1\frac{2}{3}x$

1 **a i** 3   **ii** $1\frac{1}{3}$ **iii** 1

b i $\frac{-1}{3}$ **ii** $\frac{-3}{4}$ **iii** $^-1$

2 **a i** The car starts at a steady speed (A), continues at a slower steady speed (B), stops for a while (C), then returns to the starting point at a steady speed (D).

b i Cup is full. Person takes a sip then waits a while, perhaps because it is too hot. Person drinks most of the tea, waits then finishes it or throws away the last bit.

ii The water is heating slowly to start with, then gradually quicker, then tends to a steady temperature.

iii The car accelerates, travels at a steady speed, then decelerates.

1 **a** 3   **b** 0   **c** 101

d 7

2 **a** 13 717   **b** 35 441   **c** $107\frac{2}{9}$

d 154.5

3

Fracton	Decimal	Percentage
$\frac{7}{12}$	$0.58\dot{3}$	$58.\dot{3}\%$
$3\frac{1}{4}$	3.25	325%
$2\frac{7}{10}$	2.7	270%
$\frac{1}{100}$	0.01	1%
$\frac{7}{20}$	0.35	35%
$\frac{33}{200}$	0.165	16.5%

1 **a** £16.42, 27.8%   **b** 9.5 m

2 **a** $(3600 + 400) \div 5 = 800$ **b** $\frac{(200 \div 40)}{9} = \frac{5}{9}$

1

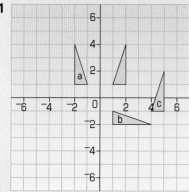

2 A $x = 4$ **B** $y = 3$

3 a Sphere   **b** Cone

  c Triangular prism

4 a $2 : 1$ **b** $1 : 3$

  c $20 : 1$ **d** $4 : 7$

1 a B, C, E

  b i Translation $\binom{3}{0}$

    ii Translation $\binom{-2}{-5}$

    iii Rotation through 90° clockwise about (1.5, 0.5)

    iv Translation $\binom{-5}{-5}$

2 a 3.8 cm, 25.2 cm

  b 96 cm   **c** 16 cm

  d $1 : 6$ **e** $1 : 36$

1 a $x = 17$ **b** $y = 4$ **c** $z = 3$

2 a $p = 3r + 2t$ **b** 5

3 a i $\frac{14}{45}$ **ii** $\frac{11}{21}$ **iii** $5\frac{7}{10}$

  b $4\frac{1}{9}$ cm

1 a i $x = {}^-11$ **ii** $x = \frac{1}{3}$ **iii** $x = 2$

    iv $x = 1\frac{1}{4}$ **v** $x = {}^-13\frac{2}{3}$

  b i $x = 3$ **ii** $x = 66$ **iii** $x = 3$

  c i You can write an inequality, $3x + 6 > 42$.

    ii It is greater than 12.

2 a i $A = \pi r^2$ **ii** $r = \sqrt{\left(\frac{A}{\pi}\right)}$

  b i $L = 10 - 2x$ **ii** $x = \frac{(10 - L)}{2}$

1

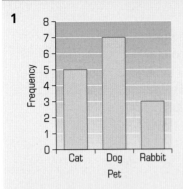

2 Mean = 5.14, Median = 5, Mode = 8, Range = 7

1 a

17	5
17	1 2 4
16	5 5 6 6 7 7 8 8 8 8 9 9
16	0 0 1 1 3 4
15	5 5
15	1 3 4 4 4

Key
17 | 5 means 175 cm

b Mean = 163.6 cm
Median = 165 cm
Range = 24 cm

c The modal class is 165–169 cm.
The median is a more representative average than the mean.

1 a 33.64 **b** 219.76

2 a 27 **b** 70 **c** 11.5
  d 6570

3 a 30 366 **b** 11 696 **c** 10.5
  d 36.62

2 a $-5\frac{1}{4}$ **b** $2\frac{2}{3}$ **c** $5\frac{1}{24}$
  d -33 **e** $\frac{11}{20}$ **f** $1\frac{59}{81}$

3 225.4 m

1 a 20, 23; T(n) = 3n + 2

b 23, 27; T(n) = 4n – 1

c 43, 53; T(n) = 10n – 7

d 10, 8; T(n) = 22 – 2n

2 a 3x + 12 **b** 8x + 24

c x^2 – 6x **d** 3x^2 + 7x – 2xy

1 a $s = 3n + 1$

b i $f = 4n + 2$

ii Middle cubes have 4 faces visible; both end cubes have an extra face visible.

2 a i $y = 2.5x + 10$

ii He is paid £10 plus £2.50 per boat.

b At birth your heart rate is 58 beats per minute. The rate increases by 3 beats per minute every 5 years.

3 a 8 camels **b** 29 camels

4 2.7 cm

1 a i 25, 36 **ii** n^2

b i 50, 72 **ii** $2n^2$

c i 26, 37 **ii** $n^2 + 1$

2

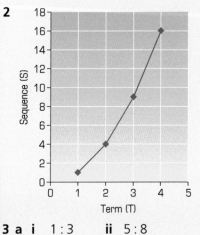

3 a i 1 : 3 **ii** 5 : 8

b i 1 : 6 **ii** 1 : 3.2

4 a £36 **b** £34

1 64

2 Klearglass

1 5

2 a 42 cm^3 **b** 8 mm^2

3 a 40 mm   **b** 4.2 cm   **c** 0.52 m

  d 1 kg   **e** 3500 ml   **f** 2 g

4

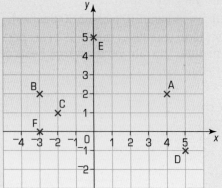

1 60 km

2 Perpendicular bisect of AB.

3 c 45°

  d The angle would be smaller.

1 Range = 7, Mean = 5, Median = 4.5, Mode = 4

2 a 2005   **b** 1.5

3

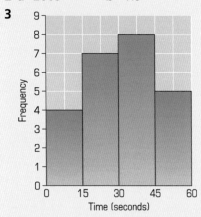

There are no unique answers.

1 HH, HT, TH, TT
2 32
3 0.73
4 a $x = 210$ b $x = 100$ c $31\frac{1}{2}$

1 b Hanif should expect to cycle home in five minutes 2 or 3 times a week.

Index

Index